Cover image by Digital Vision

ISBN 978-0-75750-467-9

Printed in the United States of America

7 8 9 10 17 16 15

Personal Fitness

Looking Good—Feeling Good

Fifth Edition

Charles S. Williams
University of Florida

Emmanouel G. Harageones
Escambia County Schools, Florida

Dewayne J. Johnson
Florida State University

Charles D. Smith
University of South Florida

Contributing Editor
Kathryn M. Hildebrand,
Northern Arizona University

KENDALL/HUNT PUBLISHING COMPANY
4050 Westmark Drive Dubuque, Iowa 52002

Contents

Introduction

How to Use the Book

This textbook was designed in such a way that you will be able to gain the necessary information on how to establish a healthier lifestyle and to better understand the close relationship between your physical health and fitness and how you see your total self. It is widely believed that how teenagers feel about their bodies directly affects their body images and self-esteem. As you will note from the U.S. Surgeon General's Report in Chapter 1, this could be the most important course you will take in high school.

Prior to reading each chapter, note the objectives at the beginning of the chapter. They are written in the form of questions to help you identify the important concepts to be learned in that specific chapter. Also review the vocabulary words that will be presented. If these words are new to you, review their meaning by using the glossary in the back of the textbook. You should then scan over the A level headings to obtain a general overview of what you will be reading about.

As you begin reading, you will note that each chapter contains helpful information that will broaden your understanding of health and wellness. The wellness connection topics include information regarding goal setting, safety, Internet resources, nutrition, stress, consumer issues, and use of technology in developing your personal fitness plan. There is a short description for each of these connections following the introduction. As you finish reading the chapter, attempt to answer the review questions. Attempting to recall information is better than just rereading with no purpose. If you can not recall an answer to a question, go back and reread that specific information rather than the entire chapter.

Wellness Connections

The following connections are in every chapter as shown.

Goal Setting

All successful athletes and business executives understand the need to set goals. We want to get you in the habit of setting goals early on. This information not only reminds you to establish a goal for personal fitness improvement, but these hints can carry over to all of life's challenges.

Safety Awareness

This may contain safety tips or issues that are specific to each chapter. We want you to start thinking about safety, as this is especially important for your age group. While cardiovascular disease is the major cause of death over one's life span, accidents are the most frequent cause of death for your current age group.

Reference information needed throughout the course to develop your personal fitness plan is centralized in the appendices. While some of the information is first presented in individual chapters, the information is repeated in the appendices so that it can be easily located.

A very unique feature of this text is that you will be assisted in establishing a personal fitness program that you will follow throughout the course. This will provide you with an excellent opportunity to set personal goals in areas you would like to improve. Getting into the habit of being physically active is not an easy habit to establish, if you are currently an inactive person. By developing and following a personal fitness program throughout this course, you will be well on your way to living a lifestyle that will enable you not only to feel good about yourself, but also to live a healthier and longer life. Your teacher will assist you in learning the necessity of practicing and working at becoming a healthy and fit person, just as you would need to work at becoming an accomplished musician or athlete.

You will have the opportunity in each chapter to explore valuable worldwide resources through the Internet to gain additional information about all aspects of fitness and health related topics. These sources will enable you to gain information about many additional questions you may have that are not included in the text. Many sites offer calculators to help you determine your training heart rate, calories burned, or help you plan your work-out program or assist with nutritional food selection and menu planning.

A key objective of this book is that you will become an advocate of the pursuit of optimal health and fitness. An advocate is a person who believes strongly in something, and in this case, you would believe strongly in trying to be as healthy and fit as possible. If this occurs, you will not only know how to establish your own personal fitness, but also help other family members understand the importance of being physically active.

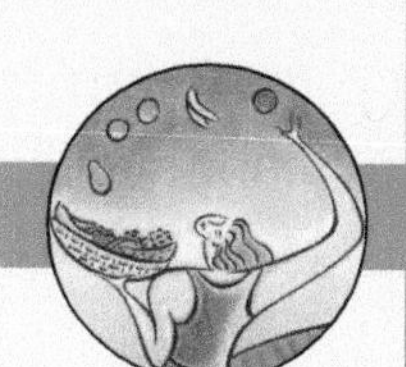

Nutrition Information

This information contains suggestions regarding your dietary selections. We want you to think about lifestyle habits in all wellness areas early on. As you will learn in this course, good health is obtained by a combination of physical activity and proper nutrition.

Stress Information

This information includes stress-management suggestions related to the chapter contents. These suggestions will assist you to implement positive stress-coping strategies to prevent the various illnesses caused by stress.

Consumer Issues

This information contains consumer issues related to the chapter contents. One of the major benefits of this course is that you will obtain the knowledge necessary to become a knowledgeable consumer. As a result of becoming a well-informed consumer, you will be able to make wise decisions in product safety to not only protect your bank account, but your health as well.

Internet Resources

This information will reference you to Internet links specific to the chapter contents. Due to technology and the World Wide Web, individuals are no longer limited to the resources of their local libraries. Resources throughout the world are now literally at your fingertips. In addition, the links will also assist you in the development of your personal fitness plan.

PFP Technology Activity

This is information about how you can use technology to help apply the chapter contents to your personal fitness program. The need for participating in physical activity will become more important as society becomes more sedentary. This section will assist you in using technology to your advantage and in maintaining your personal fitness program.

Personal Fitness

Looking Good—Feeling Good

Fifth Edition

1

Looking Good and Feeling Good

Objectives

As you read this chapter, look for answers to these key questions:

- Why is physical fitness a personal matter?
- How do some people neglect their health by choosing not to participate in physical activity?
- What are the primary health risk factors, and which ones may be controlled?
- What benefits are gained by exercising?
- What is the relationship between wellness and personal fitness?
- What is a personal fitness program (PFP)?

Goodshoot

"Success does not mean being the best, but doing your best."

V•A•L•U•E

Information presented in this chapter will help you understand the importance of being committed to the objective of becoming physically active and healthy. A clear understanding of personal fitness programs and their positive impact on students' lives is presented, and the case is made that this could be the most important class students take in high school. To summarize the findings of the U.S. Surgeon General's Report, one's involvement in physical activity could be a matter of life or death.

Chapter Preview

- Personal Fitness Is a Personal Matter
- Physical Fitness Is a Trend
- Surgeon General's Report on Physical Activity
- What Affects Your Attitude toward Physical Fitness?
- What Is Physical Fitness?
- Primary Health Risk Factors
- Contributing Health Risk Factors
- Benefits of Physical Activity
- Relationship between Wellness and Personal Fitness
- Pre-Assessment Considerations
- Physical Activity Readiness Questionnaire
- Your Personal Fitness Programs (PFP)
- Summary
- The Wrap-Up

Vocabulary

When you have completed this chapter, you should understand the meaning of these vocabulary terms:

physical fitness

health risk factors

inactivity

obesity

cholesterol

diabetes

body image

wellness

personal fitness program (PFP)

Wellness Connection

Personal Fitness Is a Personal Matter

Do you know anyone who doesn't want to look as good as possible or to feel as good as possible? Probably not. It is only natural to want to look and feel as good as possible. The fact is that everyone has a great deal of control over this desire. Although you inherit your body type from your parents and grandparents, you can still control your feelings and attitudes about yourself. One of the biggest factors that determines how you feel about yourself is the condition of your body. If you are pleased with the condition of your body, then chances are, you will feel good about yourself totally.

Personal fitness is a *personal* matter. The word *personal* is a key point to remember. Try not to compare yourself to anyone else in any way when working on self-improvement in physical fitness. Take pride in seeing yourself improve throughout this course. One of the most important things that will help you to experience success in improving how you look and feel is your *attitude.*

Try to keep an open mind about personal fitness. Do not let others influence you in a negative way. Always try your best, and give 100 percent. If you let others influence you in the wrong way, you will be the loser. Keeping a positive attitude can make a tremendous difference in almost any dimension of your life. That is certainly true when it comes to your physical fitness and lifestyle.

Corel

Physical Fitness Is a Trend

During the past twenty years, there has been a remarkable awakening of interest in physical fitness. Walkers, joggers, roller-bladers, and bikers move through parks and along highways. Tennis courts are filled, as are swimming pools. There is a huge demand for skateboard parks. Health clubs and fitness centers are extremely popular. You undoubtedly have many friends who are on personal fitness programs. Physical fitness should be an important ingredient in everyone's lifestyle.

GOAL SETTING

Identify at least one thing that you would like to change about yourself to make you a better person.

Not long ago it was common for people to get excited about some form of exercise, do it regularly for a period of time, then lose enthusiasm and stop. That is called a *fad*. For many people, however, interest in physical fitness has persisted for years and continues to be part of their lifestyles. When the interest in something, such as physical fitness, lasts for a long time, it is called a *trend*. Physical fitness continues to be a trend in this country. This is great news because personal fitness is such an important aspect of achieving greater self-respect and expanding your overall potential.

Surgeon General's Report on Physical Activity

Many people are excited about their physical fitness programs and have active lifestyles. However, research studies continue to show that a large percent of adults are not very fit and many are obese. As a result, the Surgeon General's Report on Physical Activity and Health (1996) emphasizes the importance that physical fitness has on the quality of life.

Photodisc

Personal fitness is an important aspect of achieving greater self-respect.

Although physical activity can help each of us live healthier, happier, and more fulfilled lives, one of the most alarming findings of this report is that physical activity declines dramatically during the high school years. This is a dangerous trend when you consider the fact that regular physical activity reduces the risk of developing, or dying from, some of the leading causes of illness and death in the United States.

Are any members of your family inactive and obese? If you or any of your friends are in this category, this personal fitness course will give you an opportunity to start building a healthier lifestyle. That can be a rewarding process, and you may find this course to be one of the most beneficial courses you will take in high school.

What Affects Your Attitude toward Physical Fitness?

Since feeling good about your body is such an important part of your self-image and self-concept, why do some people have a negative attitude toward improving their bodies? Several answers to this question will be discussed in this course, but you may have a few of your own to add.

Lack of Athletic Ability

Due to a lack of understanding of physical fitness, many people think that becoming a fast runner or a good ballplayer is part of being physically fit. Consequently, those students who do not have a good athletic background feel as though they cannot become physically fit. This way of thinking is unfortunate because you do not have to be a skilled person to be physically fit. Your experience in this course can be personally satisfying regardless of your athletic background.

SAFETY AWARENESS

If you have been inactive for while, start your training program at a slow pace and learn to enjoy physical activity.

Past Experience with Youth Sports

Another possible reason for the development of negative attitudes toward physical fitness is youth sports. It is estimated that more than 20 million young people, ages 5 to 16, play youth sports in this country. Youth sports have been and still are great experiences for many participants. However, a high percentage of young athletes, both male and female, drop out of youth sports at a relatively early age. The main reason is that the pressure to win increases at some point and they stop having fun. Some adolescent psychologists believe many young people

Internet Resources

Surgeon General's Report—Center for Disease Control
http://www.cdc.gov/nccdphp/sgr/adoles.htm

Benefits of Physical Activity—Center for Disease Control
http://www.cdc.gov/nccdphp/sgr/mm.htm

Ten Leading Causes of Death by Age Groups—Center for Disease Control
http://webapp.cdc.gov/sasweb/ncipc/leadcaus10.html

Software application that offers a word processing, database, and statistics system—Center for Disease Control
http://www.cdc.gov/nccdphp/dnpa/pro-trng.htm

Healthy People 2010—Center for Disease Control
http://www.cdc.gov/cvh/hp2010/objectives.htm#goal

develop a negative attitude toward themselves because of this, and this sense of inferiority may carry over into attitudes toward their physical capabilities in general.

Heredity

Heredity plays a role in your body type.

Lynelle Harrison

It is important to understand the role heredity plays in a person's final body type or build. Bone structure influences a person's measurements. Naturally, a person with large bones will have larger measurements than a person with small bones. However, people with either bone structure can have attractive body shapes. Regardless of your body type, you can maximize the attractiveness of your body through a proper physical fitness and wellness program.

Media Influence

Another factor that may foster negative attitudes about physical fitness in the minds of teens is the media coverage in magazines, television, and newspaper ads. Our society values slimness and athletic ability to a high degree. Many young women believe they should look like Abercrombie models. Young men are expected to have lean, muscular bodies. As you may be aware, very few people have the figure or body shape they perceive as being ideal. It is difficult to define what is meant by the ideal body shape, but the *thin-is-in* attitude prevails. Although the media has presented positive aspects of health and fitness, there have also been some negative aspects. Ads selling products to improve appearance frequently do so in a deceptive manner. They suggest that anyone can have the body of a model. Most young people will not attain these levels of appearance, and consequently, some will develop feelings of inadequacy.

The media also influence some parents in determining what their children should look like. As a result, they sometimes pressure their children to lose weight or to do something else to improve their appearance.

The following section explains reasons why some people are unable to attain the standards promoted in the media.

Confused about physical fitness?

What Is Physical Fitness?

Definitions of physical fitness vary widely. It is easy to understand why many people are confused about physical fitness. To some, having a high level of physical fitness means being a good athlete. It is true that most athletes are in very good shape; however, one does not have to be an athlete to be physically fit.

Body Weight Can Be Misleading

Appropriate weight is one indication of physical fitness, but it is not the only one.

Photodisc

Today there seems to be a *slimness mania,* especially among females. Individuals with this attitude frequently measure physical fitness by the bathroom scale. If the scale indicates that the person weighs just what she wants to weigh, she is happy. If, on the other hand, the scale indicates a reading that is five pounds over the desired weight, she is unhappy. This attitude is an unfortunate misconception about physical fitness.

Being obese is, without question, a factor that works against being physically fit. However, many young people believe they are physically fit just because their weight is at a desirable level. Do you know anyone who is very slender yet is in terrible physical condition? Appropriate weight is one indication of physical fitness, but it is not the only indication.

Some people have an obsession about being too fat, and in struggling to control their weight, they might be depriving themselves of important nutrients. The myth that thinness means fitness has been promoted successfully by various media. This course will help you take a closer look at the myths and fallacies that surround being physically fit.

Nutrition Information

Recognize the choices you make in choosing food. Could you make healthier choices? All of your choices add up and have a cumulative effect on your health and appearance.

Do you like what you see in the mirror? Is the mirror a friend or a foe?

Manny Harageones

Physical Fitness Defined

Teenagers are concerned with looking good and feeling good, so it is essential that you understand physical fitness. People are described as being physically fit when they are able to carry out daily tasks without undue fatigue, are able to handle emergency situations, and possess sufficient energy to enjoy leisure-time pursuits. Physical fitness is determined by the condition of your heart and circulatory system, respiratory system, muscular system, degree of flexibility, and percentage of body fat.

Primary Health Risk Factors

You can significantly change your current health, as well as the state of your future health, by controlling health risk factors associated with disease, disability, or premature death. The removal of even one of these risk factors may reduce the threat of several diseases. Although you may feel these risk factors are only relevant to older people—maybe those your parent's age—they are quite important to you, as well. Since many of these diseases start when a person is a teenager or younger, it is to your benefit to learn how you can control these factors. The most commonly identified risk factors are discussed next.

Inactivity

Those who remain active have fewer heart problems and other diseases than those who remain inactive. Inactivity limits your chances of being in charge of your life, since physical health is vitally important to your total development. Physical inactivity is caused from lack of muscle stimulation, and is largely the result of technology. Video games, television, and computers are a few of the main factors contributing to the inactivity of teenagers.

Obesity

Having excessive deposits of fat in the body is called obesity. These fatty deposits put a strain on your heart and circulatory system, as well as on all other systems of your body. It has also been reported that obese individuals may have a hard time adjusting socially and emotionally. Obesity, or the initial stages of obesity, typically begins in childhood. Many young people are unable to control this condition during their school years and end up as obese adults.

High Blood Pressure

This condition has been identified as a major cause of heart and other circulatory problems. You probably know people, either family members or their friends, who have high blood pressure. It is important to understand that high blood pressure does not just occur in older people. Many people your age have high blood pressure, caused largely by the stresses of home life, schoolwork, and peer pressure.

Stress Information

Practice visualizing positive results of implementing your personal fitness program—then just get up and move.

High Levels of Cholesterol

Cholesterol is a waxy, fat-like substance found in the cells. Although cholesterol is needed by the body, diets high in saturated fat can cause cholesterol levels to become too high. When this occurs, the cholesterol may collect in blood vessels and clog them. This is why high levels of cholesterol in the blood frequently are associated with heart disease.

The average American consumes a diet that is extremely high in fat content. Although foods at fast food businesses may be very tasty, they are generally high in fat content and can increase your cholesterol level.

Stress and Tension

Unnecessary stress and tension can place a strain on the heart and circulatory system and may lead to various types of diseases. An argument with a close friend during physical activity may cause you to experience unusual anger, doubt, fear, and similar

Stockbyte

Who said teenagers' lives were easy?

emotions, which, in turn, will have a negative effect on your body. Who has not been upset at a parent, teacher, or friend? What happened to your body? Was it "revved up" or ready for action, as evidenced by a faster heartbeat and rapid rate of breathing? The teen years can be a very challenging time. For some, it is the most difficult time in their lives.

Smoking

You have undoubtedly heard about the negative health effects of smoking on your body, as well as about the dangers of second-hand smoke. It has been firmly established that smoking causes many problems in the circulatory and respiratory systems of your body. The Federal Drug Administration has declared the nicotine contained in tobacco to be addictive. Nicotine makes it difficult to stop smoking after it has become a habit. You may, in fact, know individuals who have found it hard to break the habit. However, you are 100 percent in control of this risk factor if you never start.

Gender

In the past, men have had a higher rate of heart disease than women. The primary reason was because men were more affected by the pressures and stresses of the business world. However, the gap appears to be narrowing since more women have entered the work force and experienced the same pressures and tensions. The increased number of women smoking may also be a factor in the increased rate of heart disease among women.

Heredity

If you have family members who have had heart attacks or other circulatory problems, your chances of having heart problems increase. In other words, you not only inherit your parents' and grandparents' physical characteristics, you may also inherit the tendency to develop the same diseases. It should be pointed out that some of these diseases may be a result of lifestyle choices, rather than an inherited trait.

Age

Advancing age increases the risk of developing coronary heart disease. This is easily understood when one considers that the collection of arterial plaque is an ongoing process and the longer one lives, the greater the build-up.

Risk Factor Checklist

Following are risk factors that can and cannot be controlled:

	I Can Control	I Cannot Control
Inactivity	✓	
Obesity	✓	
High Blood Pressure	✓	
High Levels of Cholesterol	✓	
Stress and Tension	✓	
Smoking	✓	
Gender		✓
Heredity		✓
Age		✓

Six of the nine risk factors can be controlled. Are you a good lion tamer in your own life?

Contributing Health Risk Factor

Another contributing factor that is often forgotten is diabetes. The American Heart Association considers diabetes a major contributing risk factor that should not be ignored. Diabetes is the inability of the body to produce or use insulin. Insulin is necessary for the body to utilize glucose (sugar).

Without insulin, glucose absorption by the cells and liver is low, leading to high glucose levels in the blood. It is estimated that 80 percent of diabetics die with some form of heart or blood vessel disease. Changes in eating habits, weight control, exercise habits, and drug therapy are often used to keep diabetes under control.

Benefits of Physical Activity

What's in it for you? The answer to this question is highly personal. For example, everyone benefits from physical activity; however, we all place different importance on the many benefits. While you might find some of the benefits not meaningful to you now, they may be to others or will be more meaningful to you later in life.

Improved Appearance

Looking good is very important to everyone, particularly to students your age. Exercise and fitness activities help control body weight and help make your body more attractive. Music stars and other performers are very concerned about their appearance and consequently follow well-designed fitness programs. They pay personal trainers to design workouts for them, knowing that physical activity helps to tone muscles and shape the body. By following a personal fitness plan, you will see changes in your body.

If you improve your personal physical appearance, there is a great likelihood you will also improve the way you feel about yourself overall.

Photodisc

If you improve your personal physical appearance, there is a great likelihood you will also improve the way you feel about yourself overall. This improvement may create a positive cycle in your life. When you feel good about yourself, the chances are greater that you will want to continue to improve yourself, not just in a physical way, but in every way.

Consumer Issues

Have you been tempted by ads for products promising quick, easy weight loss or increased muscle mass? Unfortunately, the products usually do not deliver on their promises, whether it is a fad diet, fancy potion, or some funky machine. If it sounds too good to be true, it usually is. Being skeptical is usually a very good practice.

Photodisc

Improving your body image can also improve the total way in which you see and feel about yourself.

Improved Body Image

Body image means the way you see your physical self. Are you pleased when you look into a full-length mirror? Since many people do not like their body images, properly designed physical fitness programs may be just the answer for them. Remember, your body image is just one part of your *self-concept*. Improving your body image can also improve the total way in which you see and feel about yourself.

Improved Self-Control

People who take control of their bodies and their lifestyles generally experience less stress and depression than those who are indifferent to striving for personal improvement. Having control of these aspects of your life might also help you have greater feelings of self-confidence and self-discipline, regardless of the situations in which you find yourself.

Improved Health

Physical activity beyond the daily routine is needed to avoid heart disease and other illnesses associated with inactivity. This is particularly true for older people, but it also has relevance for you. Active people are also healthier because their digestion is enhanced through exercise, providing better elimination of waste products from the body.

Increased Muscular Strength and Endurance

The vast majority of male teenagers are anxious to be as strong as possible and to have well-developed muscles. While the majority of female teenagers do not want to develop large muscles, they do want to have firm, well-toned bodies. In both cases, the end result of a physical fitness program will be improved personal appearance and self-confidence. This leads directly to the next benefit of physical fitness.

Increased Level of Energy

Being tired during the day might be the direct result of poor lifestyle choices, such as poor nutritional and rest habits. Low energy might also be due to a body that is not "tuned-up"

Stockbyte

Is your body as important as your car? Do you know people who take better care of their cars than they do their bodies?

appropriately. Your body might be equated to an expensive car. Who would put low-octane gas in a hot sports car, or disregard all company recommendations for handling it?

Our bodies are much more valuable than the most expensive car, yet it is strange that we sometimes disregard the key guidelines for getting the maximum performance from them. Appropriate physical activities are a key factor in helping your body function near an optimal level. A higher energy level is one outcome of following a physical fitness program. A high level of physical activity will prevent fatigue and allow you to enjoy leisure-time activities to a greater degree. You will be able to play longer, gain more skill, and experience a greater degree of success and enjoyment in games and sports. You will also be able to complete your school day with little fatigue.

Stockbyte

A high level of energy will prevent fatigue.

Improved Physical Performance

If you are physically fit, you will be able to participate in sports and other physical activities for a longer period of time due to greater muscular and cardiovascular endurance. Because you will not tire as quickly, you will enhance your chances of being successful not only in sports, but in all physical activities.

Increased Success in Your Schoolwork or Job

Ancient Greeks used a phrase that summed up their belief about the importance of the body: a sound mind in a sound body. They thought this phrase was essential in the education of their children. Research studies show that increased physical fitness helps with academic achievement. As your body becomes more efficient, you function more effectively.

Photodisc

Physical fitness can increase success in your school work or job.

Helps Cope with Stress

Teenagers are frequently under many stresses and become depressed, angry, or anxious about their lives. A good exercise program can be one of the most important ways to deal with stress. Physical activity will not only provide relief from daily anxieties, but can also have a refreshing, exhilarating effect on your life. In chapter 11, you will learn several easy techniques for recognizing and handling the stress in your life.

Sleep Better

For the majority of you, sleeping may not be a problem. However, this is not the case for everyone. Exercise relieves tension, and so your body relaxes more, enabling you to go to sleep quickly and sleep soundly.

Increased Life Expectancy

This benefit may seem to be more related to your parents or some older friends than to you. But, remember the comparison of your body to an expensive car? A car motor will last much longer if it is cared for properly, and so will your body. Many diseases attributed to inactivity begin at an early age because individuals disregard the needs of their bodies and abuse them.

Physical fitness activities provide almost immediate physical and mental benefits. The physical benefits include looking good and feeling good about yourself. The mental benefits include increased self-esteem, improved self-control, reduced stress, and a feeling of confidence.

Can you think of other benefits? The important point to remember is that there are many benefits of exercise for everyone, including high school students.

Relationship between Wellness and Personal Fitness

Wellness can be defined as the total commitment to living a healthy and active lifestyle dedicated to optimal fitness and personal health. Personal fitness is one aspect of wellness. There are five other components of wellness:

1. Mental fitness
2. Emotional fitness

3. Environmental fitness
4. Social fitness
5. Spiritual fitness

One's lifestyle can have an effect on all of the components of wellness. Everyone makes decisions related to their lifestyles. You can opt to be inactive, out of shape, overweight, and without energy. Or, you can take responsibility for your life and make positive lifestyle choices. This course is designed to provide you with information that will better enable you to make positive lifestyle choices. If you desire to be an energetic and enthusiastic individual, you must invest time and effort in improving your lifestyle.

Pre-Assessment Considerations

Corel

It is important that you get started as soon as possible.

Although this entire course is designed to help you learn how to design your own personal fitness program, it is important that you get started as soon as possible. You may be asked by your instructor to record the information listed below. These data will give some indication of your readiness to increase your level of physical activity. In addition, this information could serve as a baseline to compare against later in the year.

- height
- weight
- resting pulse
- blood pressure
- previous involvement in physical activity
- current fitness level
- current health
- past medical history

PFP Technology Activity

Using a computer, create a file to save information about your Personal Fitness Program (PFP) on a disk or school server. Develop a cover page, table of contents, and dividers for your plan and save this to your PFP file. Your teacher may instruct you to add other assessment forms containing personal data to your PFP.

Your Personal Fitness Program (PFP)

A unique feature of this course is that you will establish a Personal Fitness Program (PFP) and follow it throughout the semester. A PFP is a plan designed to help you select activities that will enable you to improve your lifestyle. Part of your PFP will include physical activity to help you have more energy, become stronger, more flexible, burn calories, and most importantly, live longer. Another aspect of your PFP will be changing one or more health behaviors, such as, improving your nutritional habits, consuming water, getting an appropriate number of hours of sleep, and/or learning how to recognize conflicts and resolve them during physical activity.

The purpose of a PFP is to help you make choices that will enable you to establish physically active habits resulting in a healthy lifestyle. You cannot obtain positive results by just wishing that you looked better and felt better. Once you realize the benefits of being physically active and have the desire to improve, you must take action for positive results to take place. One of the first things you must do is assess your current health status and fitness level. Before you can correct a problem, you have to be able to recognize that a problem exists and what may be the cause. Complete the Par-Q and let your instructor and guardian know if you answered yes to any item. Place the Par-Q and any other assessment instrument your instructor assigns in your PFP.

Goal setting is another very important process to understand when you want to improve yourself. The steps involved in goal setting are covered in Chapter 3, but for now, you can establish common-sense behavioral goals. As mentioned above, you might choose to eat more nutritious meals, sleep more, and be more physically active. Use these three areas to form the basis of your PFP, which would serve as a beginning for your lifestyle improvement plan. Do not select any physical activity without the consent of a medical doctor, if you have any medical condition.

Remember, this is a beginning program; as you progress through the course, you will gain knowledge in many areas that will allow you to improve and expand your PFP. There is a PFP update section at the end of each chapter to remind you to reevaluate your goals and to record your progress. Your PFP is your personal plan, and your success in accomplishing goals will encourage you to establish additional ones to improve your lifestyle. Start your program today, and you will start taking more control of your life and future.

Physical Activity Readiness Questionnaire

Being involved in physical activity will not only help you look better, it will also help you feel better by enhancing your health. Although physical activity is safe for most individuals, some should check with their doctor before becoming physically active. Answer the following seven questions. You should answer the questions honestly to determine if you should check with your doctor before you increase your physical activity.

PAR-Q & YOU
Physical Activity Readiness Questionnaire
(A questionnaire for people aged 15 to 69)

Name: ____________________________ **Date:** ___________ **Period:** _____

This is to certify that I have read and understand the contents of the Physical Activity Readiness Questionnaire and have answered the questions correctly.

______________________________ ______________________________

Signature **Parent or Guardian Signature**

Yes	No	
_____	_____	1. Has your doctor ever said that you have a heart condition and that you should only do physical activity recommended by a doctor?
_____	_____	2. Do you feel pain in your chest when you do physical activity?
_____	_____	3. In the past month, have you had chest pain when you were not doing physical activity?
_____	_____	4. Do you lose your balance because of dizziness, or do you ever lose consciousness?
_____	_____	5. Do you have a bone or joint problem that could be made worse by a change in your physical activity?
_____	_____	6. Is your doctor currently prescribing drugs (for example, water pills) for your blood pressure or heart condition?
_____	_____	7. Do you know of any other reason why you should not do physical activity?

If you answered yes to one or more questions, talk with your doctor by phone or in person BEFORE you start becoming much more physically active or BEFORE you have a fitness appraisal. Tell your doctor about the PAR-Q and which questions you answered yes.

- You may be able to do any activity you want—as long as you start slowly and build up gradually. Or, you may need to restrict your activities to those which are safe for you. Talk with your doctor about the kinds of activities you wish to participate in and follow his/her advice.
- Find out which community programs are safe and helpful for you.

If you answered no honestly to all questions, you can be reasonably sure that you can do the following:

- start becoming much more physically active—begin slowly and build up gradually. This is the safest and easiest way to go.
- take part in a fitness appraisal—this is an excellent way to determine your basic fitness so that you can plan the best way for you to live actively.

Delay becoming much more active under these conditions:

- if you are not feeling well because of a temporary illness such as a cold or a fever—wait until you feel better.
- if you are or may be pregnant—talk to your doctor before you start becoming more active.

Please note: If your health changes so that you then answer yes to any of the PAR-Q questions, tell your fitness or health professional. Ask whether you should change your physical activity plan.

Informed Use of the PAR-Q: The Canadian Society for Exercise Physiology, Health Canada, and their agents assume no liability for persons who undertake physical activity, and if in doubt after completing this questionnaire, consult your doctor prior to physical activity.

Summary

There is no easy path to being physically fit and healthy. Some would like us to believe there is because they can make millions of dollars from our purchases. It is a fantasy to think you can take a magic pill, or do a two-minute-a-day exercise schedule and become fit. If you wish to gain, regain, or maintain a high level of personal physical well being, you must be prepared to give time and effort to attain your goals.

To be successful at this task, you need to answer the following questions honestly:

1. Are you satisfied with your current state of physical fitness?
2. Are you satisfied with your body image (what the mirror says)?
3. Does your lifestyle include vigorous physical activity?
4. Are you satisfied with your lifestyle?
5. Are you able to recognize and resolve conflicts with others during physical activity?

If you answered no to any of these questions, you should recognize the need for engaging in a personal fitness program. **The challenge is yours. Go for it.**

The Wrap-Up

Vocabulary Matching

Match the definitions to the correct term.

1. Obesity
2. Health risk factors
3. Diabetes
4. Body image
5. Physical fitness
6. Inactivity
7. Cholesterol
8. Wellness
9. Personal fitness program

A. condition in which the body is unable to produce or use insulin

B. the capacity of the whole body to function at optimum efficiency

C. factors associated with disease, disability and premature death

D. lack of physical activity and exercise

E. a condition characterized by excessive deposits of fat on the body

F. a waxy, fat-like substance found in animal tissue

G. the way one sees oneself physically

H. plan designed to help you select activities that will enable you to improve your lifestyle

I. total commitment to living a healthy and active lifestyle

Multiple Choice

Select the most correct answer.

10. Setting up a personal physical fitness program will provide:
- A. emotional benefits
- B. mental benefits
- C. physical benefits
- D. all of the above

11. The U.S. Surgeon General produced a report on the importance of physical activity so that the population would know
- A. how to have a positive self image.
- B. that engaging in physical activity is a matter of life and death.
- C. the importance of a strong military.
- D. the importance of being thin.

12. Which of the following is the most modifiable primary cardiovascular risk factor that will have the greatest impact on an individual's well-being?
A. alcohol use
B. gender
C. inactivity
D. stop smoking

13. Diets high in saturated fat can cause __________ levels to become too high, thus clogging arteries.
A. cholesterol
B. insulin
C. heart
D. stress

14. The media attempts to make people feel
A. bad so they will buy their products to look and feel better.
B. good about themselves.
C. good by choosing average looking people to do ads.
D. none of the above are correct statements.

15. What is the leading cause of death in the United States?
A. alcohol abuse
B. cancer
C. cardiovascular disease
D. drug use

16. To be healthy and physically active, one must be
A. an athlete
B. non-handicapped
C. young
D. none of the above are correct.

17. Cardiovascular risk factors that one can control include
A. inactivity, obesity, high blood pressure, smoking, and age.
B. inactivity, obesity, stress, cholesterol, and heredity.
C. inactivity, obesity, high blood pressure, cholesterol, stress, and smoking.
D. inactivity, obesity, high blood pressure, cholesterol, stress, smoking, and age.

18. Physical fitness deals with five factors:
A. cardiovascular fitness, muscular strength, muscular endurance, flexibility, and body composition.
B. cardiovascular fitness, muscular strength, athletic ability, body composition, and flexibility.
C. cardiovascular fitness, fitness test scores, muscular endurance, flexibility, and stress level.
D. stress level, muscular strength, cholesterol level, flexibility, and inactivity.

19. Which best describes the primary health risk factors?
  A. Almost all problems begin when people are older.
  B. Most health risk factors apply only to older people.
  C. Most risk factors are beyond your control.
  D. You can improve your health by controlling several health risk factors.

Authentic Assessment—Short Response

20. In what way is physical fitness related to body image?

21. What effect can advertisements have on the way people see themselves physically?

22. Why is the word *personal* so important in a personal fitness class?

23. Compare two people, one who is fit and one who is unfit. Are there any differences in them besides the amount of physical activity in their lives?

24. What is the relationship, if any, between body image and self-esteem?

Authentic Assessment—Extended Response

25. **Writing situation:** Some individuals have had a negative experience with youth sports.

    Directions for writing: Discuss why some people think you have to be a good athlete to be physically fit. Then explain why it is a mistake to believe that health-related physical fitness is just for athletes.

26. **Writing situation:** Cardiovascular disease is the number one cause of death in the United States.

    Directions for writing: List the primary health risk factors associated with cardiovascular disease, disability and premature death. Compose a letter to a family member or friend encouraging him/her to begin an exercise program by contrasting his/her lifestyle with the primary health risk factors.

2

Components of Fitness

Photodisc

Objectives

As you read this chapter, look for answers to these key questions:

- What is the difference between health-related and skill-related physical fitness?
- What are the health-related components of physical fitness?
- What are the skill-related components of physical fitness?
- Why does a person not have to be a good athlete to be physically fit?
- Why is it important to know your current level of health-related fitness?

"If it is to be, it is up to me."

V•A•L•U•E

Knowing your current level of physical fitness is essential to living a healthier and happier life. Prior to accomplishing any task, you must know where you are before you design a plan to improve. Knowledge about how to self-assess the health-related components of physical fitness and how to interpret assessment results will help you plan your Personal Fitness Program.

Chapter Preview

- Analyzing Physical Fitness
- Health-Related Fitness
- Skill-Related Fitness
- Fitness Assessment
- Interpreting Assessment Results
- Goal Setting
- PFP Update
- Summary
- The Wrap-Up

Vocabulary

When you have completed this chapter, you should understand the meaning of these vocabulary terms:

health-related fitness
skill-related fitness
flexibility
cardiovascular fitness
muscular strength
muscular endurance
body composition
body mass index (BMI)
agility
balance
power
reaction time
coordination
speed
norm-referenced tests
criterion-referenced tests
health-related fitness standards

Wellness Connection

Analyzing Physical Fitness

What is physical fitness? How can it be attained? It is very important that you understand the answers to these questions if you are going to become responsible for your own health and fitness.

Physical fitness is made up of both health-related and skill-related components. The **health-related fitness** components relate to how well the systems of your body operate. Are your heart and other muscles in good shape? This type of physical fitness is related to your overall state of health. The **skill-related fitness** items are concerned with abilities related to sports activities. Are you fast? Do you have good eye–hand coordination? The focus of this book is on the health-related components of physical fitness, why they are important, and how they can be improved. Skill-related fitness is covered later in the chapter.

Photodisc

Health-Related Fitness

Both kinds of fitness are important for successful participation in sports activities. However, only the health-related components can contribute to the prevention of disease and the promotion of health. That is why they are called health-related.

Maintaining an acceptable level of the health-related components of physical fitness is recognized as a key element in maintaining a healthy lifestyle. People who attain such levels of fitness reduce their risks of developing health problems, such as heart disease, low back pain, and obesity, and improve their body's ability to function. This is why health-related fitness should be the concern of everyone, regardless of age.

There are five health-related components of physical fitness: flexibility, cardiovascular fitness, muscular strength, muscular endurance, and body composition. Remember that fitness

GOAL SETTING

Some students do not try their best when completing a physical fitness test. Therefore, it is no surprise that the test results do not reflect their true levels of physical fitness. To help you set realistic goals for improving your physical self, give your best effort on each test item so you have an accurate understanding of your body's condition.

is for everyone. You do not have to be a good athlete to be physically fit. If you exercise regularly and follow basic training principles, you will improve your health-related fitness.

Flexibility

Flexibility describes the range of movement possible at various joints. It is probably the most frequently overlooked component of fitness. If you want to be as good as you can be, you must work on flexibility as regularly as you work on muscular strength and endurance or cardiovascular efficiency.

Because flexibility is specific to each joint, no single test can provide complete information about the flexibility of all major joints of your body. However, there are several tests that will give you an indication of flexibility in joints most likely needing

Trunk-lift test

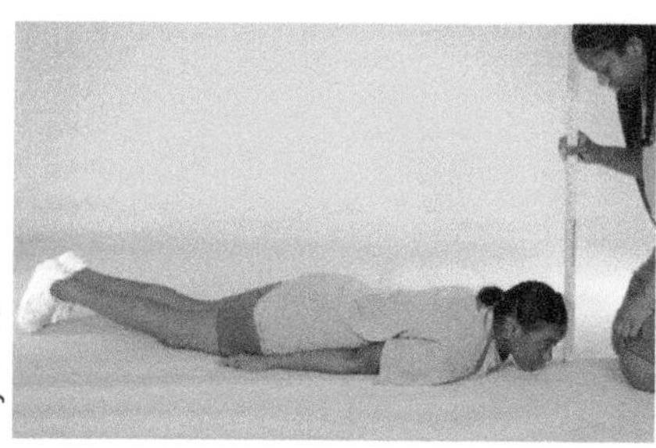

Ray Carson

Trunk Lift Test

Equipment/Facilities: This test requires a mat and a yardstick. Mark the yardstick at the 6, 9, and 12-inch mark with colored tape.

Procedures:

1. Warm up prior to testing.
2. Lie flat on the mat with the your toes pointed and your hands under your thighs.
3. Find a spot on the mat or floor that is in line with your eyes and look at it as you perform the test.
4. Lift your upper body off the mat in a very slow and controlled manner and hold that position several seconds while your partner conducts the measurement.
5. The measurement is done by your partner placing the yardstick at least one inch to the front of your chin and not directly under your chin and measures the distance from the mat to the bottom of your chin. The score is recorded to the nearest inch.
6. Perform the test twice and record your best score. Do not raise higher than 12 inches.
7. Cool down after testing.

Shoulder stretch test

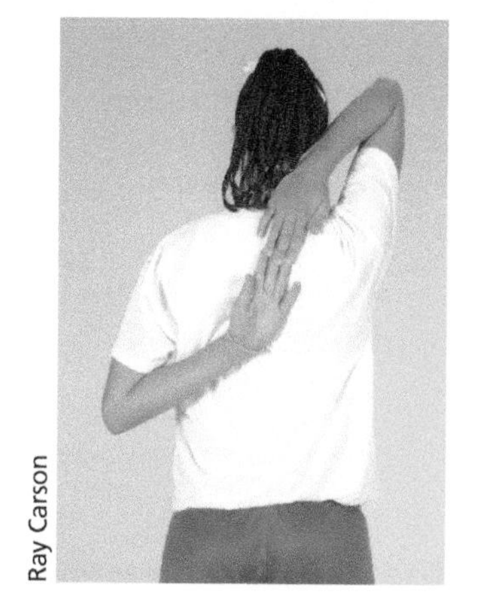

Ray Carson

Shoulder Stretch Test

Procedures:

1. Warm up prior to testing.
2. To test the right shoulder, stand straight, reach your right hand over your right shoulder and down the back as if to pull up a zipper. At the same time place your left hand behind your back and reach up, trying to touch the fingers of your right hand. If your fingertips touched together, you record a passing score.
3. Repeat the test for the left shoulder.
4. Cool down after testing.

Back-saver sit-and-reach test

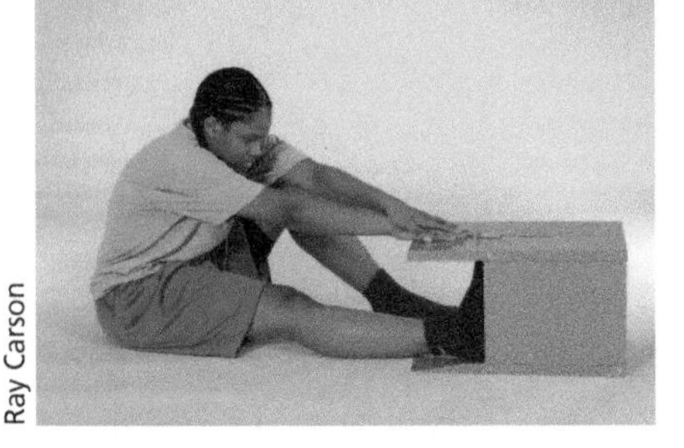

Ray Carson

Back-Saver Sit-and-Reach Test

Equipment/Facilities: This test requires a sturdy box approximately 12 inches high. Tape a ruler to the top of the box with the 9-inch mark on the edge of the box against which your foot will rest. The "zero" end of the ruler sticks out facing you.

Procedures:

1. Warm up prior to testing.
2. Remove your shoes and sit down at the test box.
3. Extend one of your legs so that your foot is flat against the end of the box. Bend your other knee with the sole of your foot flat on the floor 2 to 3 inches to the side of the straight knee.
4. Extend your arms over the measuring scale with your hands placed one on top of the other, palms down.
5. Reach directly forward along the measuring scale four times and hold the position of the fourth reach for a least 1 second. Your hands should reach forward evenly, your bent knee should move to the side allowing your body to move past it, the knee of your extended leg should remain straight, and your hips should remain square to the test box.
6. Have your partner measure the distance your fingertips reach to the nearest half-inch to a maximum score of 12 inches.
7. The trial should be repeated if your hands reach unevenly, extended leg bends at the knee, or your hips turn away from the test box as you reach.
8. After you measure one side, switch the position of your legs and measure your other side.
9. Cool down after testing.

V-sit reach test

Ray Carson

V-Sit Reach Test

Equipment/Facilities: This test requires a mat, a two feet long baseline strip, and one measuring strip. The measuring strip is placed perpendicular to the midpoint of the baseline extending two feet on each side and marked off in half-inches. The point where the baseline and measuring strip intersect is the "0" point.

Procedures:

1. Warm up prior to testing.
2. Remove your shoes and sit on the mat with the measuring strip between your legs and the soles of your feet placed immediately behind the baseline, heels 8 to 12 inches apart. Clasp your thumbs so that your hands are together, palms down and place them on the measuring strip.
3. Have your partner hold your legs flat. Slowly reach forward as far as possible, keeping your fingers on the measuring strip and feet flexed. After three practice tries, hold the fourth reach for three seconds while that distance is recorded.
4. Your score, recorded to the nearest half-inch, is read as a plus score for a reach beyond the baseline and a minus score for a reach behind the baseline.
5. Cool down after testing.

Sit-and-reach test

Ray Carson

SAFETY AWARENESS

Do not try to maintain the same level of activity when injured. Remember that you must start back slowly after being ill or injured.

Sit-and-Reach Test

Equipment/Facilities: This test requires a mat and a specially constructed box with a measuring scale marked in centimeters, with 23 centimeters at the level of the feet.

Procedures:

1. Warm up prior to testing.
2. Remove your shoes and sit on the mat with knees fully extended, feet shoulder-width apart and soles of the feet held flat against the end of the box.
3. With hands on top of each other, palms down, and legs held flat by your partner, reach along the measuring scale as far as possible.
4. After three practice reaches, hold your fourth reach while the distance is recorded. Your score is recorded to the nearest centimeter.
5. Cool down after testing.

attention. These tests include the trunk lift test, the back-saver sit-and-reach test, the shoulder stretch test, the v-sit reach test, and the sit-and-reach test.

Cardiovascular Fitness

Cardiovascular fitness relates to the ability of the heart, blood, blood vessels, and the respiratory system to supply oxygen and necessary fuel to the muscles during physical activity. The best type of physical activity for improving cardiovascular fitness is aerobic activities. Aerobic activities are those which force the body to use a large amount of oxygen for a sustained period of time. *Sustained* means that the physical activity should be done for a period of 15 to 30 minutes to get the aerobic benefits. Examples of aerobic activities are jogging, cycling, swimming, rope jumping, and aerobic dance. Certain sports, like basketball and soccer, also provide the workout needed to achieve an aerobic training effect. Aerobic activities provide a safeguard for your physical and mental health.

Cardiovascular fitness can be measured in a number of ways. The most accurate measurement is a stress test performed on a stationary bicycle or treadmill in a physical fitness laboratory or hospital. This test requires expensive equipment and highly trained personnel. Cardiovascular fitness can be more easily evaluated with step tests, distance tests, and the PACER test. The most common distance tests are the 1-mile run for time, the Cooper 1 1/2-mile run for time, the 1-mile walk for time, the 9-minute run for distance, and the 12-minute run/walk for distance. Prior to performing a distance run, you should practice running to learn how to pace yourself. It is also important to condition yourself before attempting a timed run.

Manny Harogeones

You may run for distance or time to measure aerobic endurance.

Photodisc

PACER (Progressive Aerobic Cardiovascular Endurance Run) Test

Equipment/Facilities: This test requires a 20 meter flat, smooth, non-slippery surface, CD or cassette player, PACER CD or audio cassette, measuring tape, marker cones, pencils, and copies of scoresheets.

Procedures:

1. Warm up prior to testing.
2. Begin running when you hear the starting beep on the PACER cassette tape. You need to get to the line that is 20 meters away before the second beep. At the sound of the second beep, turn around and return to the starting line, trying to beat the next beep. If you get to the line before the next beep, you must wait for the beep before running in the other direction. You will continue in this manner until you fail to reach the line before the beep for the second time.
3. The beeps on the tape are spaced to start you off at a slow pace and then gradually begin occurring more frequently to speed you up.
4. If you cannot reach the line by the time the beep sounds, you are given one more beep to attempt to regain the pace. The second time you cannot reach the line by the beep, your test is completed.
5. Have your partner record the total number of laps you completed. A lap is one 20-meter distance.
6. Cool down after testing.

One-Mile & Cooper 1-1/2-Mile Run

Equipment/Facilities: This test requires a stopwatch and a 1 mile distance (track or other measured distance).

Procedures:

1. Warm up prior to testing.
2. Start the stopwatch and cover the mile distance as fast as possible.
3. Use the fastest pace that you can sustain for the entire mile distance.
4. Walk if you have to; however, your goal is to cover the mile in the shortest time possible.
5. After you have covered the mile, stop the stopwatch and record the time (minutes and seconds) it took you to cover this distance.
6. Cool down after testing.

Internet Resources

Physical Best—American Alliance for Health, Physical Education, Recreation and Dance
http://www.aahperd.org

Fitnessgram—Cooper Institute for Aerobics Research
http://www.cooperinst.org

The President's Challenge—President's Council on Physical Fitness and Sports
http://www.fitness.gov

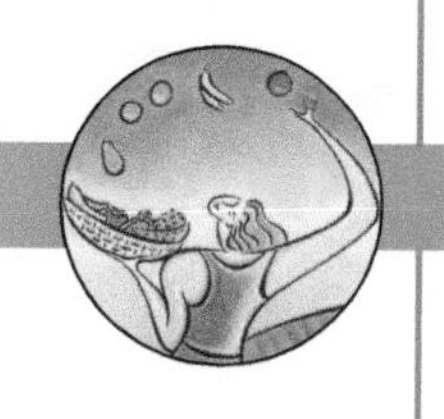

Nutrition Information

It is not wise to "super size," since these servings provide additional calories and fat. Be prepared to say, "No!" when asked, "Do you want to super size?"

Muscular Strength and Muscular Endurance

Muscular strength and endurance are closely related components that are very important to teenagers. Muscular strength is the ability of a muscle group to apply a maximal force against a resistance one time. Muscular endurance is the ability to repeat muscle movement for a long period of time.

In the past, young men were much more interested in muscular development than young women. That gap is closing rapidly, as more women are realizing the importance of developing their muscular fitness. Today, more than ever before, women want to have firm and well-toned bodies. An important fact to remember is that most females will not develop large muscles for the simple reason that they do not have enough of the necessary hormone testosterone. Males, on the other hand, have a high level of testosterone, enabling them to greatly increase muscle size and body definition. Regardless of whether you are male or female, improving your muscular development will improve your body image.

Stress Information

During physical activity become more understanding. Take thirty seconds to consider the feelings of others and how your reaction could create even more anger.

The curl-up test and partial curl-up test are used to measure abdominal muscular strength and endurance. Push-ups, pull-ups, and the flexed-arm hang are commonly used to evaluate muscular strength and endurance of the upper body.

Body Composition

Body composition is the ratio of fat to muscle, bone, and other tissues that compose your body. A certain amount of body fat is needed for good health. Extremely high or low amounts of body fat can cause health problems. Most young adults desire a low percent of body fat. Your body image may suffer if your percent of body fat is too high. Looking good and feeling good depend a great deal on what percent of your body weight is fat. The information in this text, if put to use, will help you achieve an ideal body weight and an appropriate level of body fat.

Curl-up test

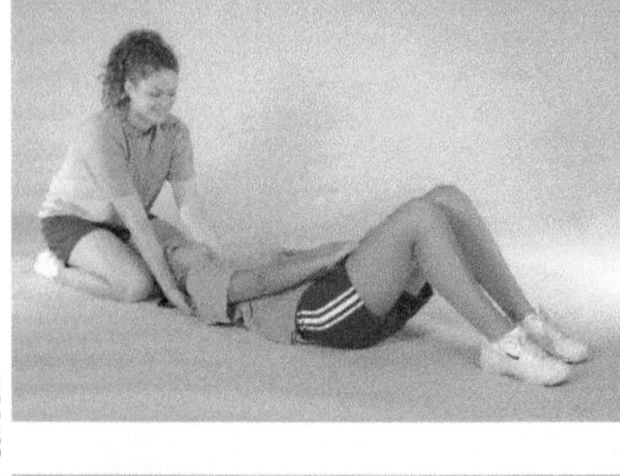

Curl-Up Test

Equipment/Facilities: This test requires a mat and a measuring strip. The measuring strip may be made of cardboard, posterboard, rubber, smooth wood, or any similar thin, flat material. The measuring strip should be 4-1/2 inches wide and 30 to 35 inches long.

Procedures:

1. Warm up prior to testing by stretching your abdominal muscles.
2. Lie on your back on the mat with your knees bent at an angle of 140 degrees. Feet should be flat on the floor with legs slightly apart. Arms need to be straight, parallel to your trunk, with palms resting on the mat with fingers stretched out.
3. Have one partner use his hands to make a resting place for your head. Have another partner place the measuring strip under your knees on the mat so that your fingertips are just resting on the nearest edge of the measuring strip. Have this partner secure the ends of the measuring strip.
4. Curl up slowly, sliding your fingers across the measuring strip until your fingers reach the other side, then curl back down until your head touches your partner's hands. Keep your heels in contact with the mat.
5. Continue performing curl-ups without pausing until you cannot continue or until you have reached the maximum of 75 curl-ups.
6. Pace yourself at a controlled rate of 20 curl-ups per minute, or about 1 curl-up every 3 seconds.
7. Have your partner count and record your results. The count is made when your head returns to your partner's hands on the mat.
8. Cool down after testing.

Partial curl-up test

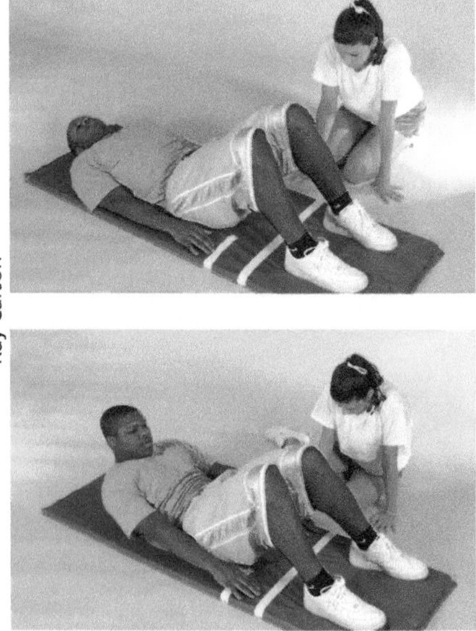

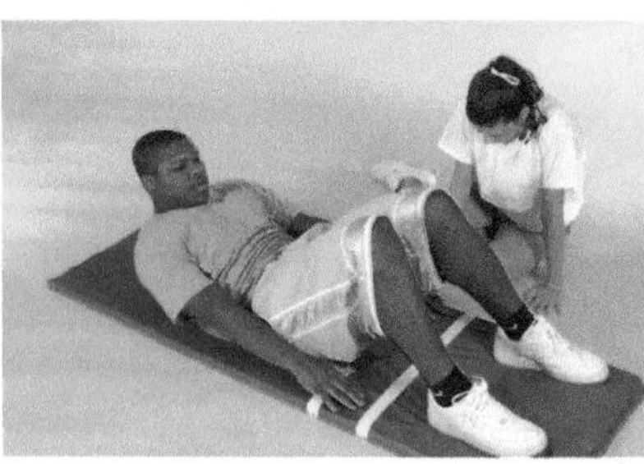

Ray Carson

Partial Curl-Up Test

Equipment/Facilities: This test requires a mat. A cadence should be called or played on a pre-recorded tape. The rhythm should be approximately 20 partial curl-ups per minute or 1 partial curl-up every 3 seconds.

Procedures:

1. Warm up prior to testing.
2. Lie flat on your back with your knees bent, feet on the floor, and heels 12 inches from your buttocks. Your arms are extended forward with fingers resting on the legs and pointing toward the knees.
3. Have your partner use his hands to make a resting place for your head.
4. Curl up slowly sliding your fingers up the legs until the fingertips touch the knees, then back down until your head touches your partner's hands.
5. Continue performing partial curl-ups without pausing until you cannot continue or until you have reached the health fitness standard.
6. Pace yourself at a controlled rate of 20 partial curl-ups per minute, or 1 partial curl-up every 3 seconds.
7. Have your partner count and record your results. The count is made when your head returns to your partner's hands on the mat.
8. Cool down after testing.

Pull-Up Test

Equipment/Facilities: This test requires a horizontal bar at a height that allows you to hang with your arms fully extended and your feet clear of the floor.

Procedures:

1. Warm up prior to testing.
2. With your arms straight, hang from the bar with the palms of your hands facing away from your body.
3. Pull your body upward until your chin is lifted over the bar, then return to the starting position.
4. Perform as many pull-ups as possible.
5. Your score is the number of completed pull-ups performed. To be counted, your pull-up must result in your chin being lifted over the bar and you returning to the full hanging position with elbows fully extended.
6. No swinging, kicking, or other jerky movements are allowed.
7. Cool down after testing.

Flexed Arm Hang Test

Equipment/Facilities: This test requires a stopwatch, chair, and a horizontal bar at a height that allows you to hang with your arms fully extended and your feet clear of the floor.

Procedures:

1. Warm up prior to testing.
2. Grasp the bar (hands are shoulder-width apart) with an overhand grip (palms facing away from the body). With the assistance of a partner or the chair, raise your body off the ground to a position where your chin is above the bar, elbows are flexed, and chest is close to the bar.
3. Have your partner start a stopwatch as soon as you take this position. Hold this position as long as possible.
4. Have your partner stop the watch when your chin touches the bar, or your head tilts backward to keep your chin above the bar, or your chin falls below the level of the bar.
5. Your score is the number of seconds you are able to maintain the correct position.
6. Cool down after testing.

Consumer Issues

Do not fall for claims that a product can burn fat off a particular part of the body (for example, the buttocks, hips, or stomach). Achieving a major change in your appearance requires sensible eating and regular participation in physical activity that works the whole body.

Ray Carson

Push-Up Test

Equipment/Facilities: **This test requires a mat. A cadence should be called or played on a prerecorded tape. The rhythm should be approximately 20 push-ups per minute, or 1 push-up every 3 seconds.**

Procedures:

1. Warm up prior to testing.
2. Lie down on your stomach on the mat. Place your hands under your shoulders, fingers stretched out, legs straight and slightly apart, and toes tucked under.
   Push up off the mat with your arms until your arms are straight, keeping your legs and back straight. Your back should be kept in a straight line from your head to your toes throughout the test.
3. Lower your body with your arms until your elbows bend at a 90-degree angle and your upper arms are parallel to the floor. Return to the starting straight arm position.
4. Continue performing push-ups without pausing until you cannot continue.
5. Pace yourself at a rhythm of about 20 push-ups per minute, or about 1 push-up every 3 seconds.
6. Have your partner count and record your results. The count is made when you return to the starting straight-arm position.
7. Cool down after testing.

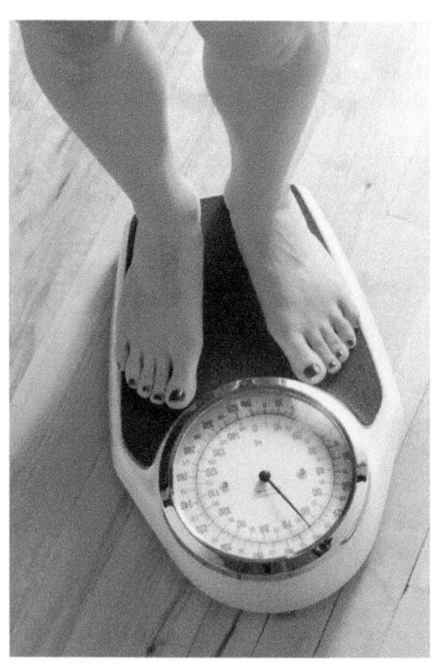

Photodisc

Body Mass Index (BMI)

Equipment/Facilities: **This test requires a weight scale and yardstick, wall measure, or weight scale with a height measuring device.**

Procedures:

1. Take off your shoes and measure your body weight on a scale. Record your weight to the nearest pound.
2. Without shoes, measure your height standing fully erect. Record your height to the one-half inch.
3. BMI is determined by dividing the body weight measured in kilograms by the height measured to the nearest meter squared.
$$\frac{\text{Weight (kg)}}{\text{Height (m)}^2}$$
4. Calculate your weight in kilograms by dividing your weight in pounds by 2.2. Calculate your height in meters by multiplying your height in inches by 2.54 and divide by 100.
   For example:
   If your weight in pounds = 180, your weight in kilograms is 180/2.2 = 82.
   If your height in inches = 72 (6'), your height in meters is 72 × 2.54/100 = 1.83.
   Square your height in meters: 1.83 × 1.83 = 3.3.
5. Calculate your BMI = 82/3.3 = 25.

Triceps and Calf Skinfolds Test

Equipment/Facilities: This test requires a skinfold caliper and a marking pencil.

Procedures:

1. Have your partner mark the following sites with a marking pencil:
   triceps: midpoint between your shoulder and your elbow on the back of your right arm
   calf: inside your right lower leg at the largest part of your calf
2. When measuring your triceps skinfold, stand erect with your right arm relaxed and your palm facing your leg.
3. When measuring your calf skinfold, place your right foot on an elevated surface, or sit in a chair so that your knee is bent at a 90-degree angle.
4. Have your partner take the measurements by pinching a fold of your skin between the thumb and forefinger slightly above the mark. Your partner should then place the skinfold caliper one-half inch below the pinch site in the middle of the fold.
5. Have your partner take one measurement at each site before doing the second measurement at each site and finally the third set of measurements. Read the skinfold to the nearest 0.05 millimeter. Disregard the highest and lowest reading and record the middle measurement.
6. Add the middle measurement of your three triceps measurements to the middle measurement of your three calf measurements.
7. Have your partner record your results (sum obtained in #6). Use the Body Composition Conversion Charts in the appendix to determine your percent body fat based on the total of your skinfold measurements.

Body composition can be evaluated in several ways. Underwater weighing is the most accurate method of determining what percent of body weight is fat. However, this method requires expensive equipment and trained personnel. Body composition is more commonly assessed by measuring the thickness of skinfolds, using a device called a skinfold caliper. Triceps and calf skinfold measurements provide a good estimate of the percent of body weight that is fat. Another common measurement of body composition widely used today is **body mass index (BMI).** The body mass index provides an indication of the appropriateness of your weight relative to your height. However, BMI does not indicate the percent of fat.

Triceps and calf skinfold measurements assess body composition.

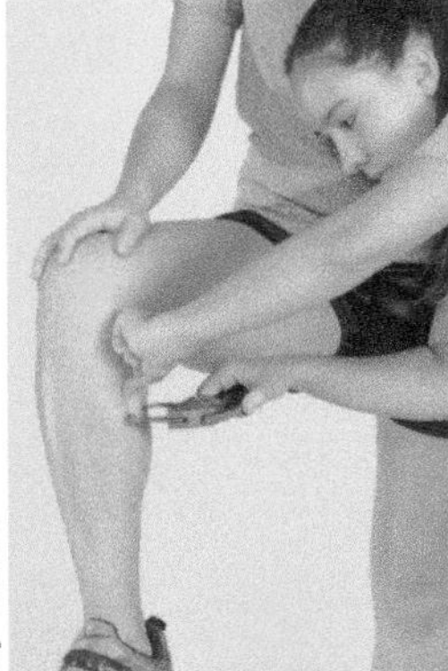

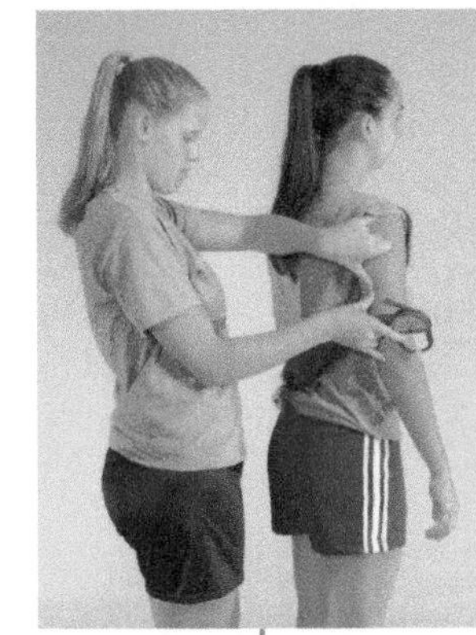

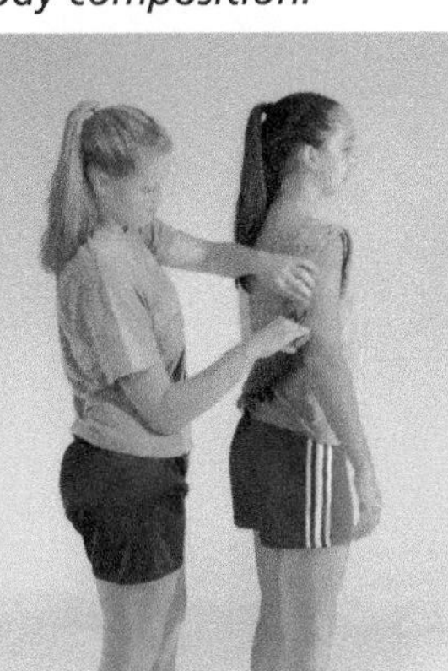

Ray Carson

Skill-Related
Fitness

There are six skill-related components of physical fitness: agility, balance, power, reaction time, coordination, and speed. These factors contribute to your ability to successfully participate in sports activities. Regular participation in sports or other recreational pursuits can have a positive influence on your health and fitness. Individuals who have a high level of skill-related fitness are more likely to be physically active than those who have a lower level of skill.

Agility

Agility is the ability to change the position of your body and to control the movement of your whole body. Agility is an important quality in many sports, because you must change direction rapidly and always have your body under control.

Corbis

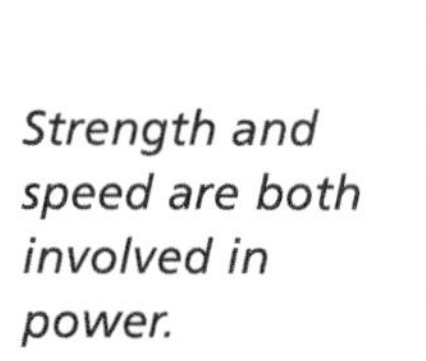

Strength and speed are both involved in power.

Agility tests are similar to conditioning and practice drills used in various sports. Shuttle runs, zigzag runs, and the hexagonal jump are some examples of ways to measure agility.

Balance

Balance is the ability to keep an upright posture while either standing still or moving. Good balance is essential to being successful in activities such as ice skating, skiing, surfing, and gymnastics.

Many challenging tasks can be used to evaluate balance. Some examples are standing as long as possible on the ball of one foot; standing as long as possible on a balance board or roller board with one foot or both feet; walking on a balance beam; doing headstands; and doing handstands.

Photodisc

Standing on one foot measures static balance. Walking on a balance beam measures dynamic balance.

Power

Power is the ability to perform with strength at a rapid pace. Strength and speed are both involved in power. Football players, swimmers, shot-putters, discus throwers, and high jumpers are examples of athletes who typically have a high degree of power.

The vertical jump and the standing long jump are commonly used to assess power.

Reaction Time

Reaction time is the amount of time it takes to start a movement once your senses signal the need to move. People with good reaction time can usually start quickly in track and swimming or react quickly in ping-pong or karate.

Photodisc

Coordination is the integration of eye, hand, and foot movements.

A very simple assessment of reaction time is the yardstick test. The object of this test is to catch the yardstick as quickly as possible when it starts to fall. Scoring is based on how far the yardstick falls before you catch it.

Coordination

Coordination is the integration of eye, hand, and foot movements. This component is necessary for success in such sports as baseball, softball, tennis, golf, and basketball, where good hand-eye coordination is essential.

Like agility, tests of coordination are similar to conditioning and practice drills used in various sports. Some examples are dribbling and shooting in basketball, place kicking and punting in football, and dribbling in soccer.

Corel

Speed is the ability to cover a distance in a short time.

Speed

Speed is the ability to cover a distance in a short time. Speed is a very important factor in many sports activities.

Short runs are used to evaluate speed. Examples of such tests are the 100-meter dash and the 200-meter dash.

Fitness Assessment

Before beginning a personal fitness program, you should know your level of flexibility, cardiovascular fitness, muscular strength and endurance, and body composition. You should also know how to assess each of these components and how to interpret the results. The first assessment, or pre-test, will help you determine your present fitness level and provide you with a basis for setting realistic goals. The post-test, at the conclusion of the instructional program, will help you determine the progress you made toward your goals and assist you in setting new goals.

Periodic self-testing is an effective way to monitor your progress, determine the effectiveness of your personal fitness program, and reevaluate and update your goals. This is why it is important for you to be able to assess yourself and interpret the results. You are encouraged to test yourself anytime you wish to check your progress. Self-testing enables you to determine when and how much to change your personal fitness program. It also allows you to check your progress toward your desired level of health-related fitness. By repeating the tests from time to time, you will develop a better understanding of your personal fitness needs and confidence in your ability to solve your own fitness problems.

Interpreting Assessment Results

Some physical fitness tests use norms to indicate fitness levels. These are called **norm-referenced tests.** Assessment results are indicated in percentile rankings. Percentile rankings represent the percentage of individuals of the same age and sex who scored at or below your test score. If you performed at the 75th percentile, you achieved a score better than 75 percent of those in your age group. Percentile rankings, however, should only be used as an indication of your strengths and weaknesses, not as a means of comparing yourself to other people. Remember that fitness is a personal matter. Compete with yourself, not with others. It is important that you do not over-train.

Other physical fitness tests use specific standards to judge fitness levels. These are called **criterion-referenced tests. Health-related fitness standards** represent satisfactory levels or ranges of flexibility, cardiovascular fitness, muscular strength and endurance, and body composition necessary for good health. Achieving these standards is important to good health. Not only will you be less susceptible to various health problems if you attain these standards, but you will also be more likely to look good and feel good.

The charts on pages 42 and 43 illustrate the health fitness standards from the *President's Challenge Health Fitness Test,* a test endorsed by the President's Council on Physical Fitness and Sports and the healthy fitness zone standards from The Cooper Institute for Aerobics Research *FITNESSGRAM*, a test endorsed by the American Alliance for Health, Physical Education, Recreation and Dance. These charts represent the health-related fitness tests described earlier in this chapter.

Achieving acceptable health-related fitness standards is important to good health.

Goal Setting

In Chapter 3 you will learn about the importance of goal setting in relation to health and fitness. When you develop your goals, it is essential that you use the information regarding your present level of fitness. That is the purpose of the pre-test.

It is important to remember that individuals will improve at different rates. If you score far below the health fitness standard in a particular component, you have the potential to make enormous progress in that area. If you score near, at, or above the standard, you may improve only moderately. The more fit you are, the harder you will have to work to make small gains. Less-fit individuals may show dramatic improvement, yet remain far below their potential. The important thing is to do the best you can. Remember that physical fitness benefits everyone.

PFP Technology Activity

Enter your pre-test health-related fitness test scores using the software program provided by your teacher or in a database software program. When finished, save the information to your PFP file and/or print out the results and place it in your PFP notebook. You will use these results in setting goals for each of the health-related components of fitness.

Health Fitness Standards Chart

Males												
Age	13		14		15		16		17		17+	
HFZ	Lower	Upper	Lower	Upper	Lower	Upper	Lower	Upper	Lower	Upper	Lower	Upper
FLEXIBILITY												
Trunk Lift (inches)	9	12	9	12	9	12	9	12	9	12	9	12
Back Saver Sit-and-Reach** (inches)	8		8		8		8		8		8	
Shoulder Stretch	Passing = touching fingertips together behind the back											
V-Sit Reach (inches)	1		1		1		1		1			
Sit-and-Reach (centimeters)	21		21		21		21		21			
CARDIOVASCULAR												
PACER (# laps)	41	72	41	83	51	94	61	94	61	94	61	94
One-Mile Run (min:sec)	10:00	7:30	9:30	7:00	9:00	7:00	8:30	7:00	8:30	7:00	8:30	7:00
One-Mile Run (min:sec)	8:00		8:00		7:30		7:30		7:30			
Cooper 1–1/2 Mile Run	12:30		12:30		12:30		12:30		12:30		12:30	
MUSCULAR STRENGTH AND ENDURANCE												
Curl-Up (# complete)	21	40	24	45	24	47	24	47	24	47	24	47
Partial Curl-Up (# complete)	25		25		30		30		30			
Pull-Up (# complete)	1	4	2	5	3	7	5	8	5	8	5	8
Pull-Up (# complete)	2		3		4		5		6			
Flexed Arm Hang (seconds)	12	17	15	20	15	20	15	20	15	20	15	20
Push-Up (# complete)	12	25	14	30	16	35	18	35	18	35	18	35
Push-Up (# complete)	10		12		14		16		18			
BODY COMPOSITION												
Skinfold Measurement (% fat)	25	10	25	10	25	10	25	10	25	10	25	10
Body Mass Index	23	16.6	24.5	17.5	25	18.1	26.5	18.5	27	18.8	27.8	19
Body Mass Index	24.7	15.4	25.4	16.1	26.4	16.6	26.8	17.2	27.5	17.7		

* Number on left is lower end of HFZ; number on right is upper end of HFZ.

** Test scored Pass/Fail; must reach this distance to pass.

*** Non-shaded rows—source: With permission from The Cooper Institute for Aerobics Research, *Fitnessgram Test Administration Manual* (Dallas, TX: 1999), 38.

****Shaded rows—source: With permission from The President's Council on Physical Fitness and Sports, *The President's Challenge* (Bloomington, IN, 2002–2003), 23.

Health Fitness Standards Chart

Females												
Age	13		14		15		16		17		17+	
HFZ	Lower	Upper	Lower	Upper	Lower	Upper	Lower	Upper	Lower	Upper	Lower	Upper
FLEXIBILITY												
Trunk Lift (inches)	9	12	9	12	9	12	9	12	9	12	9	12
Back Saver Sit-and-Reach** (inches)	10		10		12		12		12		12	
Shoulder Stretch	Passing = touching fingertips together behind the back											
V-Sit Reach (inches)	3		3		3		3		3			
Sit-and-Reach (centimeters)	25		25		25		25		25			
CARDIOVASCULAR												
PACER (# laps)	23	51	23	51	23	51	32	61	41	61	41	61
One-Mile Run (min:sec)	11:30	9:00	11:00	8:30	10:30	8:00	10:00	8:00	10:00	8:00	10:00	8:00
One-Mile Run (min:sec)	10:30		10:30		10:00		10:00		10:00			
Cooper 1–1/2 Mile Run	15:20		15:20		15:20		15:20		15:20		15:20	
MUSCULAR STRENGTH AND ENDURANCE												
Curl-Up (# complete)	18	32	18	32	18	35	18	35	18	35	18	35
Partial Curl-Up (# complete)	25		25		30		30		30			
Pull-Up (# complete)	1	2	1	2	1	2	1	2	1	2	1	2
Pull-Up (# complete)	1		1		1		1		1			
Flexed Arm Hang (seconds)	8	12	8	12	8	12	8	12	8	12	8	12
Push-Up (# complete)	7	15	7	15	7	15	7	15	7	15	7	15
Push-Up (# complete)	7		7		7		7		7			
BODY COMPOSITION												
Skinfold Measurement (% fat)	32	17	32	17	32	17	32	17	32	17	32	17
Body Mass Index	24.5	17.5	25	17.5	25	17.5	25	17.5	26	17.5	27.3	18
Body Mass Index	25.3	15.5	25.3	16.2	26.5	16.6	26.5	16.8	26.9	17.1		

* Number on left is lower end of HFZ; number on right is upper end of HFZ.
** Test scored Pass/Fail; must reach this distance to pass.
*** Non-shaded rows—source: With permission from The Cooper Institute for Aerobics Research, *Fitnessgram Test Administration Manual* (Dallas, TX: 1999), 39.
****Shaded rows—source: With permission from The President's Council on Physical Fitness and Sports, *The President's Challenge* (Bloomington, IN, 2002–2003), 23.

PFP Update

The experiences you have had in this chapter and with the health-related fitness assessments have provided you with crucial information and knowledge that will enable you to develop realistic goals for your PFP. Remember, periodic self-testing is an effective way to monitor your progress and re-evaluate and update your goals.

Changing old habits is difficult, so do not feel badly if you have found it hard to follow your plan on a regular basis. What you are undertaking is challenging, but you can be successful if you think of progress in small steps. It may have taken you a long time to get out of shape or to establish bad habits, so changing them and getting into good condition will not happen overnight. The key is to keep wanting to improve yourself. Nothing succeeds like success.

If you are having problems following through, find a friend or family member who will be supportive of your efforts to self improve. This has proven to be an important factor in success in any endeavor. Discuss your concerns with other classmates, too, because they may also be having problems with their PFPs. Be sure to ask your teacher for help.

Summary

There are two kinds of physical fitness: health-related fitness and skill-related fitness. The health-related fitness components are essential to a healthy lifestyle and the prevention of health problems. That is why they are called health-related. The five health-related fitness components are flexibility, cardiovascular fitness, muscular strength, muscular endurance, and body composition.

The skill-related fitness components are concerned with abilities related to sports activities. They include agility, balance, power, reaction time, coordination, and speed.

There are several tests to measure each component of physical fitness. Knowledge of how to conduct these tests will allow you to determine your fitness level throughout life. Some physical fitness test results are indicated in percentile rankings and are called norm-referenced tests. Others use specific standards to judge your fitness status and are called criterion-referenced tests.

Before beginning a personal fitness program, you should know your current level of health-related fitness in order to set realistic goals. Self-testing is an effective way to monitor your program. This is why it is crucial for you know how to evaluate yourself and interpret the results and keep from causing harm to your body by over-training.

Physical fitness is for everyone. You do not have to be a good athlete to be physically fit. If you regularly engage in physical activity and follow basic training principles, you will improve your health-related fitness.

Photodisc

The Wrap-Up

Vocabulary—Matching

Match the definitions to the correct term.

1. Balance
2. Cardiovascular fitness
3. Speed
4. Muscular endurance
5. Coordination
6. Flexibility
7. Reaction time
8. Body composition
9. Power
10. Agility
11. Skill-related fitness
12. Health-related fitness
13. Muscular strength
14. Body mass index (BMI)
15. Norm-referenced tests
16. Criterion-referenced tests
17. Health-related fitness standards

A. range of movement possible at various joints
B. ratio of fat to muscle, bone, and other tissue
C. ability to change the position of your body and control the movement of your body
D. ability to cover a distance in a short time
E. integration of eye, hand, and foot movements
F. amount of time it takes to get moving
G. ability to do strength performances at a rapid pace
H. ability of the circulatory and respiratory systems to supply oxygen to muscles during exercise
I. ability to keep an upright posture while either standing still or moving
J. ability to use muscles for long periods of time
K. components of fitness that helps one to be successful in sports
L. the ability of muscles to exert a force one time
M. indication of the appropriateness of your weight relative to your height
N. physical fitness tests in which norms are used to indicate fitness levels
O. satisfactory or healthy levels of flexibility, cardiovascular fitness, muscular strength and endurance, and body composition
P. components of fitness that contribute to the operation of the systems of the body
Q. physical fitness tests in which specific standards are used to judge fitness levels

Multiple Choice

Select the most correct answer.

18. The health-related components of physical fitness are most associated with
- **A.** how fast you improve.
- **B.** how well the systems of your body operate.
- **C.** how well you perform in sports activities.
- **D.** your level of athletic ability.

19. Which test measures the flexibility of the lower back and hamstrings?
- **A.** back-saver sit-and-reach
- **B.** prone trunk extension
- **C.** push-ups
- **D.** shoulder stretch

20. Which can be used to assess cardiovascular fitness?
- **A.** 200-meter dash
- **B.** 1-mile run
- **C.** 12-minute run
- **D.** both B and C

21. The ability of muscles to exert a force one time is called
- **A.** muscular endurance.
- **B.** muscular strength.
- **C.** power.
- **D.** reaction time.

22. Which item would not assess body composition?
- **A.** body mass index (BMI)
- **B.** curl-ups
- **C.** skinfold measurements
- **D.** underwater weighing

23. The purpose of the initial fitness assessment, or pre-test, is
- **A.** to compare students to each other.
- **B.** to identify your strengths and weaknesses.
- **C.** to provide you with a basis for setting realistic goals.
- **D.** B and C are both correct.

24. Periodic fitness self-testing is an effective way to
   A. determine the effectiveness of your personal fitness program.
   B. monitor your progress.
   C. re-evaluate and update your previously set goals.
   D. all of the above.

25. Physical fitness tests that indicate results in percentile rankings are called
   A. criterion-referenced tests.
   B. health-related tests.
   C. norm-referenced tests.
   D. skill-related tests.

26. Health fitness standards are best described as
   A. a method of comparing yourself to other people.
   B. percentage of individuals of the same age and sex who scored at or below your test score.
   C. satisfactory levels or ranges of flexibility, cardiovascular fitness, muscular strength and endurance, and body composition necessary for good health.
   D. scoring at the 85th percentile.

27. When you develop your personal fitness goals, it is essential that you
   A. compare the fitness level of friends of the same age.
   B. compare the fitness level of friends of the same weight.
   C. utilize the information regarding your current level of fitness.
   D. A and B are correct.

Authentic Assessment—Short Response

28. What is the difference between health-related fitness and skill-related fitness?

29. Why should everyone be concerned about health-related fitness?

30. What are some tests for assessing each of the health-related components of fitness?

31. Why is it important to know how to assess your own physical fitness level?

32. Describe the difference between norm-referenced tests and criterion-referenced tests.

Authentic Assessment—Extended Response

33. **Writing situation:** You do not have to be a good athlete to be physically fit.

    Directions for writing: Think about individuals you know who you think are physically fit. Describe the individuals, explaining why you think they are so fit.

34. **Writing situation:** The health-related fitness components are essential to a healthy lifestyle and the prevention of health problems.

    Directions for writing: Write public service announcements that promote regular participation in physical activity. The focus of the PSAs should be on the enhancement of the health-related components of fitness.

3

Goal Setting for Teenagers

Photodisc

Objectives

As you read this chapter, look for answers to these key questions:

- How can you take more responsibility for your health and fitness?
- What are goals?
- What is goal setting?
- What is the difference between long-term goals and short-term goals?
- What are the steps necessary for successful goal setting?

"Nothing can stop people with the right mental attitude from achieving their goals."

—Thomas Jefferson

V • A • L • U • E

Goal setting is a process that can provide guidance to improve yourself. It is a simple process but one that has excellent potential to help you achieve new levels of accomplishment. Goal setting does not just apply to personal fitness. The process applies to all aspects of your life such as how to get along with others. Specific steps are presented that will help you become a proficient goal setter.

Chapter Preview

- Teen Years: A Topsy-Turvy Time
- Taking Control of Your Health and Fitness
- What Are Goals?
- What Is Goal Setting?
- Goal Setting Is Like a Ladder
- Goal-Setting Steps
- Goal Setting In Action
- PFP Update
- Summary
- The Wrap-Up

Vocabulary

When you have completed this chapter, you should understand the meaning of these vocabulary terms:

goal setting

long-term goals

short-term goals

timelines

desire

obstacle

Wellness Connection

Teen Years: A Topsy-Turvy Time

The term *topsy-turvy* means that things are not very certain or are in disorder. That is why the term seems appropriate to teenage life. As a teenager, you might disagree with this point, because you are one of the lucky people who are happy with their lives. However, it is true that many teenagers find this period of time confusing and frustrating. As a teen, you are in a transition from childhood to adulthood. During this transition, you experience physical, social, emotional, and mental changes. These changes bring both good and not-so-good experiences. The good changes include physical maturation, a sense of independence, the discovery of new abilities, and the satisfaction of taking care of yourself. The not-so-good changes include unusual physical differences between peers, moodiness, self-consciousness, discovery of personal limitations, and difficulties involved in taking on new responsibilities.

Although the teen years are an emotionally unsettled time, they are also a fantastic time of learning how to take more and more control of your own life. Up until this time in your life, your parents have probably made the majority of the decisions on what you ate, what you wore, where you went, who your friends were, and the activities in which you were involved. Now you must take more responsibility in making these decisions. Of course, you will still need some guidance from your parents and teachers to help you refine your decision-making ability.

Taking Control of Your Health and Fitness

Now that you are starting to have more control over your own life, you need to accept responsibility for it. Two of the most obvious aspects that need a tremendous amount of attention are your health and fitness. Making responsible decisions on diet, exercise, and the use of your time have an important impact on your lifestyle. As you know, your body image has a direct effect on how you feel about yourself overall. Learning to make appropriate decisions about your personal program of health and fitness behaviors (PFP) is essential to becoming happy and successful.

Teen years bring about good and not-so-good feelings caused by changes in a person's physical, social, emotional, and mental being.

Photodisc

Do you have friends who would like to be stronger, weigh a few pounds less, or play some sports activity? Undoubtedly you do. The question therefore arises, if they want these things, why don't they do them? Unfortunately, there is a big gap between wanting something in your life and making it happen. Wouldn't it be nice to just wish for something and have it happen? Who wouldn't like a money tree in the backyard? However, having a money tree is a wish and not an attainable goal. A *realistic* goal of having additional spending money will take more than a wish; it will require effort on your part.

One major reason why people are not as healthy and physically active as they desire to be is that they have never been taught how to attain these goals. This personal fitness course is a great start in the right direction, but the responsibility for making proper decisions about your own health and physical fitness is yours. This chapter will discuss goal setting as a means of helping you realize more of your potential.

What Are Goals?

Almost anything you desire can be a goal. Buying a car, getting better grades, changing your body weight, getting stronger, or making the track team could be personal goals. Goals serve as a guide for what you do and give you something to work toward. Setting personal goals help you do your best and achieve the things you want in life.

GOAL SETTING
Reward yourself when you accomplish a goal.

In this course, the focus is on health-related fitness. Therefore, you will be encouraged to set goals in flexibility, cardiovascular fitness, muscular fitness, and body composition. You will also be encouraged to set health-related goals in nutrition, weight control and stress management.

What Is Goal Setting?

Goal setting is a process that can help you improve yourself and, therefore, feel good about yourself. It is a means of getting you motivated about self-improvement and lifestyle. The following sections on long-term goals, short-term goals, and the steps involved in the goal-setting process will help you understand goal setting. It is not a difficult process, but it will take effort and commitment on your part.

Safety Awareness

Being fortunate is more often associated with making good decisions than having luck. For example, never enter a street between two parked cars when you are jogging, unless you wish to increase the odds of having bad luck. Always attempt to cross a street at a traffic signal.

Long-Term Goals

Although you might not realize it, you probably set goals all the time. Some of your goals might take a long time to reach, perhaps years. An example of a long-term goal would be to go to college and study to become a doctor or computer programmer. Another long-term goal could be to save money to buy a car. But long-term goals do not have to take years. You might want to accomplish the goal of becoming a leader in student government, during this semester; that would also be a long-term goal. None of these examples can be achieved in a short period of time. But all can be achieved with the use of short-term goals.

Photodisc

Goals help you take control of your life.

Short-Term Goals

Short-term goals are goals that can be established to help you either achieve a long-term goal, or help you accomplish something in a short period of time. Short-term goals can be reached in a few days or weeks. Short-term goals are usually specific, while long-term goals may be more general. Examples of some short-term goals include studying hard to get a good grade on next week's algebra test or earning enough money to buy concert tickets for this weekend.

Goal Setting Is Like a Ladder

The establishment of goals can be compared to a ladder. Think of the top rung of a ladder as your long-term goal and the rungs leading to it as your short-term goals. Each rung (short-term goal) you climb will put you in a better position to reach your long-term goal. Notice how the ladder in the drawing illustrates this analogy. In this situation, the person wants to lose 10 pounds—the long-term goal represented as the top rung on the ladder. Instead of just setting a long-term goal of losing 10 pounds, which is difficult for many people, this person set 10 short-term goals of losing one pound per week, represented by each of the 10 rungs on the ladder. It is important for anyone who is just beginning to set goals to start by setting short-term goals. These goals should not be too difficult to achieve, and you will feel good when you've reached one. Reaching one can act as motivation to encourage you to reach the next rung (short-term goal) on the ladder. By setting goals using the ladder method, you will see concrete progress and develop a sense of confidence. An increased feeling of self-confidence can inspire you to want to reach for higher rungs on your performance ladder.

Long Term Goal

-10 Pounds	Week 10
-9 Pounds	Week 9
-8 Pounds	Week 8
-7 Pounds	Week 7
-6 Pounds	Week 6
-5 Pounds	Week 5
-4 Pounds	Week 4
-3 Pounds	Week 3
-2 Pounds	Week 2
-1 Pounds	Week 1

Use short-term goals to reach a long-term goal.

Goal-Setting Steps

The following information on how to set personal goals will be of value to you only if you sincerely wish to make a change in your lifestyle.

Internet Resources

On Line Activity Log—The Center for Health and Health Care in Schools
http://www.healthinschools.org/2003/july18_alert.asp

Fitness Awards Program—The President's Council on Physical Fitness and Sports
http://fitness.gov/sports/sports.html

Find Your Exercise Profile—American Heart Association
http://www.justmove.org/diary/login.cfm

Desire

Desire is the most important factor in goal setting. Wanting to improve yourself in some way is essential before you can start setting goals. Goals are personal. Parents, friends, or teachers cannot set goals for you. It is completely up to you. Other people can help you only after you have decided how you want to change. In what ways would you like to improve yourself?

Belief

Wanting to make a change and doing it are two different things. You undoubtedly know people who want to stop smoking or lose 15 pounds but never do it. Why do you suppose this is the case? In all probability, they simply did not believe they could do it. An important point to remember is that if you believe you cannot do something, you probably cannot. On the other hand, if you really believe you can do something, you have a chance of accomplishing it. Want power can become will power.

Analyze Where You Are Now

Knowing your starting point is essential to establish both short-term and long-term goals. For example, if you wish to lose ten pounds, you need to know exactly what you weigh now. Or if you want to improve your diet, it would be important to know what you currently eat over a two- or three-day period of time. Recording everything you eat and drink provides valuable information needed in identifying the steps to take for improvement to occur. You may have already taken a pre-test on your physical fitness level. If you have, you know what your starting points are in regard to your flexibility, cardiovascular efficiency, muscular strength and endurance, and body composition.

Nutrition Information

Are you aware of certain "cue" foods you eat? A bag of cookies or bar of candy gives you the cue to pick it up and eat it, even when you are not hungry. If your goal is to lose weight, remove the cue foods in your house, car, or backpack.

Photodisc

A winner is someone who has moved out of the "comfort zone." Such an individual has learned to set goals that are neither too hard nor too easy.

Set Realistic Goals

It is important for you to set goals that are realistic. A realistic goal is one you can reach. If your goals are too hard to reach, you may become discouraged and give up. If they are too easy, you may lose interest in them. Try to set goals that will stretch you and will move you out of a comfort zone.

Accomplishing something that has pushed your mental strength to a new level will make you feel good about yourself and prepare you to want to reach for higher goals. Realistic goals are those both reachable and challenging.

Realistic goal setting is based on your current level of physical fitness. For example, if you are only able to jog 440 yards without stopping, setting a goal of being able to jog a mile in 8 minutes in a month's time is probably unrealistic. A realistic goal for someone with this level of fitness may be to jog a mile in 12 minutes at the end of a month's time. In a four-month period of time, the individual would be able to jog the mile in 8 minutes. Similarly, if you can only do one pull-up, setting a goal of 10 additional pull-ups in a month's time may be unrealistic. On the other hand, setting a goal of 3 pull-ups in a month's time is realistic. Over a longer period of time, a goal of 10 pull-ups could be obtained and would be a realistic goal.

Stress Information

Reduce a big project down into small parts. Select the easiest part of the project to work on first. By breaking down large projects, you will not become overwhelmed and delay starting the project.

Write Your Goals in Detail

Putting your goals down on paper helps you to clarify what you want to do. When you think of something you want, it is just a wish. When it is on paper, you are moving the idea along the road to success. Writing down your goals will allow you to get a clearer picture of what you want to do. You may need to go back and be more specific with the goals in your PFP.

List the Benefits You Will Receive

Identifying how you will benefit from accomplishing your goals is a very important step because the benefits you list will help make your desire stronger and, therefore, make your belief in yourself stronger. For example, if you want to begin a weight-lifting program so that you will look

Corel

Realistic goals are those both reachable and challenging.

better, what personal benefits would you list? The following are just a few of the benefits you would probably hope to gain:

- Improved body image
- Energy
- Improved endurance
- Increased self-confidence and self-esteem
- Greater enjoyment of all types of physical activities

The more benefits you can list for accomplishing your goal, the greater will be your desire to make it happen. Remember the discussion in Chapter 1 about the health benefits of being physically active? The benefits obtained from this course, as is the case in all classes, is a direct result of the efforts you put forth. The only difference here is that the benefits could become a matter of life or death.

Identify Obstacles

If you have never set goals before, you may not foresee the blocks or obstacles to attaining your goals. On the other hand, if you have tried to do something and failed, an obstacle may have been the doubt that you could really follow through and achieve your desired goal. Some obstacles may center on you, while other obstacles may center on your friends or your family. There is very little you cannot achieve in the areas of health and fitness if you have the will power and belief in yourself. In your own life you are in the driver's seat and have the power to shape your lifestyle.

Consumer Issues

When shopping for a health product that you think would help to achieve your goals, report any product you believe is being falsely advertised. Contact your state attorney general's office, state department of health, or the local consumer protection agency. These offices are often listed in the blue pages of your telephone book.

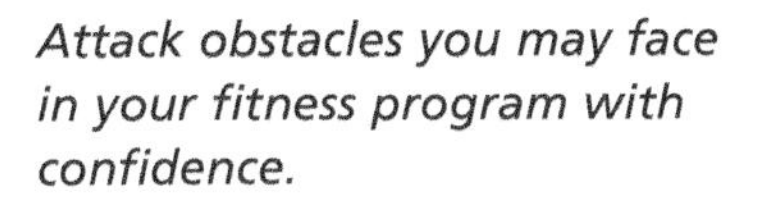
Attack obstacles you may face in your fitness program with confidence.

Identify Knowledge You Will Need

Wanting something and achieving it are two different things. If you want to reduce the stress in your life, you cannot wish it away. You will need to know how to reduce your stress before it can actually be reduced. This need for knowledge applies to any goal you set. Your physical education teacher will be able to help you gain the knowledge you need to reach your goals.

Make a Plan of Action

Photodisc

Wanting something and achieving it are two different things.

After all information has been collected, make a game plan; that is, outline a step-by-step strategy for accomplishing your goals. If your game plan is set up properly, you will experience success quickly and insure your continued progress toward attaining your goals.

Develop a Timeline

While it is not easy to know exactly when you can accomplish your fitness goals, you may be able to get a pretty good idea, particularly if you seek advice from your physical education teacher. Setting timelines, times when something will be completed, is a simple and effective method to organize and plot your course to a major goal. Think of a physical fitness goal you would like to achieve this semester. For example, suppose you want to jog without stopping for 30 minutes by the end of the semester. The drawing of a timeline shows how this could be done. Notice that while a timeline does not provide you with the strategies to reach your long-term goal, it does set deadlines for making progress toward that goal.

Writing out your goals and putting them on a timeline makes it easier to accomplish them. A timeline does the following:

- gives you a better sense of control, organization, and direction
- promotes greater commitment to your goals
- helps relieve worry and confusion, especially as your individual deadlines approach
- helps you pace your efforts
- creates a sense of urgency to reach goals

A timeline helps you to pace your efforts toward reaching your goal.

Jogging Time in Minutes

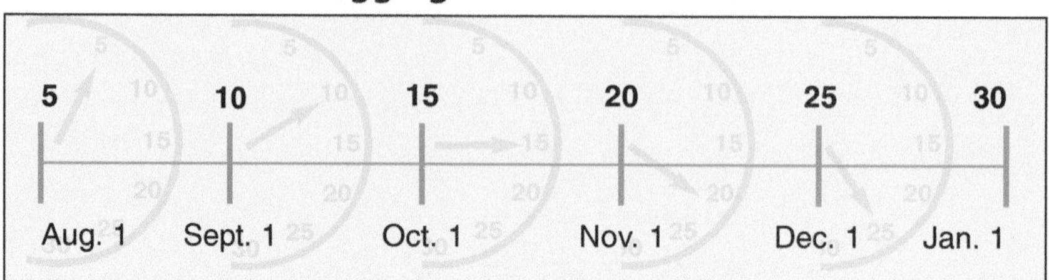

Monitor Your Progress

Any goal setting should be accompanied by continuous monitoring to determine whether your goals are still reasonable. You might find that you need to readjust your short-term goals or even your long-term goals. A good monitoring process will keep you from wasting time or losing interest in your goal. Losing the belief that you can stick to your program is self-defeating. If this happens, get feedback from your parents, physical education teachers, or supportive friends.

Corbis

Never give up on your goals.

Never Give Up

Back your plan with a determination that you will never give up. If you are just beginning to set goals, it could be very easy to give up. Do not be led astray by yourself or by others. Avoid sharing your goals with anyone who is not supportive. Be determined to take control of your lifestyle. Such determination will mean a lot to you.

Goal Setting in Action

The following case study is an example of a course of action one high school student undertook to reach her goals.

Jodi was a 15-year-old tenth-grader who did not feel comfortable in sports activities. Like most teenagers, she was concerned about looking as good as possible and feeling good about herself. Jodi was 5 feet, 4 inches tall and weighed 128 pounds. When she took the physical fitness test at the beginning of the semester, she scored at the 25th percentile level in the mile run (12:21), and her percent of body fat was much higher than she wanted. Jodi did not like scoring so low in the mile run or having such a high percent of body fat. One problem she had with her weight was the fact that some of her clothes were not fitting as well as they had a few months earlier. An even greater concern was her fear that other students would see she was gaining weight.

As a result of a discussion on goal setting in her personal fitness class, she made up her mind to lose 10 pounds, which would help reduce her percentage of body fat. She also decided she wanted to be able to run the mile at least 2 minutes and 15 seconds faster, which would raise her to the 50th percentile level (10:15) for her age. Jodi wanted to do this in 9 weeks, by the time of her next physical fitness test.

Manny Harageones

Jodi did not like scoring so low on the mile run.

Goal One

Jodi knew that in order to successfully reach her two long-term goals, she would have to set several short-term goals. She developed the following plan to meet her goals:

Manny Harageones

Jodi realized that she was eating too much junk food.

Jodi recognized that her diet contained too much junk food, but she did not know how much. Her first step was to monitor and record everything she ate and drank for 3 days. This provided her with a baseline of information about the amount and kinds of foods she was eating. An analysis of her food intake revealed that she ate very few fruits and vegetables, frequently went to fast-food restaurants, and ate too much junk food.

Based on her findings and information obtained in Chapter 9 on Nutrition, she resolved to do the following:

- Eat at fast-food restaurants no more than twice a week and to make good choices when she did.
- Reduce the amount of junk food she was eating and replace it with nutritious snacks.
- Eat at least two fruits and three vegetables every day.

Jodi knew these three changes in her nutritional behavior would not be easy, but she was tired of being just a "little overweight."

Goal Two

Manny Harageones

Jodi made a decision to eat more appropriately.

In order to reduce her mile-run time by 2 minutes and 15 seconds, Jodi knew the answer was not only to run more often, but also to be more active overall. To meet this long-term goal, she resolved to take these actions:

- Buy a pair of comfortable jogging shoes that would provide good arch support.
- Walk/jog three times a week at school for 15 minutes without worrying about distance traveled during the next four weeks.
- Cycle or play tennis with one of her parents or a friend at least twice a week.
- Jog continuously for 15 minutes by the end of the fifth week.
- Reduce her time for the mile run at least one minute (11:20) by the fifth week.

Manny Harageones

Jodi decided she needed to be more active overall.

- Increase her three training runs at school to 20 minutes duration the sixth week.
- Retake the test for the mile run and achieve the 50th percentile level by the end of the ninth week.

After writing down her goals, Jodi made the following list of benefits she would gain from accomplishing her two goals:

1. Her appearance would be improved.
2. She would be less self-conscious with her friends.
3. She would feel good about herself because she had accomplished a difficult task.
4. She would be more physically fit and confident in physical education class.
5. She would be more willing to dress out for physical education.
6. She could wear clothes at least one size smaller.
7. She would feel more confident to tackle other challenges in her life.

Throughout the 9 weeks, Jodi planned to weigh herself at the same time each Friday with the anticipation of losing from 1 to 1 1/2 pounds each week. To help her accomplish her goals, she decided to keep a personal log of her efforts in both areas. She thought that recording her feelings and activities throughout the 9 weeks would motivate her to maintain her momentum. She also planned to share her log with her physical education teacher and close friends whom she knew would give her feedback and encouragement.

When she reached the end of the 9-week time period and achieved her goals, she planned to celebrate by buying herself a new outfit. Jodi believed strongly that she would reach her goals.

Do you think Jodi was successful in reaching her goals? What were the steps she took? She certainly had all of the elements necessary to be successful:

1. She had both the desire to improve and a belief that she could do it.
2. She assessed herself and knew where she was in both of her goal areas.

Manny Harageones

Jodi felt good about herself and her appearance.

3. She identified how she would benefit from reaching her goals.
4. She set a very specific plan with specific time lines as to when she hoped to accomplish certain things.
5. She monitored her progress and planned to get the help of her physical education teacher to give her feedback and direction.
6. She believed in herself and did not give up.

Jodi had concerns similar to those of many young people. She not only wanted to look and feel as good as possible, but also wanted to perform as well as she could. If you develop a plan tailored to meet your needs, there is no doubt that you will become a successful goal setter.

PFP Technology Activity

Using a word-processing software, create a list of goals to assess your own personal physical fitness needs. Place one copy in your PFP and post another copy in your room. Additional information on HOW you will achieve these goals and WHY the goals are important to your health should also be identified.

List of Goals

1. Be more physically fit
2. Improve appearance
3. Wear clothes one size smaller
4. Improve self-confidence
5. Be more confident to tackle other challenges
6. Feel good about myself

PFP Update

Success with your PFP depends on how well you can understand and apply the "steps of goal setting." Although it might seem like there are many of them, each is important. For example, it is important that you list the benefits you believe you will gain if you follow your program goals. Most teens want to improve their physical appearance, and this certainly is a benefit of following a PFP.

Another important step is to identify obstacles or barriers. Would it be a wise decision to hang around someone who made fun of your efforts to self improve? The answer is obvious—no one needs friends like that. Confide in friends who want you to succeed and who will be urging you to achieve a higher goal.

Seek help from your teacher to write behavioral goals. By changing your behavior, you will have more success in reaching your long-term goals. It would also be helpful to work with another person in class so that each of you could encourage the other. Are you keeping a diary of your activities?

Summary

The teen years can be a difficult time as well as a positive time. Learning to take control of your life through good decision making can be very rewarding. You will find that effective goal setting will be a natural, positive force in your life. If done properly, the process will give you added confidence and a stronger belief in yourself as you take control of various aspects of your life.

The following are steps in goal setting:

1. Have the desire to improve.
2. Believe that you will be successful.
3. Analyze where you are right now.
4. Set realistic goals.
5. Write down both your long- and short-term goals in detail.
6. List benefits you will receive by reaching your goals.
7. Identify the obstacles that may be in your way.
8. Identify the knowledge you may need to reach your goals.
9. Make a plan of action to reach your goals.
10. Develop timelines for both short-term and long-term goals.
11. Monitor your progress closely with a personal log.
12. Never give up.

Goal setting is a lot like golf. It's the follow-through that counts.

By keeping your goals appropriate, attainable, and as specific as possible, you will gain momentum to continue on to the next challenge. Remember that goal setting and planning are ongoing processes; therefore, feel free to modify and adapt your plans so that they remain appropriate for you. Do not be upset with yourself if you deviate from your program on a given day. That is only human nature. Goal setting may not be easy at first, but it will become easier as you gain experience. Goal setting can become an exciting process in your life. Do not hold back; give it your best shot.

The Wrap-Up

Vocabulary—Matching

Match the definitions to the correct term.

1. Goals
2. Long-term goals
3. Short-term goals
4. Timeline
5. Desire
6. Obstacle

A. the attitude to want to achieve something
B. a goal that takes a long time to reach
C. anything that gets in the way of achievement
D. a goal that can be reached in a short period of time
E. something that one wants to achieve that is accomplished through work
F. a tool used to organize and plot the course toward a major goal

Multiple Choice

Select the most correct answer.

7. A good change that may occur during the teen years is the
A. discovery of self-limitations.
B. freedom from parental pressure.
C. freedom from peer pressure.
D. opportunity to take more control of your life.

8. Taking control of your health and fitness means
A. accepting the way you are.
B. learning how to set appropriate goals.
C. learning how to set very high goals.
D. wishing for positive changes in your fitness level.

9. Which best describes goal setting?
A. a process that can help everyone improve themselves
B. achieving something in a short period of time
C. making something happen with little effort
D. wishing for something to happen

10. Which is true about goal setting?
A. Getting in over your head will positively challenge you.
B. Realistic goals keep you excited about self-improvement.
C. Unreasonable goals frequently challenge people.
D. You should first set very long-term goals.

11. In setting goals, you should consider
   A. development of a physical fitness game plan.
   B. obstacles in your path.
   C. use of time lines.
   D. all of the above.

12. Making a detailed plan to reach your goals is
   A. a step that guarantees success.
   B. a very important step to take for all goal setters.
   C. excellent, but mostly for athletes.
   D. primarily for beginners.

13. Success in reaching your goals will add to your sense of
   A. dependence on others.
   B. personal limitations.
   C. self-confidence.
   D. self-consciousness.

14. You are better able to achieve your goals if you
   A. believe you can be successful.
   B. have the desire to improve yourself.
   C. understand the benefits you will receive when successful.
   D. understand that all of the above are true.

15. Which is the most important factor in setting goals?
   A. analyzing where your friends are now
   B. getting advice from friends on how to reach goals
   C. having the desire to improve yourself
   D. writing your goals down in a nonspecific way

16. Which of the following would be a good strategy in setting goals?
   A. Complete a self-assessment of where you are at first.
   B. Do not worry about obstacles for they will disappear when you get started.
   C. Just start exercising, and see how you like it.
   D. Since it is your program, avoid any advice from your friends.

Authentic Assessment—Short Response

17. List two changes that can make your life topsy-turvy.

18. What goals could you set that might make your life less stressful?

19. How are *desire* and *belief in oneself* important in accomplishing goals?

20. What are the steps necessary for successful goal setting?

21. Identify five goals that you would like to accomplish this year.

Authentic Assessment—Extended Response

22. You have a close friend who is overweight and wants to reduce his percent of body fat. What advice would you give him on how to go about setting goals to help him lose weight?

Directions for writing: Discuss the best method of losing weight, including an optimal amount of weight to lose weekly.

23. Jane is a junior in high school and is under a lot of stress. Her parents are going through a rough time, and she feels that she is to blame. She is getting depressed.

Directions for writing: Persuade Jane that she needs to consider different coping strategies to reduce the stress in her life.

4 Guidelines for Exercise

Photodisc

Objectives

As you read this chapter, look for answers to these key questions:

- What should you consider when beginning an exercise program?
- What clothing considerations should be made for an exercise program?
- What precautions should be taken when exercising in hot weather? In cold weather?
- What are the symptoms of heat exhaustion and heat stroke?
- What other safety factors should you consider when you exercise?
- How do you maintain a proper fluid balance during physical activity?
- What are the steps in warming up and cooling down?
- What injuries could you encounter when beginning an exercise program?

"Exercise is to the body, as reading is to the mind."

Initiating a sound personal fitness program requires considerable information. The information in this chapter provides guidelines that will help you establish a safe and appropriate personal fitness program. Being knowledgeable about heat illnesses, for example, is crucial for individuals living in hot climates. The importance of an adequate amount of water is another topic that should be thoroughly understood.

Chapter Preview

- Getting Started
- What You Wear Can Make a Difference
- Exercising In Hot Weather
- Exercising In Cold Weather
- Additional Safety Precautions
- Warming Up
- Cooling Down
- Common Injuries
- PFP Update
- Summary
- The Wrap-Up

Vocabulary

When you have completed this chapter, you should understand the meaning of these vocabulary terms:

hyperthermia

heat cramps

heat exhaustion

heat stroke

hypothermia

warm-up

cool-down

shin splint

stitch in the side

diaphragm

Wellness Connection

Photodisc

Getting Started

The purpose of this chapter is to help you with a positive start in your personal fitness program. Although this entire course is designed to help you learn how to design your own personal fitness program, it is important that you get started safely. Prior to beginning a physical fitness program, you should keep in mind a number of important guidelines. The guidelines covered in this chapter should be considered regardless of age; they become even more important with the increase of age.

Basic Health Indicators

Do a self survey of basic health indicators—weight, resting pulse, blood pressure, previous involvement in physical activity, your fitness level, and your past medical history. Even though you might have recorded these items in Chapter 1, it is always a good idea to keep them in mind when you are planning on increasing your level of physical activity or you are planning on starting again after being ill.

Medical Exam

If you answered no to all seven items in the Par-Q that was covered in Chapter 1 and have not been ill, you will not need to have a medical exam before beginning a personal fitness program. However, it is recommended that anyone who answered yes to any one item on the Par-Q, has experienced ill health, or is over 30 years of age should have a medical exam before beginning a personal fitness program. This is especially important if a person has not been physically active. The medical exam should include an exercise stress test. During this test, the heart's response to exercise is monitored closely by a physician.

Fitness Evaluation

You should evaluate your level of physical fitness prior to beginning a personal fitness program. This will allow you to set realistic goals and to determine your progress over a period of time. Recall that the methods of assessment were discussed in Chapter 2. The assessment should cover all health-related components of physical fitness, including flexibility, cardiovascular fitness, muscular strength and endurance, and body composition.

Your current level of physical fitness will determine where you should begin exercising and how to progress. Your fitness level data will also help you choose activities that will maintain or improve your current level of physical fitness. Once you have determined your level of fitness, you will be ready to set realistic and challenging goals for your personal fitness program. Your current level of fitness will be the standard by which you will be able to judge your improvement during periodic reevaluations.

Goal Setting

Water is an extremely important substance for our bodies, yet many people do not drink an adequate amount. How would you go about reaching a goal of drinking six to eight glasses of water a day? People who drink an adequate amount of water try to always drink one to two glasses of water before leaving home in the morning. This gives them a good start for the day.

Goal Setting

As you know from Chapter 3, goal setting is a key component in establishing a personal fitness program. When setting goals for your personal fitness program, you are really setting lifestyle goals. Your goals should include long- and short-term goals, be realistic, and serve as motivators. Set specific goals that are both attainable and challenging for each health-related component of physical fitness. Evaluate your short-term goals periodically, modifying them as necessary. Your long-term goals may remain the same. Concentrate on improving your lifestyle over a long period of time. Celebrate the fact that you are on a personal trip to becoming a better person.

What You Wear Can Make a Difference

Your program and the weather determine what you should wear. The general rule is to have good shoes, clean socks that fit, appropriate undergarments, and loose-fitting clothing. Keep in mind that your body's cooling process requires that air pass over the skin to evaporate sweat. Loose clothing allows this evaporative process to take place.

Shoes

Proper footwear is the major requirement for effective care and protection of your feet. Shoes should be designed well, constructed from the best possible materials, and fit comfortably.

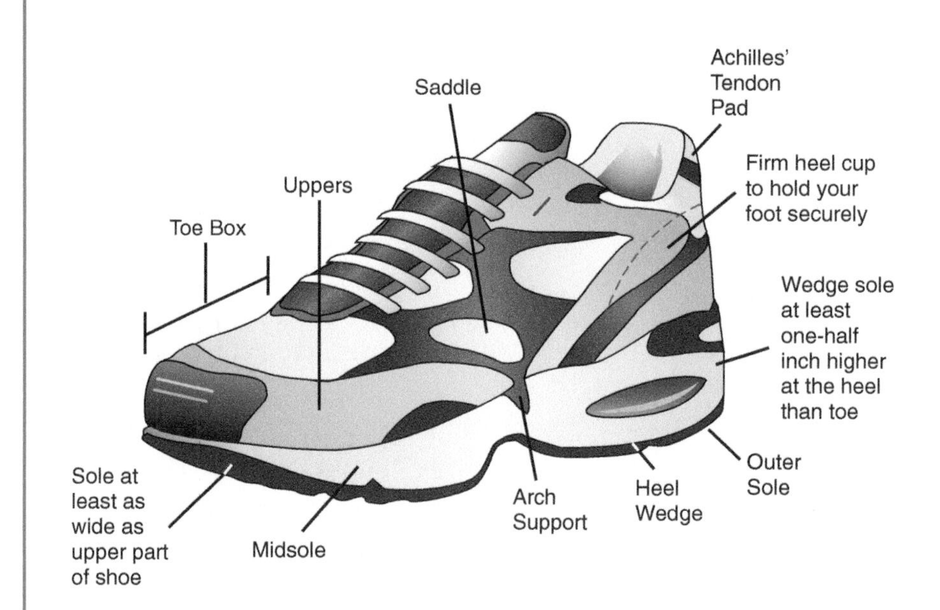

Construction of a jogging shoe

Purchasing quality athletic shoes is a wise investment. The drawing shows the major features to look for in a jogging shoe. As you will note, jogging shoes have no side walls, whereas, basketball shoes do. This is because basketball requires movements from side to side and pivoting. Therefore, a side wall is necessary to keep your foot from rolling over the edge of the shoe.

When buying athletic shoes, take time to examine them carefully and answer these questions:

- Is the sole appropriate for the type of activity?
- Do they have a side wall or are they designed for straight ahead movement?
- Do they have good arch supports?
- Do they have firm heel cups to hold your feet securely?
- Do they have soft, well-cushioned inner soles?
- Are there any rough seams or edges inside the shoe that may cause blisters?
- Are they the correct size in terms of both width and length?

Once you have purchased your shoes, keep them clean, dry, and in good condition.

Safety Awareness

Safety precautions in hot weather include exercising during the cool hours of the day, drinking a lot of water, avoiding overexertion, and wearing lightweight, loose-fitting clothing that allows the circulation of air around the body to help it cool.

Socks

When you try on athletic shoes, be sure to wear the same type of socks you will be wearing when you participate in your fitness

activity. A minor factor such as socks can change the fit of the shoes slightly and cause them to feel uncomfortable when you exercise. Socks prevent direct friction of the skin against the shoes, which may cause blisters. In general, it is better to wear two pairs of socks, since this provides more comfort and protection against blisters. Regardless of whether you wear one or two pair of socks, be sure your socks are clean and fit properly. Make sure there are no wrinkles or folds in your socks before putting on your shoes.

Shirts

A cotton T-shirt is appropriate for most activities. Such a shirt provides excellent absorbency and allows the body to breathe. In addition, T-shirts are comfortable, durable, easy to wash, and inexpensive. Nylon shirts make cooling more difficult because this material traps sweat, thereby not allowing body heat to be transferred to the air. Common sense tells you never to wear dark-colored shirts at night because of safety considerations. Wear a white shirt in hot weather because white best reflects the sun's rays.

Shorts

The main concern in choosing shorts is that they should not be too tight around the thighs. A tight fit may rub and chafe the body. To reduce irritation and chafing, rub petroleum jelly on your legs where your shorts contact the skin.

Nutrition Information

Eat a light meal before engaging in physical activity. It only takes 1 1/2 to 2 hours for it to be digested. A big meal takes 3 to 4 hours to digest. If you exercise too soon after eating, digestion is interrupted and you could feel sick.

Exercising in Hot Weather

The maintenance of your body's internal temperature is very important. When you exercise, blood flow is concentrated in the working muscles, creating a heat build-up. This causes an increase in body temperature because blood transfers internal heat from your working muscles to the skin, where it is given off to the outside air. You rely on the air's absorption of heat from your skin surface to keep your body temperature from climbing too high.

Dress as lightly as possible when exercising in hot weather.

Manny Harageones

A warm environment with high humidity makes the transfer of heat to the air very difficult. Although sweating occurs, the sweat produced fails to evaporate because the air is full of moisture, and there is no place for the liquid sweat to go. This causes less body heat to be transferred to the air. Your body temperature continues to rise and could create a fluid deficiency in your body, if you keep exercising.

A reduction of body fluids or an increase in body temperature, called **hyperthermia,** can create conditions that are uncomfortable and even life threatening. It is, therefore, very important for those who exercise in warm or hot environments to learn the symptoms, treatment, and preventive measures for the heat related body conditions of heat cramps, heat exhaustion, and heat stroke.

Heat cramps are the least serious heat-related problem. If you are dehydrated from not drinking enough water or from sweating a lot, you might notice that certain muscles (frequently the calf muscle) will start contracting involuntarily and cause pain. If this happens to you, stop the activity, apply direct pressure, rest in a cool place, and drink plenty of water.

Stress Information

Improve organizational and work skills to reduce possible stressors. Practice good time management and learn how technology can make you more efficient.

Exercise with caution in a hot environment.

Heat exhaustion is a condition characterized by heavy sweating, accompanied by dizziness and extreme weakness. You should stop physical activity and immediately try to cool the body. Take fluids continuously until the symptoms have passed. Moving to a shaded area and applying wet towels will also help. If the symptoms last more than an hour or the person has heart problems or high blood pressure, medical attention should be sought.

Consumer Issues

Drink water before, during, and after exercising to avoid dehydration. The body cells can not function properly until the fluid is restored. Buying expensive sport drinks is not necessary unless you are involved in athletic training.

Heat stroke is a medical emergency and medical assistance should be called immediately. This form of heat illness is the most severe and occurs when the body ability to regulate its temperature has failed. This condition is characterized by hot, dry skin, and a rising body temperature that may reach 106 degrees. On occasion, unconsciousness may follow. Every attempt must be made to cool the body with an ice massage, cool water immersion, or by any other means.

Heat illness, symptoms, and treatment

The following table presents an outline of heat illnesses. Everyone should be familiar with these conditions and how to protect against them.

	If you have any of the symptoms below, you may be developing a heat injury.		Be prepared to take appropriate actions.	
Heat Cramps	• Thirst • Chills • Clammy skin	• Throbbing heart beat • Nausea	You should: • Drink 1/2 cup of water every 10–15 minutes	• During breaks, move to shade and remove as much clothing as possible
Heat Exhaustion	• Profuse sweating • Dizziness • Headache • Shortness of breath	• Weak, rapid pulse • Lack of saliva • Extreme fatigue	You should: • Stop exercise and move to a cool environment • Drink 2 cups of water for every pound lost	• Take off wet clothing and sit on a chair in a cold shower • Place an ice bag on your head
Heat Stroke 911	• Lack of sweat • Dry, hot skin • Lack of urine • Hallucinations • Swollen tongue • Deafness	• Visual disturbances • Aggression • Unsteady walking • Excessively high body temperature	You should: • Call for emergency medical treatment • Until help arrives, place icebags on back and front of head	• Remove clothing and rub alcohol over most of the body • Sit on chair in cold shower

Drink fluids before, during, and following your exercise session.

Heat Illness Prevention

There are several important points to remember when exercising in a hot or humid environment:

- On extremely hot and humid days, it is recommended that you confine your exercise to a water environment and/or exercise early or late in the day when the heat is less intense.
- The average person loses about 10 cups of fluid a day. When you are exercising, you are losing even more. Drink fluids before, during, and following your exercise session. Do so whether you are thirsty or not. Interestingly enough, when your body is in some stage of dehydration, thirst is not always a good indicator of your body's need for fluids. In addition to the guideline of drinking the normal 8 to 10 glasses, drink 1 cup of water for every 20 minute exercise period. You should drink water even if you are not participating in a physical fitness program. Drink water with meals, snacks, and anytime you eat sweet or salty foods. You should be well hydrated if you find that you must relieve yourself every two hours and your urine is clear or pale yellow in color.
- Lightweight and perforated clothing with adequate exposure of arms and legs promote the escape of heat from the skin surfaces. Lighter colors are preferred because they reflect rather than absorb the sun's rays.
- Wear a lightweight and light-colored cap to shade your head from the sun.
- The use of salt tablets is not recommended. Excessive salt tends to irritate the stomach lining and has also been indicated as a risk factor in high blood pressure.

Internet Resources

Locker Room Survival Skills—Center for Disease Control
http://www.bam.gov (search: safety)

Importance of Hydration—National Athletic Trainers Association
http://www.nata.org/industryresources/parentandcoachesguide.pdf

Sport and Exercise Safety—The Nemours Foundation
http://kidshealth.org/teen/safety/

If you are exercising with a friend whose skin becomes flushed and hot, whose breathing becomes difficult, or who appears incoherent, get him or her immediate medical help. Follow these safety guidelines even in cooler weather because the body can have difficulty cooling itself even when the weather is not hot.

Exercising in Cold Weather

Exposure to severe winter-like conditions including below-freezing temperatures, icy winds, and precipitation, can also create serious problems. These conditions can result in an excessive decline in body temperature, or **hypothermia,** as well as cause frostbite—freezing of the limbs and exposed portions of the face. Even if you are fit, be sure to increase your warm-up time and start your exercise slowly, with a more gradual energy output than normal. Be aware of the fact that the colder you are, the lower your potential level of operational effectiveness.

Photodisc

Dress in layers and cover your head and hands to prevent heat loss during cold weather.

If you participate in such cold weather activities as jogging, ice skating, skiing, or sled riding, you can offset the effects of your exposure to very cold temperatures and winds by taking the following precautions:

- Use thermal underwear and outerwear.
- Wear a turtleneck shirt, gloves, face mask, and hat to reduce body heat loss.
- Wear several layers of light clothing. These are more protective and less cumbersome than one heavy, bulky layer and can be discarded more readily if no longer needed.
- Do not overdress, since too much clothing can cause you to perspire excessively, making your clothes wet. Damp clothing can be uncomfortable and also cause you to feel chilled.
- Wear water-resistant outer garments when exposed to snow or a cold rain. Hypothermia tends to occur more rapidly when clothing is wet, even in temperatures above freezing. Wet clothing provides little insulation and actually accelerates the loss of internal body heat.

Additional Safety Precautions

Illness

If you are not feeling well, you should stop exercising until you feel better. Whenever there is a chance that physical activity may aggravate a minor illness, infection, or injury, you should quit exercising until you are feeling better. If you are recovering from an illness, begin physical activity at a lower level than that at which you were exercising before your illness.

Eating Schedule

Should you exercise after a big meal? The answer to this question centers on the definition of a big meal. If you have just eaten a typical Thanksgiving dinner, you should decrease or suspend vigorous physical activity for 2 or 3 hours. However, a leisurely walk with family or friends after the meal will not interfere with digestive processes. School lunches are not considered big meals; therefore, you do not have to worry about how much you eat prior to physical activity. Whenever you are going to participate in a vigorous sports activity, eat a light meal, so you will be able to perform more efficiently and feel good while you are performing.

It has been found that exercising before a meal will reduce your appetite. If you want to lose weight, participating in your personal fitness program before a meal may be the best time to do so.

Air Pollution

If you live near a big city, you may see people exercising near heavily traveled highways or other areas where there is a high degree of air pollution. If at all possible, find another area, such as a park, in which to exercise. On one hand, the upper portion of your air passages has an outstanding filtering system for most of the large particles found in air. On the other hand, it has been shown that very small particles are not filtered out of the air and can end up in your lungs. The benefits of exercise tend to outweigh the dangers, but exercising outdoors during smog alerts should be avoided.

Dogs

Dogs can pose a problem for walkers, joggers, and cyclists. Although their bark is usually more serious than their bite, the exceptions can be very hazardous. Dogs tend to be very protective of their territory, so avoiding them makes sense.

Personal Safety

If possible, exercise with another person or with a group. Many people find it easier to stick with an exercise program if they exercise with friends. There is also safety in numbers. People can sometimes be far more dangerous than dogs. Females, in particular, must be alert to dangerous situations. Exercising with others, staying away from unpopulated areas, eliminating outdoor, nighttime exercise, and staying alert can help avoid danger.

Warming Up

The warm-up is a 10- to 15-minute period during which you prepare your body for vigorous exercise. Some people want instant success and forgo the warm-up. Such impatience invites pain and injury. A warm-up is very helpful from both a physical and mental standpoint and may determine, whether or not you continue to participate in the activity selected.

Manny Hargeones

Start with a brisk walk or slow jog, then stop and do 7–10 minutes of stretching exercises.

Benefits of Warming Up

It makes sense that warm muscles are safely stretched more than cold muscles. The more flexible your muscles are, the more you can minimize injuries sustained during a slip or stumble. In addition, a loose and flexible body can better react to and absorb sudden falls and awkward positions that are encountered during vigorous sports. In summary, a warm-up will not bring about early fatigue or hinder performance, but it will prepare the body for activity and help prevent injury. A warm-up will energize you and make exercising more fun.

Engaging in a proper warm-up period before you exercise does three things:

1. It helps you mentally focus your effort and makes you feel like moving.
2. It increases your heart rate and the blood supply to your muscles, thus preparing your cardiovascular and muscular systems for the workout.
3. It generates heat in the muscle and joint tissues, which makes them more flexible and resistant to injury.

How to Warm Up

A warm-up usually includes a general and a specific component. The general component has two stages. The first stage includes some type of large muscle activity such as jogging in place or slow jogging. This activity is designed to raise the heart rate slowly while increasing muscle temperature. The second stage involves *static stretching*. Muscles should be stretched slowly for 15 to 30 seconds and progressively to the point of discomfort; not pain. *Dynamic stretching* is also an effective method of warming up the muscles. It involves a similar position but in a slow and controlled manner.

The specific component of a warm-up involves participation in the activity to be performed or a related activity. For example, if you are jogging, you might jog the first half-mile of the workout at a leisurely pace, slowly increasing to the desired speed. In this way, your body is allowed to gradually adapt to the specific stress being imposed upon it. Some people use the movements of their sport to warm up. If you are going to play tennis, for example, you will want to warm up your shoulder and arm muscles. You might want to volley the ball back and forth across the net with your partner or practice a few serves before starting the game.

There is a misconception that warm-ups should be done only when you engage in aerobic activities. Warming up is important in all activities. The concepts of general and specific warm-up apply to biking, jogging, racquetball, rope jumping, swimming, tennis, weight lifting, and all other activities.

The warm-up must become a habit. Many people do not warm up properly but come through without any apparent problems. To be on the safe side, warm up.

Cooling Down

The **cool-down** is a 10- to 15-minute period of mild exercise that follows your training session and allows your body and heart rate to return to their resting states slowly. Cooling down from exercise is as important as warming up. Just as your body was allowed to speed up gradually, it must also be allowed to slow down gradually.

Benefits of Cooling Down

Photodisc

For your cool-down, repeat some of the same stretching exercises you performed during the warm-up.

The explanation for a cool-down period following a rigorous workout is not difficult to understand. Blood returns to the heart through a system of vessels called *veins*. The muscles squeeze the veins and thus push the blood toward the heart. If you stop exercising suddenly, the return blood flow through the veins is reduced. When this happens, the blood return to the heart will drop quickly and may cause the blood to pool in your legs. This will result in less oxygen going to other body parts, such as the head.

Engaging in a proper cool-down period after you exercise will help:

- prevent blood from pooling in the muscles you were using. Without a cool-down, less blood reaches your heart, and you may feel light-headed;
- prevent waste products from building up in your muscles, keeping them from becoming sore;
- muscles and tendons relax, keeping them from becoming stiff and tight.

How to Cool Down

Your cool-down should be as long as, or even slightly longer than, your warm-up. The first phase of cooling down should consist of walking or some other light activity to prevent blood from pooling in the muscles you were using. Your cool-down period should continue until your heart rate is around 100 beats per minute.

The second phase of a cool-down should focus on the same stretching exercises that were used during the warm-up period. You will probably find that stretching is easier after exercising, due to the increase in muscle temperature. Stretching at this time loosens tightened muscles and helps prevent muscle soreness.

Bent-leg sit-ups may be added to the cool-down routine. Strong abdominal muscles are a postural aid because they provide support for the upper torso. Many researchers and physical education teachers believe the cool-down is as important or more important than the warm-up.

Common Injuries

If you start your program sensibly and in a gradual manner, the likelihood of incurring any injuries is greatly reduced. It is equally important to obey rules, wear protective gear, and use sound judgement when participating in physical activities. However, it is important to be able to recognize the symptoms of some of the more common injuries that people involved in physical activity encounter.

Muscle Strains

Muscle soreness is a common problem that usually appears within the first 12 to 24 hours following exertion and is called muscle strains. In almost all cases, the soreness is the result of starting a program that is too strenuous for you. The discomfort is due to chemical changes in the muscles and/or microscopic tears in the muscle fibers and connective tissues. The soreness may be very noticeable and may persist for one to two days. It does diminish gradually. Light massage, easy static stretching, and mild exercise may also be of value in reducing the discomfort. The key point is that nearly all of this pain can be eliminated simply by starting your program in a cautious manner.

Muscle strains are common in sports. Symptoms of a muscle strain can include muscle spasm, discoloration, tightness, partial loss of function, or tenderness. Severity of a muscle strain can be graded:

- First degree—mild muscle soreness
- Second degree—moderate—some tearing of muscle fibers
- Third degree—severe tearing or rupture of a muscle or tendon

The use of the term *muscle strain* is sometimes confused with the term *sprain*. A strain involves muscle and/or a tendon, whereas, sprains involve ligaments and joints such as with an ankle sprain.

Blisters

A *blister* is the result of friction creating heat, tissue damage, and fluid accumulation between the layers of skin in an attempt to prevent further tissue damage. The fluid may be clear or it may be bloody, creating a blood blister.

A blister can be extremely painful. If it breaks, it must be treated as if it were an open wound. After the wound is cleansed, a sterile dressing should be applied. If the blister is unbroken, then three approaches may be considered. First, it may be protected from pressure by applying appropriate gauze padding to it. Another way of protecting the blister is to place a doughnut-shaped piece of foam over it. A third method of treating a blister is to puncture its side with a sterilized needle to release the accumulated fluid. Then it must be treated with an antiseptic and covered tightly. The dressing must be kept clean to reduce the chances of infection. Never remove the layer of skin that covers a blister unless it has been torn loose. This skin covering aids in protecting the sensitive underlying and newly forming layer of skin.

Shin Splints

A **shin splint** is an *overuse* syndrome (you did too much too quickly) that will typically develop in poorly conditioned individuals at the beginning of their programs. The pain may be caused by a strain to one or several muscles located in the lower leg or from inflammation of tissue connecting the two bones of the lower leg. Hard surfaces, improper shoes, running on the balls of your feet, and overdoing it are the primary reasons for developing shin splints. Treatment consists of rest, ice packs, taping the sore area, and elevation of the leg or legs.

Stitch in the Side

A **stitch in the side** may develop in individuals who are beginning a jogging program. It is a sharp pain in the side, just under the ribs. While the cause is unknown, there are a number of theories. Some think it is caused by faulty breathing, reduced blood flow to the area, or an accumulation of lactic acid in and around the **diaphragm,** a large muscle in your upper abdomen. Recent reports suggest that a stitch in the side may be caused by stretching the ligaments that attach the liver and diaphragm. You breathe out once for every two steps. About 70 percent of us breathe when the left foot hits the ground. The other 30 percent, who breathe when the right foot hits the ground, are the ones who most frequently experience a stitch in the side. When the right foot hits the ground, it causes the liver to go down when the diaphragm goes up during breathing out. This causes the ligaments to be stretched and thus inducing the stitch in the side. If you experience this pain, stop running and apply pressure to the affected area, stretch to the opposite side and breathe deeply. Once you are in good physical condition, you will rarely experience this type of pain.

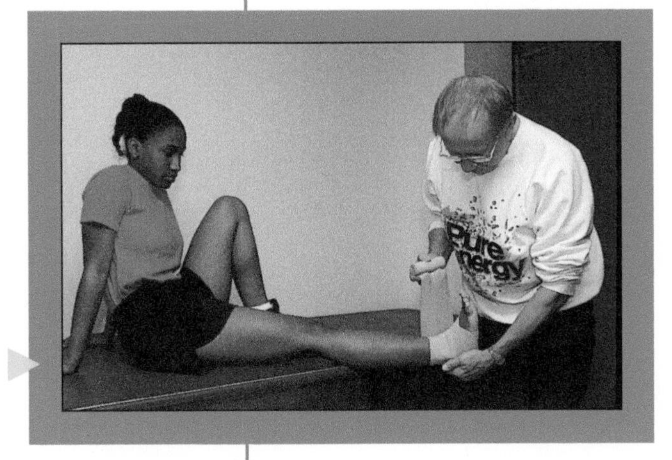

Start your program gradually to reduce the likelihood of injuries.

Sprained Ankle

It is estimated that 27,000 Americans sprain their ankle daily. Many of these sprains are a result of physical activity. Sprains are injuries to ligaments surrounding a joint or to the capsule-like sac, that surrounds a joint. Although a severe sprain may not be distinguishable from a more serious fracture, except by X-ray, you should stop the activity, apply ice, elevate the injured part, and immobilize the ankle. To help prevent such an injury, stretch, warm up, wear appropriate footwear, and check the field for rocks and holes before beginning the activity.

PFP Technology Activity

Using a word-processing software, design a warm-up/cool-down routine to be used with the specific type of physical activity that you enjoy doing.

PFP Update

This chapter provides information that relates directly to helping you be successful with your PFP. Identify the critical guidelines that are appropriate for you and your environment. You should also select stretching exercises that help you increase your flexibility fitness. Planning a warm-up and cool-down that is specific to the activities you wish to engage in is important and should be also included in your PFP.

Did you help anyone with his or her PFP recently? There undoubtedly are classmates who may be having difficulty in following their programs. You may be just the person to help them by giving verbal support or helping them to reassess their goals. If you happen to be one of those who is having trouble following through with your self-improvement plan, be sure to ask your teacher or a classmate for ideas on how to help you get back on track. Remember, progress is best approached in small steps.

Summary

It is very important when beginning a personal fitness program to follow certain guidelines. The first step is to clearly outline what you want to do and then begin in low gear. Many people begin too quickly and become injured. Understanding weather conditions and heat-related illnesses that may occur when exercising outside is of extreme importance. In hot weather, people may exercise too hard and lose too much water from their bodies by sweating. Drinking plenty of water before, during, and after exercise is a step you should always follow. Warming the body up before exercise and cooling it down after exercise are also very important steps for success in your quest for self-improvement.

This chapter provides information that relates directly to helping you be successful with your PFP. Success is the name of the game. There is nothing like self-improvement to offset a bored attitude toward your program. Knowing the level you started at and the progress you have made are key factors in success.

Photodisc

The last step is having patience. Seeing real changes in your performance may take a few weeks. If your body is out of shape, remember that it took a long time for it to get that way. It will take you more than a few days to get it back into shape. However, as soon as you get started on your program, you can expect to feel good about yourself because you will be following a positive game plan to improve your lifestyle by looking and feeling as good as possible.

The Wrap-Up

Vocabulary Matching

1. Hyperthermia
2. Heat cramps
3. Heat exhaustion
4. Heat stroke
5. Hypothermia
6. Warm-up
7. Cool-down
8. Shin splint
9. Diaphragm
10. Stitch in the side

A. the least serious heat-related problem
B. an excessive decline in body temperature
C. a 10- to 15-minute period in which you prepare your body for vigorous exercise
D. an increase in body temperature
E. a 10- to 15-minute period, after exercising, in which the body is helped to regain a resting state
F. a condition characterized by profuse sweating, dizziness, and extreme weakness
G. sharp pain in the side, just under the ribs
H. a large muscle in your upper abdomen
I. a condition characterized by hot, dry skin and a rising body temperature that is a true emergency
J. a pain in the lower leg caused by overuse

Multiple Choice

Select the most correct answer.

11. Evaluating your current fitness level prior to beginning an exercise program
  A. is only important for physically inactive people.
  B. is usually not important.
  C. will have nothing to do with the activities you choose for your program.
  D. will help you set realistic goals.

12. Proper athletic footwear is
- **A.** overrated as a factor in setting up an exercise program.
- **B.** the main requirement for the care and protection of your feet.
- **C.** the same regardless of the physical activity you do.
- **D.** worthwhile only if you are involved in a sports program.

13. Which of the following would be important to do when exercising in hot weather?
- **A.** dressing in layers
- **B.** taking salt tablets
- **C.** wearing a sweat suit if you want to lose weight
- **D.** wearing light-weight, light-colored clothing

14. Which of the following best describes the symptoms of heat stroke?
- **A.** clammy skin, no sweat, visual disturbances
- **B.** hot, dry skin, no sweat, unsteady walking
- **C.** no sweat, average body temperature, lack of urine
- **D.** unsteady walking, no sweat, chills

15. Which of the following is the most serious heat illness?
- **A.** excessive sweating
- **B.** heat exhaustion
- **C.** heat stroke
- **D.** muscle cramps

16. Which best describes a preventive measure for a heat illness?
- **A.** Do not wear a hat because your head cools more quickly without one.
- **B.** Drink fluids, before, during, and after exercise.
- **C.** Wear a rubberized suit since it will help you sweat more.
- **D.** Wear dark-colored clothing in hot weather.

17. Which of the following would be important to do while exercising in cold weather?
- **A.** dressing in layers
- **B.** drinking a glass of water before exercising
- **C.** wearing a rubberized suit
- **D.** wearing light-colored clothing

18. The process of warming-up
  A. generates heat in the muscle and joint tissues.
  B. helps to make you feel like moving vigorously.
  C. increases the blood supply to your muscles.
  D. involves all of the above benefits.

19. The process of warming-up
  A. is adequately done by stretching for one or two minutes.
  B. is probably not important for most activities.
  C. involves stretching as well as some aerobic activity such as easy jogging.
  D. is usually done by a majority of people.

20. Cooling down after working out is a process that
  A. most people do very well.
  B. takes only a couple of minutes.
  C. very few people build into their programs.
  D. allows the body to return to normal after exercise.

Authentic Assessment—Short Response

21. What are two reasons for not running near a busy highway?

22. What are two situations when you should not wear a dark-colored shirt when exercising?

23. What causes hyperthermia?

24. What is the purpose of cooling down after exercising?

25. Why do so many people complain about muscle soreness the day after a vigorous physical workout?

Authentic Assessment—Extended Response

26. Kyle and his friends are getting ready to play 3-on-3 basketball and they are taking a few practice shots. One of the guys said, "Let's get started," and so they began to play without warming up.

Directions for writing: Explain the importance of warming up before vigorous activity and also explain how to warm up for this activity.

27. Your friend invites you to go on a 20-mile bicycle ride with a cycling club and you agree. It is a very hot day with high humidity and your friend shows up at your house without any water.

Directions for writing: Persuade your friend that since it is such a hot, humid day, he should take an adequate amount of water on the bicycle ride. Include information about heat illnesses.

5

Principles of Training

Objectives

As you read this chapter, look for answers to these key questions:

- How does the principle of overload increase your fitness level?
- In what three ways is overload accomplished?
- Why is it important for you to progress at a safe rate in your exercise program?
- What principle would you apply if you wished to improve a specific muscle?

Corel

"You will only get out of training what you put into it."

V•A•L•U•E

The principles of training are used in every form of physical development. How these principles are used determines the amount of increase in one's physical fitness level. Being at or above the health standard, enhances the quality of your health as well as the quantity of your life.

Chapter Preview

- Efficient and Safe Training
- Principle of Overload
- Principle of Progression
- Principle of Specificity
- PFP Update
- Summary
- The Wrap-Up

Vocabulary

When you have completed this chapter, you should understand the meaning of these vocabulary terms:

principle of overload

FIT

frequency

intensity

time

principle of progression

principle of specificity

Wellness Connection

Efficient and Safe Training

In order to look good, feel good, and enjoy a healthy lifestyle, it is essential that you engage in regular physical activity. Some people understand the benefits of regular physical activity and make it a part of their regular daily lifestyle. Others, however, either have forgotten or have never known the joys of being physically fit. Often during adolescence, habits of inactivity are developed and permitted to become a part of daily living. We ride to school, take the elevator to the second floor, use machines to do our work, and spend our leisure time watching television. Research studies have documented the cost to both the individual and society when such behavior is a part of one's lifestyle. Not only can physical activity make you look better and feel better, it lowers the risk of disease, including heart disease, high blood pressure, stroke, diabetes, obesity, and colon cancer. Physical activity also helps you to be more productive and able to concentrate for longer periods and enhances your ability to cope with stress.

Once you understand the importance of being physically active, it is only a matter of organizing your lifestyle to include fitness activities in your daily schedule. When you decide to start a personal fitness program, remember your initial performance should match your degree of current condition. After all, if it took you several months or years to get out of shape, it is going to take you more than a couple of weeks to get back into shape.

To operate efficiently and avoid injury, you must follow a carefully planned and deliberate training program. There are three basic training principles to be followed in developing your program: overload, progression, and specificity.

Principle of Overload

In general terms, the various systems of the body will become stronger and function better if increased demands (overload) are placed on them. Although it is important to overload your body so improvement can occur, the stress should not be so severe that your body is unable to adjust. For example, your body would not be able to adapt to an overload of lifting 300 pounds on your first attempt to increase muscular strength. Not only would you be unsuccessful and not enjoy the exercise session, but you might also cause harm to your body.

As previously mentioned, physical fitness is a personal matter. The amount of overload needed varies with each individual. Some of your friends may have to work more on flexibility, whereas you may have to work harder on muscular endurance. The amount of overload needed by different individuals can easily be seen when comparing a young person and an older person. For example, if your grandmother has been inactive for some time, she may find a fast walk stressful, while you may have to jog for 2 miles to achieve an overload.

One of the first known examples of the principle of overload was traced back to the legendary Milo of Crotona. This famous Greek athlete increased his strength by lifting a small calf several times a week. As the calf grew heavier and heavier, Milo's muscles became stronger, allowing him to lift more and more weight. Milo's use of the overload principle made him the only person in his village to have the strength to lift a full-size bull.

Goal Setting

Remember to set challenging goals that are within your physical ability. The principle of progression is the calendar in which you should apply the overload variables and should be considered when establishing goals.

Milo of Crotona—legendary use of overload principle to develop strength

Frequency/Intensity/Time (FIT)	
The principle of overload may be accomplished by increasing one of three variables:	
• **F**requency	How often you exercise
• **I**ntensity	How hard you exercise
• **T**ime	How long you exercise

FIT is the word formed from the first letter of each of the three variables. FIT serves as a reminder of the three ways to achieve overload in your physical fitness program.

Frequency

Frequency refers to the number of times you exercise a week. Exercise must be performed regularly if you intend to reach and maintain an adequate level of physical fitness. Ideally, your exercise program will become a daily habit, just like brushing your teeth. You can imagine the effects of not brushing your teeth on a regular basis. Similarly, there is a connection between how frequently you exercise, your outward appearance (looking good), and how healthy you are (feeling good). Limiting your exercise to weekend recreational activity is like brushing your teeth only on these days. Exercising three days a week is the minimum frequency (how often you exercise) and will increase your level of fitness if the time (how long you exercise) is increased.

FIT can be used to remember the methods to increase overload.

How often you exercise depends on your goals. If you want the cardiorespiratory benefits of aerobic exercise, you should exercise at least three times a week. Exercising five times a week, however, is more effective. If you want to lose weight, most experts recommend exercising moderately six days a week. Weight training, however, requires time for the muscles to rest and recover. Therefore, a specific muscle should not be overloaded more than every other day for muscular strength or endurance training.

SAFETY AWARNESS

To avoid injury, use the principles of training in developing your workout program: overload, progression, and specificity. This will allow you to start at the appropriate level and progress safely without causing injury.

Intensity

The intensity of all exercise should be increased enough to demand more effort than usual from the body. How hard you must work is a critical question, because strenuous exercises may cause injury, while not training hard enough will result in little or no improvement. If you have been playing soccer on a regular basis, jogging 1 mile twice a week will not be enough of a workout to improve your cardiovascular fitness.

How hard should you exercise to develop an acceptable level of fitness? It depends upon the fitness component: cardiovascular, muscular strength and endurance, or flexibility. It also depends upon your present level of fitness. To improve your cardiovascular fitness, you must make your heart work

Photodisc

The intensity of all exercise should be increased enough to demand more effort than usual from the body.

harder than it normally does. The intensity of a cardiovascular workout is indicated by the number of times per minute your heart beats during the workout. The more intense the exercise, the faster your heart rate. Making your heart work harder by running faster would be one application of intensity that would improve cardiovascular fitness. Examples of other activities that improve cardiovascular fitness include swimming, bicycling, and aerobic dance. For muscular strength and endurance you must work harder, or increase intensity, by lifting more weight. To increase intensity for flexibility improvement, you have to work harder by stretching the muscle beyond its normal length.

Internet Resources

Fitness Calendar—Centers for Disease Control and Prevention
http://www.bam.gov/fit4life/fitt.htm

Online Exercise Diary
http://www.justmove.org/diary/login.cfm

Progress Chart—Think Quest
http://library.thinkquest.org/12153/pchart.html

Nutrition Information

Did you know that one soda can contain 10 to 12 teaspoons of sugar? Skip those excess calories and replace those drinks with a glass of water, milk, or 100 percent fruit juice, which contains essential nutrients.

Time

Time refers to how long you exercise. How many minutes do you jog (cardiovascular), lift weights (muscular strength and endurance), or perform stretching exercises (flexibility)? In order to be effective, a training session must be maintained for a certain length of time. For example, to develop cardiovascular fitness you need to maintain the activity for at least 20 to 60 minutes.

Research shows that as time is increased, intensity is decreased. This means that a person can spread the training session over a longer period of time at an easier pace. Rather than biking 4 miles in 15 minutes, bike the same distance in 20 minutes at an easier pace. People who are excessively overweight should walk instead of jog (lower intensity level) and limit the workout to a 15- or 20-minute session. Gradually they should work up to a longer period of time.

Skipping a workout session to permit the body to rest is acceptable and may help prevent injuries. However, be careful not to let a one-day layoff turn into two days, then three, and so on, until you stop exercising altogether.

Gradually increase overload. Train—Don't strain!

Principle of Progression

As you work harder (overload), your body adapts. Because your body becomes accustomed to the workload, you must progressively increase the amount of work for improvement to occur. If you progressively increase the load, as Milo of Crotona did, you will improve fitness and prevent injuries. For example, cardiovascular fitness would be improved if you began a training program that involved running a mile a day in 8 minutes for several weeks. However, if you continued to run the same distance in the same amount of time after your body had adapted to this workload, cardiovascular improvement would stop. To continue improving, you would have to increase your intensity by running a mile in 7 minutes or increase your distance to 1 1/2 miles. This would again put the overload principle into effect. Over a period of time, additional overload would have to be added.

Stress Information

Learn how to view change and challenges as exciting experiences. We learn from change and grow as a result of challenges.

It is important that you know when it is safe to progress. Think of the principle of progression as the schedule for the application of overload. You want to slowly and progressively apply stress to the body only when it is needed and not before. This is especially true during the first 4 to 6 weeks of your program, in which you should increase the overload very slowly. If your exercise level is too intense or your exercise session too long, you may feel unusually tired during the session or even for a few hours after it. This is a signal that you have placed too much overload on your body. Other signs of overexertion include nausea or vomiting during or after a workout and muscle or joint aches and pains that do not go away quickly. If you experience any of these symptoms, you need to reduce your exercise intensity and time. This is why it is important to evaluate the health-related components of physical fitness and to record daily achievements. With records of progress and knowledge of training principles, you will know when it is safe to progress and increase your overload.

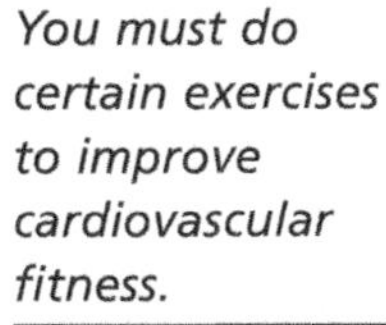

You must do certain exercises to improve cardiovascular fitness.

Photodisc

Principle of Specificity

The principle of specificity refers to the specific exercises that improve specific components of physical fitness in specific body parts. For example, flexibility exercises will increase flexibility but will not necessarily improve cardiovascular fitness. Stretching your legs will not increase flexibility in your arms. Another example is when a person who has trained for a specific sport such as gymnastics attempts to play basketball and quickly becomes fatigued. Each physical activity requires specific demands, and doing the activity is the best way to train for it.

Consumer Issues

Having knowledge about the principles of training will provide you with a powerful weapon against fraud and assist you in evaluating products and fitness facilities.

PFP Update

The information in this chapter has provided you with knowledge that will enable you to make sound decisions about achieving your goals. For example, it was suggested in Chapter 1 that you make some common-sense decisions about what kind of and how much activity to do to get started on your personal fitness program. Some of you might have wanted to improve your energy level, so you started a cycling program. You rode 3 days a week at a leisurely pace for 25 minutes each day with a friend, and you have followed this schedule since the beginning. This was a good start; however, as you have learned in this chapter, you did not overload your body effectively.

Now that you understand the overload principle and overload variables (frequency, intensity, and time), you know how to go about setting up a cycling program that will push your body harder and, consequently, help you improve your total physical health.

Take time now and reflect on the physical fitness goals you have set for yourself and how you might change your workout schedule. If you are still unsure about the principle of overload, be sure you get help from the teacher or from your friends.

PFP Technology Activity

Using a computer spreadsheet software program, create a workout regiment based on the principle of overload variables for each health-related fitness component. After you have created the spreadsheets, print it out and put it in your PFP notebook.

Summary

Three basic training principles (overload, progression, and specificity) must be observed when you design an exercise program. An overload must be added beyond what is normally placed on the body in daily activity. You can place overload on the body by increasing one or more of the overload variables: frequency (how often you work), intensity (how hard you work), and time (how long you work). A good way to remember the three overload variables is to think of the word FIT = Frequency, Intensity, Time.

Body systems adapt to the specific stresses placed upon them. As your body adapts to stress, you must progressively increase the overload to improve your level of fitness. The principle of progression allows you to increase overload gradually without injury or discomfort.

The principle of specificity permits you to improve a specific component of physical fitness in specific body parts. To improve a specific component, you must select the appropriate physical activity. The overload for a given exercise will vary for each individual. Remember that injuries result when progression is not gradual and overload is added too quickly.

See the Training Guidelines chart on page 100.

Minimum Principles of Training Guidelines as Established by the American College of Sports Medicine

Summary of Flexibility Training Guidelines

Frequency	At least three times per week.
Intensity	Stretch slowly until mild tension is felt.
Time	Static: Hold each stretch 15 to 30 seconds. Dynamic: Do 10 to 20 repetitions and one to three sets.

Summary of Cardiovascular Endurance Training Guidelines

Frequency	Perform at least three times per week.
Intensity	Maintain 60 to 90 percent maximum heart rate. Maintain 50 to 85 percent maximum heart rate reserve.
Time	Maintain continuous large muscle group activity for minimum of 20 to 60 minutes.

Summary of Muscular Fitness Training Guidelines

Muscular Endurance

Frequency	Every other day for each muscle group
Intensity	Low resistance (30 to 50 percent 1 RM)
Time	High repetitions (12 to 20 reps, one to three sets)

Muscular Strength

Frequency	Every other day for each muscle group
Intensity	Heavy weights (60 to 90 percent 1 RM)
Time	Low repetitions (4 to 8 reps, one to three sets)

The Wrap-Up

Vocabulary—Matching

Match the definitions to the correct term.

1. Principle of overload

2. FIT

3. Frequency

4. Intensity

5. Time

6. Principle of progression

7. Principle of specificity

A. how often one exercises

B. a progressive increase in the level of exercise in order to sustain improvement in physical fitness

C. how long one exercises to improve fitness

D. the three ways to achieve overload in a physical fitness program

E. the degree to which one should exercise to improve fitness

F. the performance of specific exercises in order to improve specific components of physical fitness in specific body parts

G. exposing the muscles, joints and cardiovascular and respiratory systems to more work and stress than is normally experienced

Multiple Choice

Select the most correct answer.

8. When starting a physical fitness program, you do not need to consider your
   A. health status.
   B. present fitness level.
   C. prior physical activity involvement.
   D. all of the above are correct.

9. The legendary Milo of Crotona became stronger by applying the principle of
   A. all or none.
   B. overload.
   C. regression.
   D. specificity.

10. The three basic training principles to be followed in developing your physical fitness program are
- **A.** frequency, intensity, and time.
- **B.** overload, intensity, and time.
- **C.** overload, progression, and specificity.
- **D.** safety, exercise, and diet.

11. When you increase the workload of your training session, you are increasing
- **A.** frequency.
- **B.** intensity.
- **C.** time.
- **D.** specificity.

12. When you increase the length of your workout, you are increasing
- **A.** frequency.
- **B.** intensity.
- **C.** specificity.
- **D.** time.

13. Frequency refers to how
- **A.** fast you exercise.
- **B.** hard you exercise.
- **C.** long you exercise.
- **D.** often you exercise.

14. Progression means
- **A.** changing from running to tennis.
- **B.** slowly increasing the amount of exercise.
- **C.** starting easy and going for a long period of time.
- **D.** starting fast to improve quickly.

15. Why is it important to follow the principle of progression?
- **A.** to impress all of your friends with the amount of weight you can lift
- **B.** to gradually increase intensity of training program to reduce chance of injury
- **C.** to know how to cross train thereby obtaining a total body workout
- **D.** to make sure you exercise the right body part for improvement to occur

16. Applying the principle of specificity means that you can increase

A. abdominal strength by doing leg extensions.
B. arm strength by doing push-ups.
C. leg strength by doing pull-ups.
D. shoulder strength by doing half squats.

17. Teenagers who score below the health standard in a specific fitness component may need to

A. decrease the length of time of their exercise sessions.
B. increase the intensity of their workouts.
C. increase the overload to the maximum.
D. both A and B are correct.

Authentic Assessment—Short Response

18. Why must an overload be placed on the body to improve physical fitness?

19. Why does the amount of overload vary from individual to individual?

20. How did Milo of Crotona progressively increase his workload?

21. Why must you progressively increase the amount of work in order for improvement to occur?

22. Give an example of an exercise or activity you engage in and state how the principle of specificity is involved.

Authentic Assessment—Extended Response

23. **Writing situation:** Some individuals believe that you have to run as fast as possible to increase cardiovascular fitness.

Directions for writing: Discuss why this is not based on sound training concepts. Then explain the proper application of the principle of progression to cardiovascular training.

24. **Writing situation:** Angelique scored very low on her cardiovascular test. In addition to walking more each day, her brother told her that she needed to lift weights and apply the principle of overload to improve her leg strength.

Directions for writing: Discuss why this is good advice and what direction you could give Angelique in implementing her brother's suggestion.

Corbis

6

Flexibility

Objectives

As you read this chapter, look for answers to these key questions:

- How is joint movement limited?
- Why is flexibility important?
- What is the difference between static stretching and dynamic stretching?
- How may the training principles be applied to improve flexibility?
- What safety precautions should be taken when you are engaging in flexibility exercises?
- How is flexibility evaluated?

"The rubber band theory applies to each of us; we will be no good until stretched."

Flexibility is an essential fitness component in both your everyday life, as well as when you engage in physical activity. It is important that you stretch to increase the length of both your muscles and tendons. The more range of motion you have, the more your joints can move without injury. Stretching will not only help reduce the chance of injury, minimize muscle soreness, stimulate blood flow, and it is also a great stress reliever.

Chapter Preview

- What Is Flexibility?
- Types of Stretching
- Application of Training Principles
- Flexibility Safety Precautions
- Flexibility Assessment
- Setting Goals to Improve Flexibility
- Flexibility Exercises
- Harmful Stretching Positions
- PFP Update
- Summary
- The Wrap-Up

Vocabulary

When you have completed this chapter, you should understand the meaning of these vocabulary terms:

joint

ligament

muscle

tendon

static stretching

dynamic stretching

PNF stretching

ballistic stretching

WHAT IS FLEXIBILITY?

What comes to your mind when the word *flexibility* is mentioned? Do you think of a circus acrobat tumbling about, a yoga instructor with legs behind his head, or a dancer doing splits? Everyone has flexibility to some degree, even the armchair athlete.

Flexibility is the ability to move body joints through a full range of motion. A **joint** is the point at which two bones come together. Examples of joints are the wrists, elbows, shoulders, hips, knees, and ankles. Notice that all joints do not move in the same way or to the same degree. The amount of movement in a joint is limited by the way it is formed. Pivot joints, such as the neck, permit a rotating motion. Hinge joints, such as the knee, permit a back-and-forth motion, while the hip and shoulders have a ball-and-socket formation, allowing for movement in many different directions. Your wrists and ankles have gliding joints that allow bones to slide over one another.

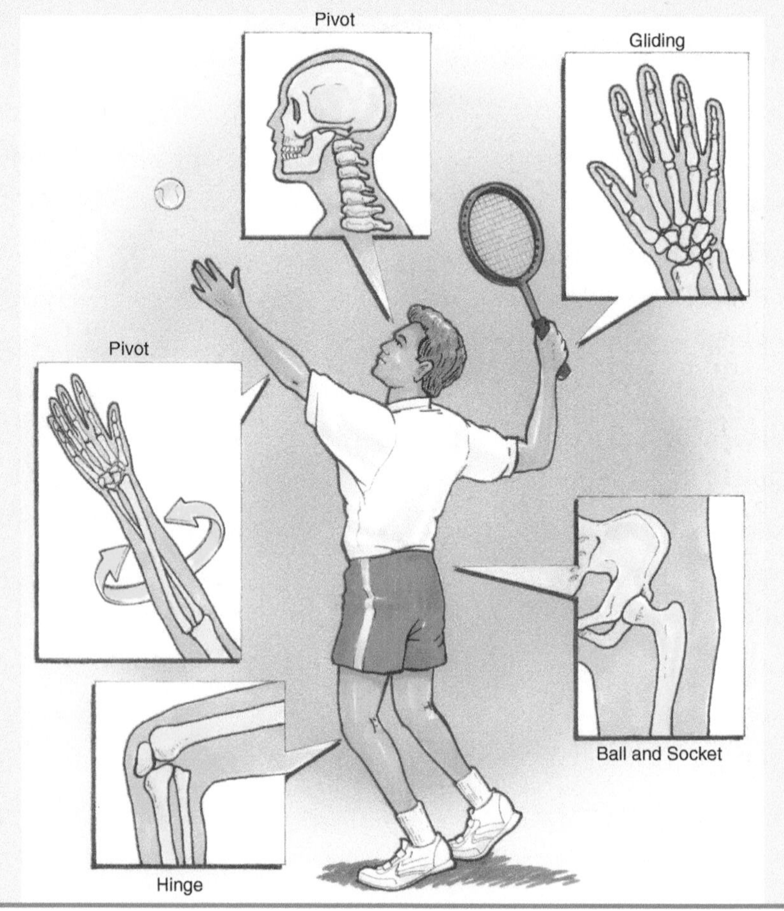

Joints of the human body

How Is Joint Movement Limited?

The direction in which a joint moves cannot be changed because of bone structure. For example, the bone structures of the elbow and knee joints set a very definite limit on how far the arm and leg can extend. These are mechanical factors that cannot be greatly modified. In other joints, such as the ankle and hip, the limitation on range of motion is imposed by soft tissue and can be modified. This soft tissue is in the form of ligaments, muscles, and tendons. It is possible to improve the amount of motion in a joint by performing exercises that alter these soft tissues.

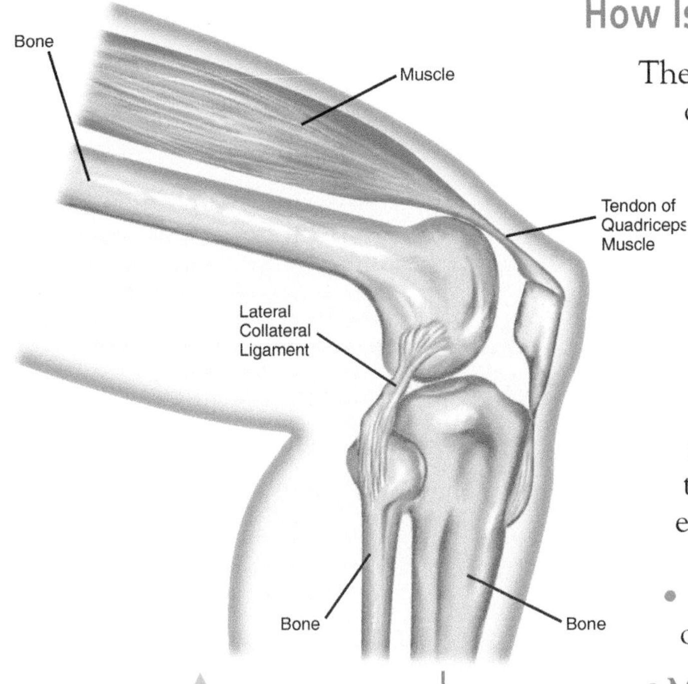

Soft tissue limits flexibility.

- **Ligament:** strong fibrous tissue that attaches one bone to another
- **Muscle:** meaty tissue that surrounds bones
- **Tendon:** connective tissue that anchors the muscle to bone

To help you remember what makes up soft tissue, think of the terms in alphabetical order. First, ligaments attach bone to bone. Muscles cover over or surround the bone. Finally, tendons anchor the muscle to the bone.

Goal Setting

While you may not be able to achieve the flexibility of a gymnast, you can definitely realize the benefits of improved flexibility by using the overload variables (FIT) as applied to stretching. Make a habit of stretching while talking on the telephone or during television commercials.

Why Is Flexibility Important?

A reasonable amount of flexibility (joint movement) is required to live a healthy and functional life, both at work and play. Since the loss of flexibility occurs gradually, you probably will not realize you are experiencing a decrease in flexibility until a problem arises. Almost everyone has observed older adults and noticed that some are more flexible than others. As one ages, some individuals are more active, while others allow their muscles to be underused. Eventually, attempting to do simple motions causes discomfort. This is due in part

Goodshoot

Individuals of the same age may have different levels of flexibility due to past and present physical activity.

to the level of present physical activity in which they are involved and the amount of past physical activity.

Reduces Injuries

A lack of flexibility can result in joint or muscle injury during exercise or daily activities. While your strength and aerobic capacity will increase with exercise, your flexibility, in some cases, may decrease with weight training and aerobic conditioning. For this reason, every muscle strengthened must also be stretched to maintain and improve flexibility as much as possible. All athletes, including professional football players, now supplement their weight training and conditioning programs with stretching exercises that improve flexibility. The great benefit of stretching is that you are able to increase the length of both muscles and tendons. This helps to increase your range of movement, enabling you to move your joints and limbs further before an injury occurs. The better conditioned your muscles and tendons are, the better they can handle sport and exercise, thereby decreasing the chance of injury.

Prevents Post-Exercise Pain

Post-exercise pain and stiffness caused by muscle spasms can be prevented or reduced by stretching exercises. Including warm-up and cool-down sessions in your workout will stretch shortened muscles and, therefore, help prevent muscular soreness. The warm-up increases the blood supply to your muscles, raises their temperature, and makes them more flexible and resistant to injury. After exercising, a cool-down period of mild exercise can prevent muscle problems by gradually stretching the muscles you used. It can also prevent blood from pooling in the area exercised.

SAFETY AWARNESS

It is important to warm up before physical activity and cool down afterward. This involves stretching your muscles before and after contracting them to prevent injury.

Helps Relieve Emotional Tension

Tight muscles arise from many causes including emotional tension. Stretching is an exercise that can help relax tense muscles. Stretching the muscles in your neck, shoulders, and upper back is an especially useful way to relax because these muscles often become tense when you sit for long periods. Have you ever seen adults who work in an office stretch or bend their heads from side to side? Have you ever stretched your wrist and arm when taking a written exam? These movements are attempts to relieve tight muscles caused by tension.

Reduces Chance of Low Back Pain

Low back pain is one of the most common ailments. It has been estimated that 80 percent of the population in the United States suffers from backaches. To maintain a healthy back, you must have a balance of flexibility, strength, and endurance. The major considerations are

- Low back lumbar flexibility
- Hamstring flexibility
- Hip flexor flexibility
- Strength and endurance of the forward and lateral abdominals, and
- Strength and endurance of the back extensor muscles

Types of Stretching

When you compare the effectiveness and safety of the various stretching methods, there are only two types that can safely improve flexibility: static and dynamic. **Static stretching** is the more acceptable method of increasing flexibility. The process involves slowly moving the muscle to its stretching point and holding this position for 15 to 30 seconds. **Dynamic stretching** involves a similar position but is done in a continuous, slow, and controlled manner. This method of stretching should not be confused with ballistic or bouncing type stretching in which the motion is done rapidly. **Ballistic stretching** usually involves bobbing, bouncing, or jerky movements that use the body's momentum. This type of stretching is sometimes harmful because you may exceed the stretchable limits of the tissues involved.

Internet Resources

Physical Fitness and Healthy Low Back Function—The President's Council on Physical Fitness and Sports
http://www.fitness.gov/activity/activity7/lowback/lowback.html

Exercises/Stretches—Georgia St. University
http://www.gsu.edu/~wwwfit/flexibility.html

Personalized Interactive Web Site to Plan Program—Centers for Disease Control
http://www.bam.gov/fit4life/index.htm

Photodisc

Hold the stretch for a minimum of fifteen seconds.

One other type of stretching is called PNF or prioceptive neuromuscular facilitation.

This method is based on a *contract and relax* technique and requires the help of another person. To perform this type of stretch, you would position the body part that is to be stretched. The assistant would then hold the body part in this position while you contract the muscles. After contraction, relax the muscles; your partner then slowly aids in stretching the selected body part. The primary disadvantage to using PNF stretching is that the partner cannot know how much pain you are experiencing and may force a body part too far, causing injury. This form of stretching should only be done by trained subjects or sports medicine personnel and is not recommended in a personal fitness program.

Ballistic stretching—rapid and bouncy-type stretching movements—should never be done. These types of movements rely on momentum to force the muscles to lengthen, and will cause injury and muscle soreness due to small tears in the muscle tissue.

Comparing the Effectiveness and Safety of Stretching Methods

Type of Stretch	Static	Dynamic	PNF*	Ballistic
Effectiveness	medium	high	high	high
Risk of injury	low	low	medium	high
Soreness	low	low	medium	high

*PNF requires trained subjects and sports medicine personnel.

Application of Training Principles

Stretching for relaxation can be performed anywhere at any time. However, to increase flexibility, you must engage in a more deliberate training program. This could be in the form of a separate flexibility program, or it could be combined with the warm-up and cool-down phases of your overall personal fitness program.

Nutrition Information

Cut down on your intake of salt, as it contributes to high blood pressure. Salt is a learned taste that can be unlearned. The next time you add salt, ask yourself if the food really needs it, or if you have developed a habit of adding it without first tasting the food. Better yet, remove the shaker from the table.

It is very important to raise the muscle temperature prior to developmental stretching. This may be done by brisk walking, jogging, or other mild exercise.

Principle of Overload

To improve flexibility, you must stretch the soft tissue (ligaments, muscles, and tendons) farther than you are accustomed to doing. This additional overload can be placed on the body by an increase in frequency, intensity, or time of the flexibility exercise program.

- **Frequency**—Stretching exercises should be done a minimum of three times a week. Performing them daily is best.
- **Intensity**—The muscle is stretched beyond its normal length to reach what is called the *stretching point*. To reach the stretching point, you stretch slowly until mild tension is felt.
- **Time**—The length of time a static stretching position is held may be increased gradually from 10 to 30 seconds. Another way to increase time would be to increase the number of repetitions of an exercise, regardless of whether it is a static or dynamic stretch.

Stress Information

If you can learn from a failure, it has been a meaningful experience.

Summary of Flexibility Training Guidelines	
Frequency	At least 2 to 3 times per week.
Intensity	Stretch slowly until mild tension is felt.
Time	Static: Hold each stretch 10 to 30 seconds. Dynamic: Do 3 to 4 repetitions and 1 to 3 sets.

Principle of Progression

You may gradually increase the overload by increasing: (1) the number of sessions per day or week (frequency), (2) the distance the muscle is stretched (intensity), or (3) the amount of time the position is held or the number of repetitions and sets (time). Regardless of how you progressively increase the overload, remember to do so in a slow, easy manner.

Principle of Specificity

Stretching exercises will improve flexibility only in the joints you exercise. You may be flexible in one joint, but this does not mean you have the same degree of flexibility in all joints.

Some of your joints may be unusually flexible, while others may be only somewhat inflexible. Flexibility is also specific to each individual. Females tend to be more flexible than males of the same age. Because flexibility differs with each person, you should not compete with others in how far they stretch. Some sports require flexibility in specific joints not required in other sports. Even within the same sport, flexibility requirements vary widely. For example, a quarterback needs shoulder-joint flexibility in order to throw a perfect pass, while a punter requires greater hip-joint flexibility.

Flexibility Safety Precautions

The following safety precautions should be considered when performing flexibility exercises.

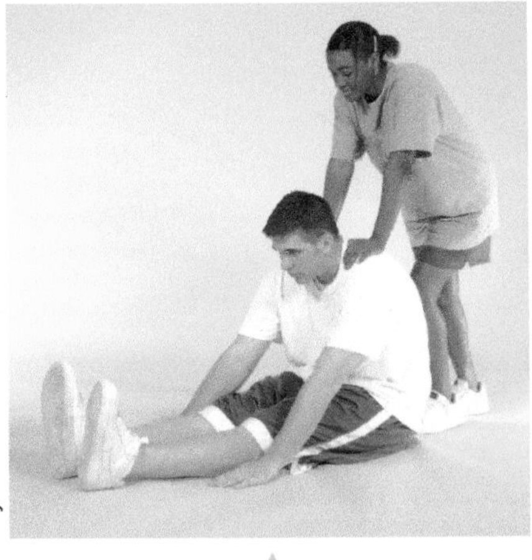
Ray Carson

Warning: Partner-assisted stretching can cause injury.

1. All ballistic stretching exercises that use the body's momentum to force a muscle beyond its stretching point have the potential for causing injury and should be avoided.
2. Using partners to help you get extra stretch can cause injury because others cannot know how much pain you are in and may force your body too far.
3. Start at a proper level and know when to increase the frequency, intensity, or amount of time of flexibility exercises.
4. There is danger of injury if you attempt to imitate the stretching ability of others. Stretch according to what you feel, not according to what others do.
5. Stretch all major muscle groups equally to include opposing muscle groups.
6. Include flexibility exercises with cardiovascular and muscular strength and endurance programs. This will help to prevent a muscle imbalance, such as the tight hamstring muscles frequently experienced by joggers.

You should know your current level of flexibility before beginning an exercise program. Testing the flexibility of each joint would take too much time and require elaborate

Consumer Issues

Stretching exercises should be performed slowly, deliberately, and carefully, allowing the muscles to relax and "let go." Vigorous straining encourages tightness and may harm the body. The numerous rubs, creams, and gels on the market provide only temporary relief to tightened muscles.

equipment. The flexibility tests described in Chapter 2 will give you an indication of flexibility in joints most likely to need attention.

A word of caution before you begin testing: (1) always warm up properly, (2) avoid ballistic (bouncing-type) movements when performing the tests, and (3) move into the testing position in a slow, controlled manner.

Setting Goals to Improve Flexibility

Flexibility can be improved rapidly if a person appropriately applies the training principles and the variables of overload. If your flexibility test score is more than 10 centimeters below the health fitness standard, you should set 3-month improvement goals within a range of 5 to 15 centimeters. If you are close to the standard, set goals with a range of 1 to 4 centimeters of improvement. If you exceed the health fitness standard, set your goal at 0 to 2 centimeters.

Flexibility Goal Setting

	Distance from Health Fitness Standard		
	Less	Close	Exceeds
Difference between Test Score and Health Fitness Standard	more than 10 cm	1 to 10 cm	at or above standard
Recommended Range for Goals	5 to 15 cm	1 to 4 cm	0 to 2 cm

Flexibility Exercises

Even if you score high on the flexibility tests, you should stretch your shoulders, lower back, hips, chest, backs of thighs, and calves on a regular basis. You will need to select specific stretching exercises before engaging in an exercise session or sports activity. The following exercises stretch each of the different parts of the body and will serve as a starting point.

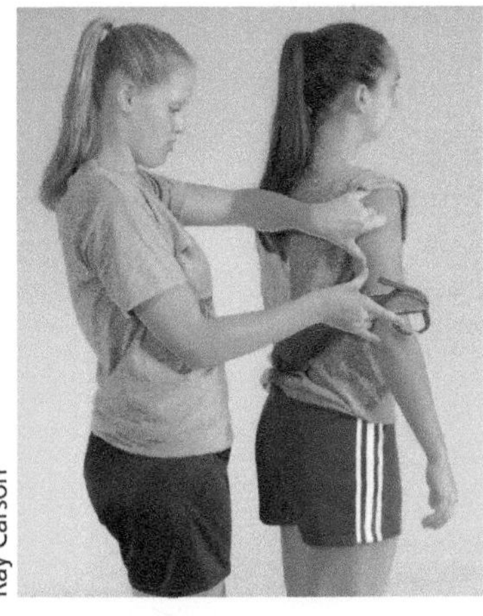
Ray Carson

Upper Body and Torso Stretch

1. Bend the knees of both legs slightly.
2. Tuck the buttocks under to keep the spine in a straight line.
3. Slowly extend one arm overhead as high as possible while extending the other arm downward.
4. Keep the head straight; do not allow it to tilt back.
5. Hold the stretch for 15 seconds.
6. Repeat with the other arm.

Neck Stretch

1. Emphasis should be on stretching in the various positions and not on rotation.
2. Hold each position for 15 seconds.
    a. Slowly bend your neck to the right and then to the left.
    b. Slowly turn your head to each side.
    c. Lower your chin to your chest.
    d. Rotate your head first to the right and then to the left.
3. Never bend your neck to the back (hyperextend).

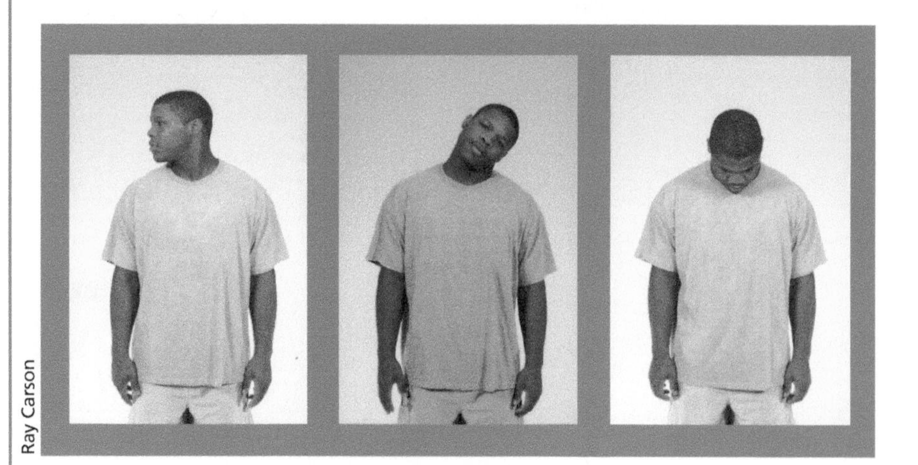
Ray Carson

Neck Stretch

Triceps Stretch

1. Reach over your head toward your back with one hand.
2. Place the opposite hand on the elbow and push the elbow upward.
3. Hold for 15 seconds.
4. Repeat with the other arm.

Ray Carson

Triceps Stretch

Chest and Biceps Stretch

1. Grasp your hands behind your back.
2. Slowly pull your arms toward one another.
3. Hold for 15 seconds.

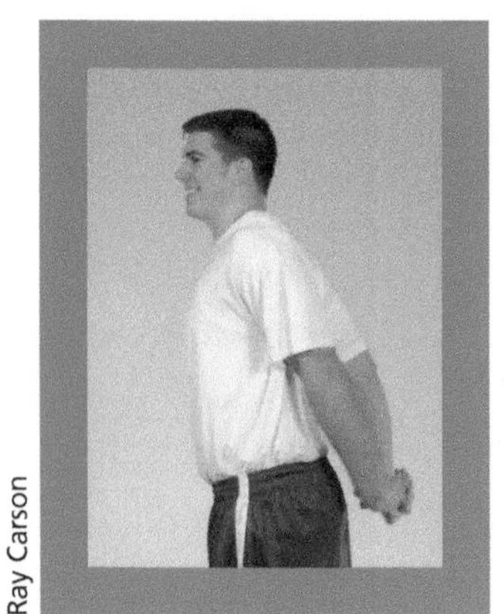
Ray Carson

Chest and Biceps Stretch

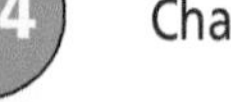

Ray Carson

Shoulder Stretch

Ray Carson

Knee-to Chest Stretch

Shoulder Stretch

1. Reach across your chest with one arm.
2. Slowly pull this arm with your other hand.
3. Hold for 15 seconds.
4. Repeat with the other arm.

Three-Prong Support Side Stretch

1. Kneel on one knee.
2. Bend to the same side as the bent knee, and support part of your weight on one arm.
3. Extend the other leg out to the side.
4. Slowly extend the opposite arm over your head.
5. Stretch from the extended leg to the extended arm.
6. Hold for 15 seconds.
7. Repeat to the other side.

Knee-to Chest Stretch

1. Lie on your back.
2. Grasp one or both legs underneath your thigh(s).
3. Pull knees to your chest.
4. Raise and lower head slowly.
5. Hold for 15 seconds.

Modified Hurdlers Stretch

1. Sit with one leg straight.
2. The opposite leg should be flexed with sole of the foot against the other leg.
3. Lean forward.
4. Hold for 15 seconds.

Hip Extension

1. Stand with pelvis in neutral position.
2. Extend leg backward at hip.
3. Hold for 15 seconds.

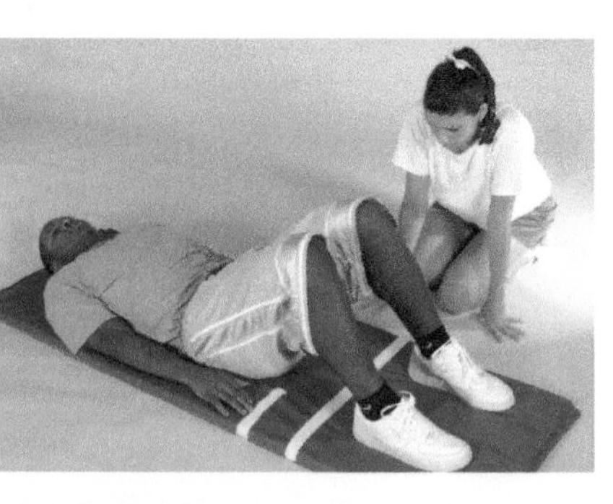

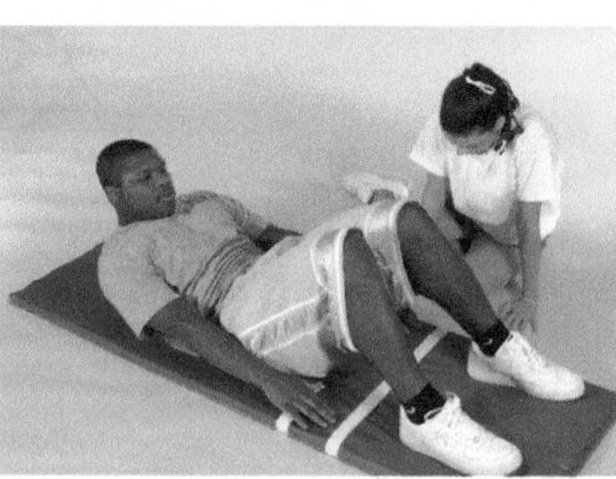

Ray Carson

Partial Curl

Back Extension

1. Lie face down with hands at thighs.
2. Keep neck and chin in neutral position.
3. Raise shoulders off floor.
4. Hold for 15 seconds.

Mad Cat

1. Place hands and knees on the floor.
2. Slowly tuck your chin and round your back, lifting it as high as possible.
3. Hold position for 15 seconds; then raise your head.

Partial Curl

1. Lie face up and with legs bent and feet flat on the surface.
2. Curl up and slide hands at side 3 to 5 inches.
3. Hold position for 15 seconds.

Hamstring Stretch

1. Place one foot on a low step or bench.
2. Keep the knee bent, and bend from the hips.
3. Hold for 15 seconds.
4. Repeat with the other leg.

Groin Stretch

1. Sit on the floor, and place the soles of your feet together.
2. Pull your feet a comfortable distance into your groin.
3. Place hands on the floor to your side to support the back.
4. Slowly press the knees down.
5. When you feel tension, hold for 15 seconds.

Quadriceps Stretch

1. Place left hand on your partner's shoulder or on an object for balance.
2. Flex your right leg backward.
3. Grasp your right ankle with your right hand.
4. Press the foot into your hand.
5. Do not pull on the foot or touch the heel to your buttocks, because this will cause a strain on the knee ligament.
6. When you feel the stretch in the front of the leg, hold for 15 seconds.
7. Repeat for the left leg.

Calf Stretch

1. Stand slightly more than an arm's length from a wall.
2. Place your feet a shoulder width apart, flat on the floor.
3. Hands should be flat, with knees and body straight.
4. Lean forward by bending the elbows.
5. When you feel tension in the lower calves, hold for 15 seconds.

Achilles Tendon Stretch

1. Stand 2 to 3 feet from a support.
2. Place one foot behind the other.
3. Lean forward keeping the heels flat.
4. Slowly bend the knee of the front leg until the Achilles tendon is stretched.
5. Hold for 15 seconds.
6. Repeat with the other foot.

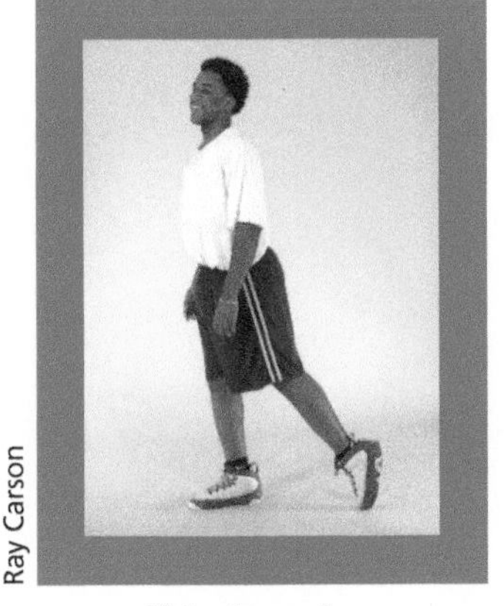

Ray Carson

Shin Stretch

Shin Stretch

1. Stand 2 feet from a support.
2. Place one foot behind the other.
3. Bend the knee of the rear leg with toes to the ground, as shown in the photo.
4. Slowly bend until you feel a stretch in the front of the lower leg.
5. Hold for 15 seconds.
6. Repeat with the other leg.

Harmful
Stretching Positions

The following stretching positions can be harmful. Many of them put stress on your joints, ligaments, tendons, and muscles, and may lead to injury. If you choose to perform any of the exercises listed, remember to stretch in a safe and controlled manner. Always avoid rapid, jerky, bouncy, ballistic movements because they may cause injury.

Head Circles

Never hyperextend your neck or do full head circles.

Arm Circles

Arm circles are actually ballistic stretches of the shoulder joint.

Plow

The plow position compresses the cervical vertebrae of the back and puts a large amount of stress on the lower back.

Sitting Quadriceps Stretch

Sitting on your heels to stretch the quadriceps overbends the knee joint.

Head Circles

Plow

Arm Circles

Sitting Quadriceps Stretch

Four-Count Toe Touch

The four-count toe touch is a traditional exercise that has been done for years, so it may be difficult to resist doing. Just remember that there are alternatives that do not place undue pressure on the disks of the lower spine, such as the hamstring stretch. Also, some people tend to lock their knees as they reach downward doing the toe touch. This can hyperextend the knee joint and cause an injury.

Hurdle Stretch

The hurdle stretch forces sideway movement of a hinge joint (bent knee joint) that is designed only for flexion and extension.

Deep Knee Bends

Bending at the knees is essential for safe lifting techniques. However, while keeping the heels flat on the ground, your knees should not bend beyond the point at which your thighs are parallel to the floor. Going beyond this limit may cause injury to any of the structures around the knee, including cartilage.

Hurdle Stretch

Four-Count Toe Touch

Deep Knee Bend

PFP Technology Activity

Create or use an online database to plot your flexibility work out regimen based on FIT so that days of participation and nonparticipation will be recorded.

PFP Update

Have you included flexibility exercises in your PFP? If you did not, you are urged to add selected stretches to your program. Why? Because flexibility is the health-related component of fitness that usually gets the least attention, yet it plays an important role in everyone's daily life. The benefits discussed in this chapter are worth the effort, and they are very attainable, if you give a little bit of time every day to stretching and being loose. If you expect your muscles and joints to function optimally, they must be warmed up and cooled down appropriately.

How did you do with the flexibility test earlier in this course? Congratulations if you did well. If you did not do as well as you would have liked, your course of action is simple: Just get after it. You should have set a goal for your next flexibility test after you took your first test. The key to success is simply to utilize the information about the overload principle presented in this chapter.

Review the stretching exercises in this chapter and add them to your PFP. They do not take much time, can be performed anywhere, and do not cost any money. For example, rather than getting out of bed quickly in the morning, do a few stretches. They will feel great. Observe cats and dogs when they wake up. Usually they do a full body stretch before moving on to the day's activities. We should probably imitate them. Stay determined to achieve your PFP goals!

Summary

Flexibility is the ability to move body joints through a full range of motion. The direction of joint movement is limited by the way it is structured. Some joints have a very limited range of motion, while others allow for movement in all directions. The four types of joints are the pivot, hinge, ball-and-socket, and gliding joint. Flexibility improvement can be made by performing static stretching, if the limitation on range of motion is imposed by soft tissues (ligaments, muscles, and tendons).

Everyone needs flexibility to some degree, both at work and play. An adequate degree of flexibility can reduce injuries, prevent post-exercise pain, reduce the chance of low back pain, and help in relieving emotional tension.

Photodisc

Static and dynamic stretching can be safely used to improve flexibility. These stretches can be performed as part of the warm-up and cool-down phases of your overall personal fitness program or as a separate flexibility program.

All principles of training are important in the development of flexibility. You should assess your current level of flexibility before beginning the flexibility phase of your personal fitness program.

Ballistic stretching and exercises that hyperextend the neck should not be performed. In addition, activities that compress the vertebrae, overbend a joint, or force sideward movements should be avoided.

Matching

1. Joint
2. Ligament
3. Muscle
4. Tendon
5. Static stretching
6. Dynamic stretching
7. Ballistic stretching
8. PNF stretching

A. point at which two bones come together
B. stretching done in a continuous, slow and controlled manner
C. form of stretching in which the body is pushed beyond its initial limit
D. strong, fibrous tissue that attaches one bone to another
E. connective tissue that anchors muscle to bone
F. stretching that involves bobbing, bouncing or jerky movements that make use of the body's momentum
G. the slow movement of a muscle to the stretching point at which it is held for 15 seconds
H. meaty tissue that surrounds bones

Multiple Choice

Choose the most correct answer.

9. The ability to move body joints through a full range of motion is known as
   A. exercise.
   B. flexibility.
   C. stretching.
   D. none of the above.

10. Wrists, shoulders, hips, knees, and ankles are all examples of
A. joints.
B. ligaments.
C. muscles.
D. tendons.

11. Post-exercise pain and stiffness caused by muscle spasms can be prevented or reduced by
A. cool-down exercises.
B. stretching exercises.
C. warm-up exercises.
D. weight training exercises.

12. What kind of stretching is done in a continuous slow and controlled manner?
A. ballistic stretching
B. dynamic stretching
C. PNF stretching
D. static stretching

13. Which of the following are examples of harmful stretching positions?
A. arm circles
B. head circles
C. plow position
D. all of the above

14. One can reduce injuries, prevent post-exercise pain, reduce chances of low back pain, and help relieve emotional tension by having an adequate degree of
A. exercising.
B. flexibility.
C. stretching.
D. none of the above.

15. The two types of stretching that can safely improve flexibility are
A. ballistic and dynamic.
B. dynamic and static.
C. PNF and ballistic.
D. static and isostatic.

16. To improve flexibility based on the principle of progression, you may gradually increase the overload by increasing the
    A. frequency.
    B. intensity.
    C. time.
    D. all of the above.

17. Strong fibrous tissue that attaches one bone to another is called
    A. joints.
    B. ligaments.
    C. muscles.
    D. tendons.

18. Which of the following is a type of joint?
    A. ball and socket
    B. hinge
    C. pivot
    D. all of the above

Authentic Assessment—Short Response

19. Why does a person lose flexibility?

20. What is the major difference between static and dynamic stretching?

21. How can the overload principle be used to improve flexibility?

22. Why should you not use partners when performing stretching exercises?

23. Name a sport or recreational activity in which you participate. List three stretching exercises you could perform to warm up for this activity.

Authentic Assessment—Extended Response

24. Both of my grandmothers are 70 years old. My maternal grandmother is very active and swims laps every day in her pool. My paternal grandmother is not very active and finds it hard to walk around the grocery store. What role does flexibility play in determining my grandmothers' level of activity?

25. Reshonda recently purchased an aerobic dance videotape and has invited you over to work out. During the first 10 minutes of the videotape, the celebrity shown on the video suggests that you warm up by performing the following exercises:

Head circles
Sitting quadriceps stretch
Deep knee bends
Plow
Hurdle stretch
Leg lifts

What advice would you give Reshonda regarding the videotape?

7 Cardiovascular Fitness

Photodisc

Objectives

As you read this chapter, look for answers to these key questions:

- How can you measure your pulse rate?
- What benefits are gained from participation in activities promoting cardiovascular fitness?
- Which health risk factors can be controlled with cardiovascular training?
- How can the training principles be applied to improve cardiovascular fitness?
- How do you determine the rate at which your heart should be exercised?
- How do you know when it is safe to progress with your cardiovascular training?

"The race is not always to the swift but to those who keep on trying."

V • A • L • U • E

Information in this chapter will not only help you obtain additional energy and make you feel better, it will assist you in combating cardiovascular disease, the number-one cause of death in the United States. It is estimated that more than half of deaths caused by cardiovascular disease could have been prevented with a change in the person's lifestyle. All of us have control over six of the nine risk factors associated with cardiovascular disease. Engaging in physical activity to improve your cardiovascular fitness is perhaps your most important lifestyle decision.

Chapter Preview

- Why Is Cardiovascular Fitness Important?
- Circulatory and Respiratory Systems
- Monitoring the Heart
- Cardiovascular Disease
- Cardiovascular Benefits of Exercise
- Application of Training Principles
- Setting Goals for Cardiovascular Improvement
- PFP Update
- Summary
- The Wrap-Up

Vocabulary

When you have completed this chapter, you should understand the meaning of these vocabulary terms:

pulse

resting heart rate

recovery heart rate

blood pressure

atherosclerosis

maximum heart rate

target heart rate

aerobic

anaerobic

Wellness Connection

Why Is Cardiovascular Fitness Important?

Cardiovascular fitness is said to be the most important of all physical fitness components. No matter how strong you look, if your circulatory and respiratory systems cannot meet your muscles' demand for oxygen, you cannot continue activity for a long period of time.

Exercising to improve cardiovascular fitness will increase your energy level, making it possible for you to exercise longer without tiring, and making you feel good. Additionally, exercising for cardiovascular fitness will help you look good, since the exercises will help you control your weight, improve your appearance, and improve your ability to meet the problems you face daily. You may be one of many people who have a low level of cardiovascular fitness if you find you are short of breath, tire easily, are unable to swim, run, bike or perform physical activities.

Cardiovascular fitness is the body's ability to provide oxygen continuously to muscles as work is performed over an extended period of time. This component of fitness includes the circulatory system (heart, blood, and blood vessels) and the respiratory system (lungs and air passages).

Developing cardiovascular fitness will help you enjoy life to its fullest.

Corbis

Research has shown that body functions improve with use and decline with disuse. In other words, the heart, lungs, and muscles become stronger and more efficient in their utilization of oxygen as they are used more. To understand how to improve your cardiovascular fitness, you must first understand how the circulatory and respiratory systems function and which diseases may result if these systems are neglected.

Circulatory and Respiratory System

People often take oxygen for granted and do not think of it as fuel for the body. The fact is, the more oxygen that muscles receive, the more energy they can produce and the better you feel. The circulatory and respiratory systems work together to provide muscles with necessary oxygen. As air is breathed in, the blood picks up oxygen from the lungs and carries it to the heart.

The heart is a remarkable muscle that serves as two pumps. The ventricle on the left side of the heart forces blood containing oxygen throughout the body through elastic blood vessels called arteries. Arteries always carry blood away from the heart.

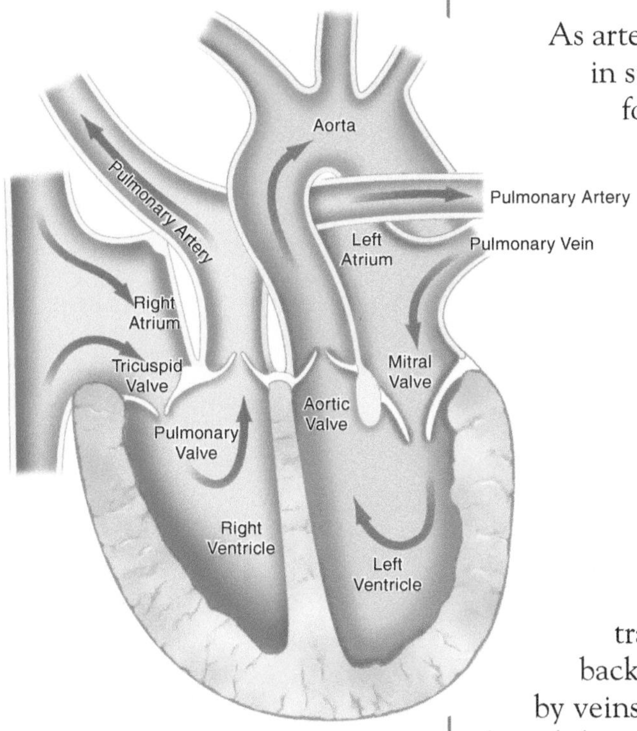

As arteries branch out in the body, they gradually decrease in size until they form tiny capillaries. This is where food and oxygen are delivered from the blood to cells throughout the body. In the drawing below, notice how the capillaries serve as bridges between arteries and veins. Veins always carry blood toward the heart.

Cross section of the heart: *Note the left ventricle muscle walls are thicker than the right ventricle walls, since this chamber pumps blood throughout the body compared to the right ventricle, which only has to pump it to the nearby lungs.*

Just as ashes are left after a fire, waste materials remain when cells use up oxygen. These wastes are picked up by the blood in the capillaries and are transported back to the heart by veins. Blood is forced through the veins by contracting muscles. The blood in veins can only move toward the heart, because one-way valves keep the blood from flowing backward when the muscle relaxes. The right ventricle of the heart pumps the returning blood to the lungs, where wastes are exchanged for more oxygen, and the process repeats itself.

An average person's body holds only about 12 pints of blood.

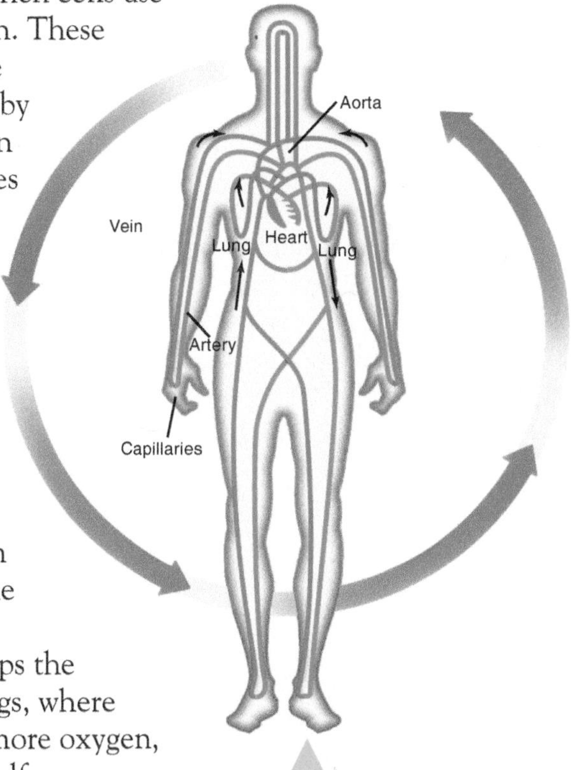

Simplified map of circulatory system: *Arrows indicate blood flow out of the heart through arteries and back by way of veins.*

Goal Setting

Individuals have different goals at different times in their life. What is important at age 15 may not be important at age 50. Likewise, the things that a 50-year-old values are also different from when that person was a teenager. The long-term goal of living a healthy and long life, however, spans all these years. The lifestyle habits developed at age 15 affect whether health goals are met at age 50.

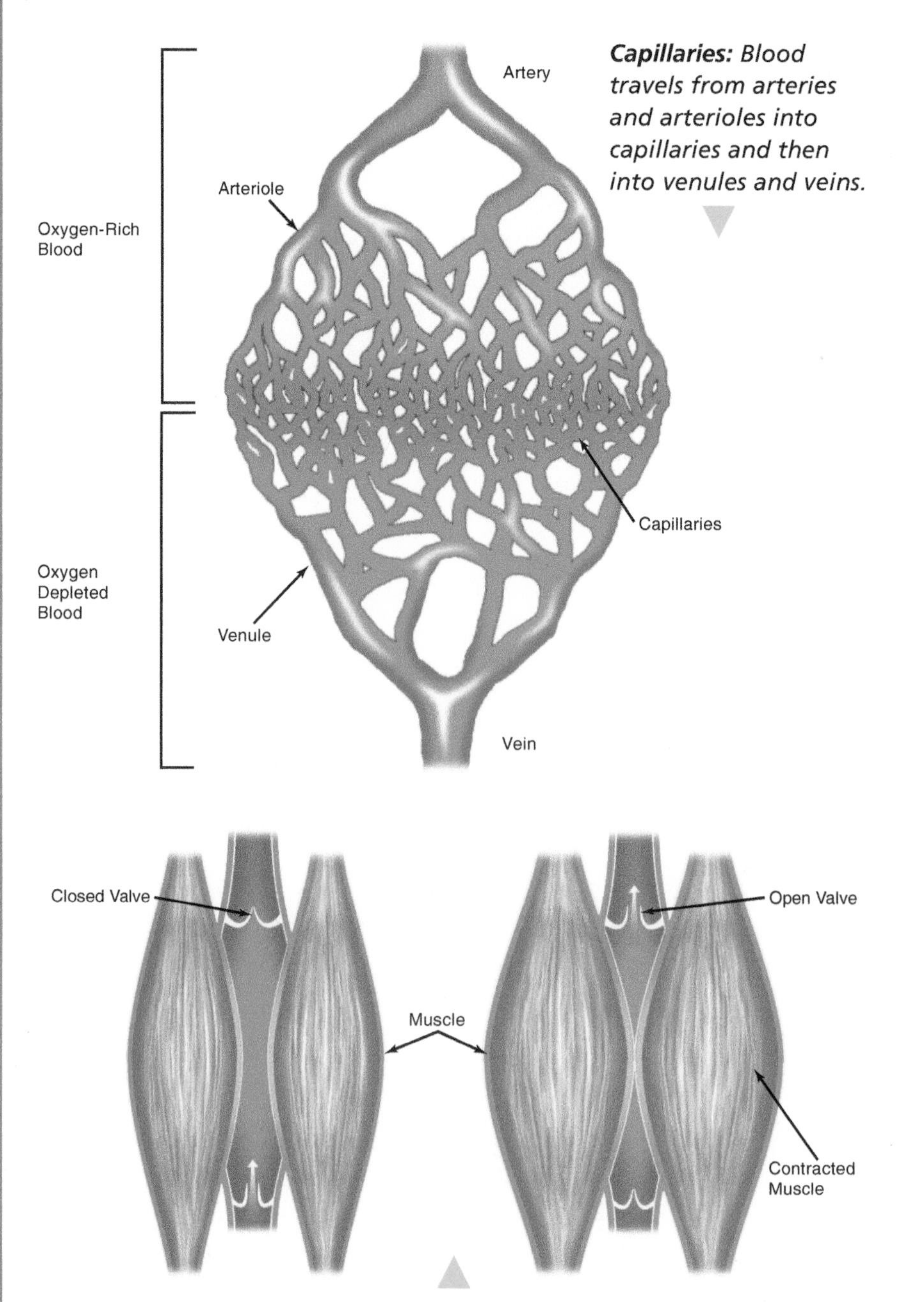

***Capillaries:** Blood travels from arteries and arterioles into capillaries and then into venules and veins.*

Contracting muscles squeeze the blood through one-way valves toward the heart.

Safety Awareness

Be alert when you are exercising outdoors near cars or people. Headphones are not advised. Stay focused on what is going on around you.

Therefore, the blood must circulate throughout the body to supply all the body cells continuously with oxygen and nutrients and to remove wastes. That is why the heart, blood vessels, and blood are called the circulatory system.

Monitoring the Heart

How fast must the heart beat to pump blood? Your heart rate varies with the changing needs of your body. When you are lying down, your heart rate is less than when you are standing. Running produces a higher heart rate than doing a less vigorous activity such as walking. Your size also has an effect on your heart rate. The average heart rate for adults is 70 beats per minute. In children, the heart beats about 100 times per minute. It is important for you to know how hard your heart muscle is working. One way of knowing is to count your pulse rate.

Internet Resources

The Heart: An On-Line Exploration—Franklin Institute Science Museum
http://www.fi.edu/biosci/heart.html

On-Line Exercise Diary—American Heart Association
http://www.justmove.org

Tracking Conditions and Risk Behaviors—National Center for Chronic Disease Prevention and Health Promotion
http://www.cdc.gov/nccdphp/tracking.htm

Risk Reduction through Lifestyle Modification—National Stroke Association
http://www.stroke.org

Pulse

Your pulse is caused by pressure of the blood on the artery wall, and it corresponds to your heartbeat. The most accurate way of checking your heart rate during exercise is with a heart rate monitor that straps around your chest. The monitor provides feedback on a digital watch at any specific time in your exercise session. The other way is to take your pulse. The best locations for feeling your pulse are at the wrist and neck, where arteries lie just below the skin. To take your pulse at the wrist, place your index and middle finger against the skin at the base of your thumb on the soft area of the wrist.

Photodisc

Pulse may be taken at the wrist or carotid artery. Take the pulse for ten seconds and multiply by six for a one-minute heart rate count.

To measure your pulse rate at the carotid artery in the neck, place your index and middle fingers from the ear lobe midway toward your Adam's apple. Once your hand is in the correct position, count the number of beats for 6 seconds and place a zero at the end of that number, or count the beats for 10 seconds and multiply by 6 to obtain a one-minute pulse rate. Be advised that the quickest method is not the most accurate. Counting for 30 seconds and then multiplying that number by 2 will give you a slightly more accurate reading. Regardless of the method used, be consistent.

Several factors may cause the pulse rate to vary. For example, exercise increases the pulse. The higher the intensity of exercise, the higher the pulse. Other factors that may affect the pulse rate include excitement, position of the body, and illness. Since your pulse rate varies throughout the day, it is recommended that you take your pulse at rest if you wish to compare pulse rate readings while exercising.

Resting Heart Rate

Since the heart is a muscle, it becomes stronger when exercised. By keeping a record of your resting heart rate, you can measure the progress gained in your cardiovascular fitness program. An active person has a lower resting heart rate than someone who is inactive. The heart of an active person pumps more blood with each beat, thus working more efficiently. After a few months of cardiovascular training, a sedentary person will note a decrease in the resting heart rate of 10 to 25 beats per minute. This illustrates that your heart is becoming stronger and more efficient.

To measure the **resting heart rate,** take your pulse just after waking in the morning and before getting out of bed. Your pulse should be taken while you are in a sitting or lying position. The American Heart Association has established a range of 50 to 100 beats per minute for resting heart rate as normal. However, research shows that adults with resting heart rates over 70 have a greater risk of heart attack than those with resting heart rates below 70.

Recovery Heart Rate

To determine when it is safe to progress in your training program, you should check your pulse after the exercise session to determine your **recovery heart rate.** The guiding principle is that your heart rate should drop to about 120 beats per minute (BPM) within 5 minutes after the workout and be less than 100 beats per minute after 10 minutes.

5 minutes after exercise = 120 BPM
10 minutes after exercise = 100 BPM

If after 5 minutes your pulse does not drop to 120 beats per minute, or after 10 minutes to 100 beats per minute, you need to reduce the intensity of your workout. However, you may elect to increase the intensity of your workout if your recovery heart rate is below 120 beats per minute 5 minutes after exercising and below 100 beats per minute 10 minutes after exercising.

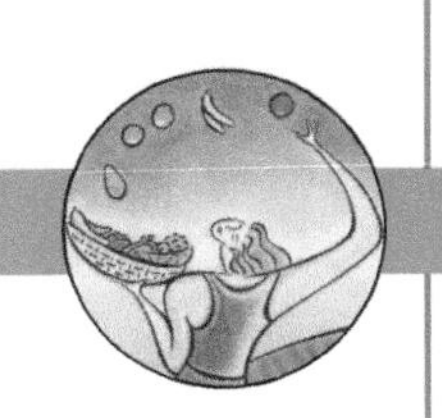

Nutrition Information

An apple a day may keep the doctor away, especially if you suffer from asthma or respiratory disease. Research findings show that people who ate five or more apples a week had better lung function than those who did not. Researchers have reported apples may reduce the risk of lung cancer.

Blood Pressure

Blood pressure is the measure of blood force against the walls of the arteries. Blood pressure is recorded with two numbers. The higher number recorded is the systolic pressure and is your blood pressure at the moment blood is pumped from the heart by the ventricles. The lower number is the diastolic pressure and represents the blood pressure when the heart is relaxed and filling with blood. The normal range for blood pressure is stated as:

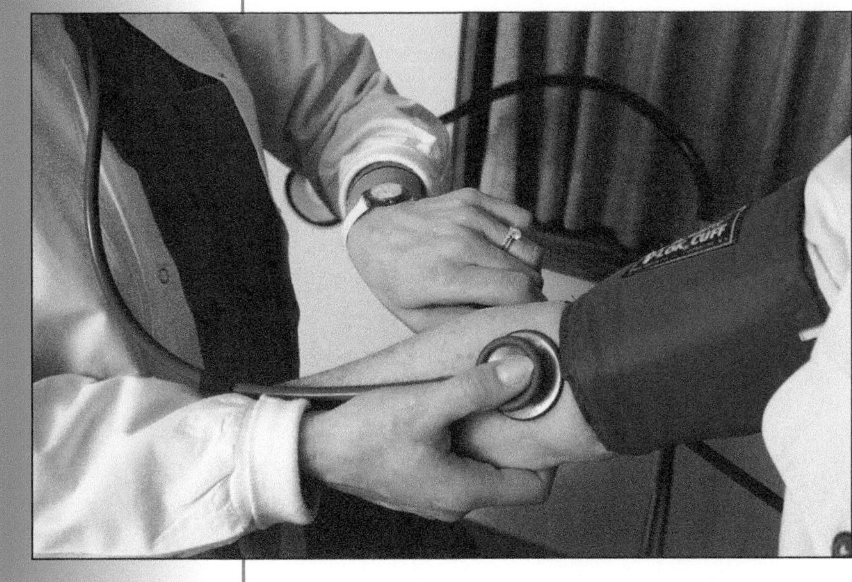

Photodisc

Blood pressure is one external method of monitoring your circulatory system. A high reading indicates an inefficient system.

$$\frac{120 \pm \text{systolic pressure}}{80 \pm \text{diastolic pressure}}$$

Aerobic exercises contribute to blood pressure control. Both systolic and diastolic pressures can be reduced as a result of aerobic training. Long-term research studies have shown that the lower the blood pressure, within normal limits, the lower the risk of having a heart attack.

Cardiovascular Disease

When people are young, they have a tendency to feel indestructible. Many teenagers believe they will live forever and give little thought to illnesses, much less death. What is needed is a mature evaluation of your lifestyle and how it will affect your health in 20 or 30 years. Scientists have found that many illnesses affecting older people start very early in life.

One illness that starts at an early age is cardiovascular disease, which is the major cause of death (40 percent) in the United States. To put it another way, for every American who dies of cancer, the second-ranking cause of death, two die of a heart-related illness.

STRESS INFORMATION

Becoming physically fit will increase your tolerance to stressful situations in sports and daily life.

Causes of Cardiovascular Disease

The primary cause of cardiovascular disease is a build-up of fatty deposits on the inner walls of the arteries. These deposits cause an arterial passageway to become smaller, leading to a condition called **atherosclerosis.** This restricts the blood flow, much like placing your thumb over a garden hose restricts the flow of water. Just as your thumb causes a higher water pressure in the hose, the fatty deposits on the inner walls of the arteries cause a higher blood pressure, which makes the heart work harder.

These fatty deposits can become so great that blood will not flow through the artery. In addition, blood vessels can also be blocked by a blood clot (thrombosis) lodging in a narrowed passageway. When this happens to an artery that feeds the heart (coronary artery), a heart attack occurs. When it happens to an artery that supplies blood to the brain, a stroke occurs. While a heart attack or stroke happens suddenly, the factors causing the blocked arteries can be traced back to many years earlier.

Developing stages of atherosclerosis

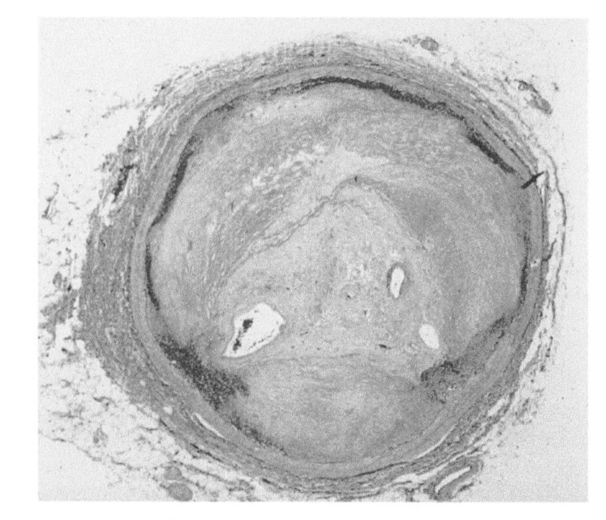

Consumer Issues

It is true that the simple act of walking can help you feel better. However, this simple physical activity does require shoes that provide good foot support. Walking helps circulation of blood throughout the body. As a result, walking directly affects your overall feeling of well being. Just get moving!

Risk Factors

A study of medical records indicates that ailments of the heart and blood vessels have decreased in recent years. However, cardiovascular disease continues to hold the deadly distinction of being the number-one killer in the United States. In fact, heart and blood vessel diseases cause almost as many deaths as cancer, accidents, pneumonia, influenza, and all other causes of death. As you will recall from Chapter 1, there are nine risk factors associated with heart attacks:

1. Inactivity
2. Obesity
3. High blood pressure
4. High levels of cholesterol
5. Stress and tension
6. Smoking
7. Sex of individual
8. Heredity
9. Age

As you review the nine risk factors, notice that the first six are controllable. The choices you make today in your lifestyle will have an effect on how well and how long you live. In fact, many people your parents' age and older wish they had learned the values of exercise and other good health habits when they were much younger.

Cardiovascular Benefits of Exercise

Have you thought about how accustomed our society has become to the use of technology? Although technology saves us labor, our bodies have not adapted well to not moving and being physically active. Just as eating additional calories has a cumulative affect, so does engaging in physical activity. Make a conscious decision to choose physical activity when given the option.

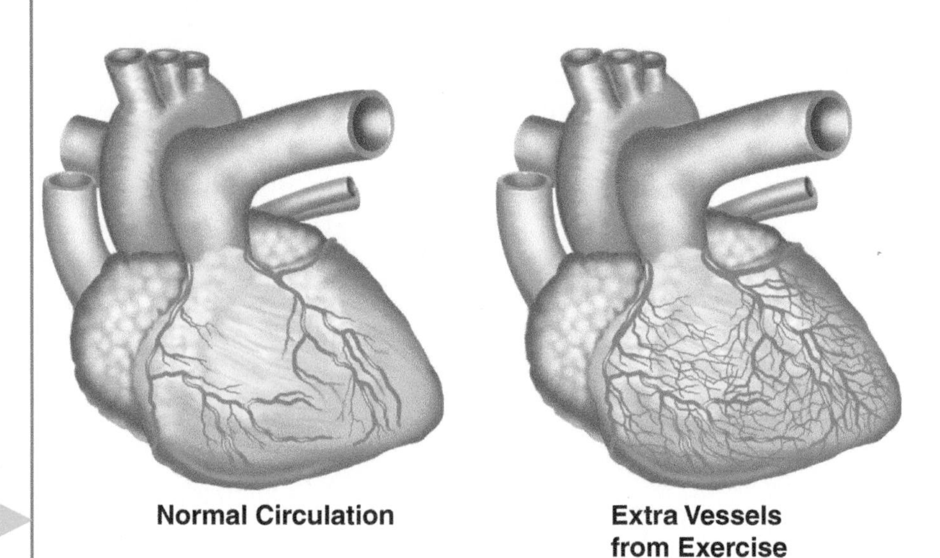

Research has shown that people who engage in regular exercise develop extra arteries in the heart muscle.

Participating in activities that promote cardiovascular fitness strengthens the heart and reduces atherosclerosis. Active people are better able to clear fats from their blood stream as a result of exercise. Therefore, fatty substances are less likely to form on the walls of the arteries. Research has shown that active people have less heart disease and are less likely to die from a heart attack than inactive people.

Everyone would like to have enough energy to take part in a favorite sport or activity without feeling tired. One way to obtain additional energy is to increase the oxygen supply to muscles by exercising the heart. Your heart muscle gets stronger as you engage in cardiovascular activities. Thus, it works more efficiently because it is able to pump out more blood with each

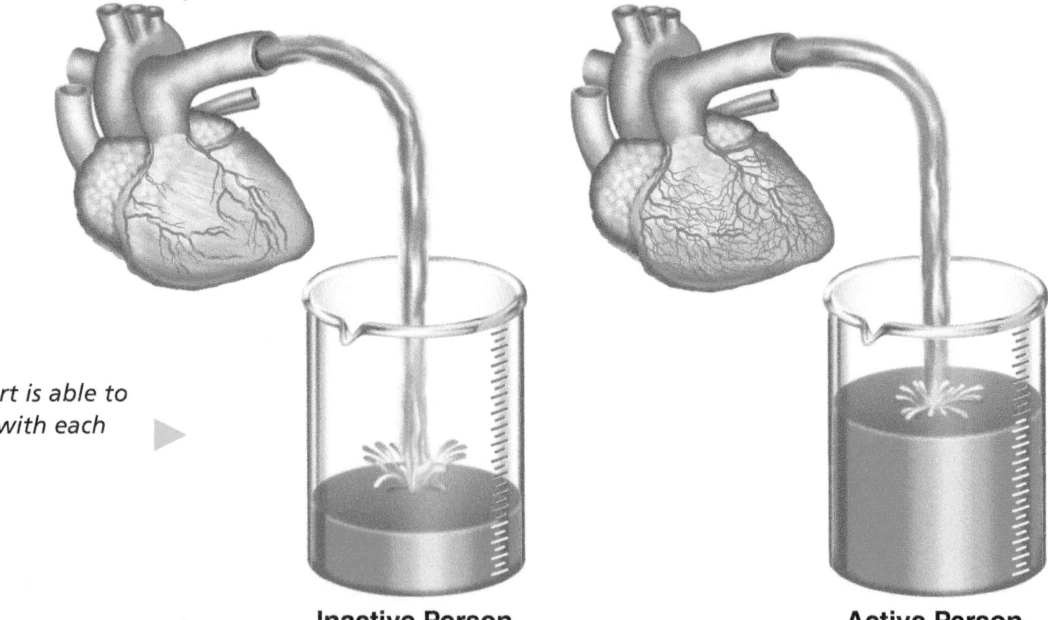

The active person's heart is able to pump out more blood with each beat.

beat. In addition, the trained heart beats fewer times per minute when compared to the heart of someone who is not physically fit. The result is that the muscles receive more oxygen and do not tire as easily.

Not only do you lessen your chances of developing heart disease and make your cardiovascular system more efficient through training, you can also obtain mental benefits. Concentration, ability to cope with stress, and positive self-concept are also improved.

Application of Training Principles

The main purpose of any cardiovascular fitness program is to increase the body's ability to utilize oxygen. To increase cardiovascular fitness you must engage in exercises that involve movements of the large muscles of the body. You must be able to maintain these exercises continuously for at least 15 to 30 minutes. Such exercises are called *aerobic*, since the working muscles continue to receive as much oxygen as they need. Brisk walking or jogging are activities that would meet the requirements.

Considerable research has led to the development of the principles of training. By following these principles, you will be able to train efficiently and avoid possible strain and injury.

Principle of Overload

One way to increase the oxygen supply to the muscles is to develop the muscle that serves as the pump. Since the heart is a muscle, it responds to training, as do all other muscles.

To develop the heart muscle, you must push it beyond its normal range and make it pump more blood with each beat. This additional overload can be placed on the heart by an increase in the frequency, intensity, or time of the exercise program.

Swimming is an aerobic activity and will develop cardiovascular fitness.

Photodisc

Frequency

The exercise selected must be performed regularly to reach an adequate level of cardiovascular fitness. Ideally, your training program will become a daily habit; however, benefits can be achieved with fewer workouts. Aerobic activities must be performed at least three times per week to reach an adequate level of cardiovascular fitness.

As a beginner you may elect to walk, swim, or bike three days per week, then increase the overload by doing your selected activity four days, then five days, and finally on a daily basis. Participating in such activities two days a week will not significantly increase cardiovascular fitness. However, such a schedule may maintain the level you have acquired.

Intensity

In cardiovascular training, you are trying to strengthen the heart and improve the body's ability to utilize oxygen. Even though the heart is a muscle, you cannot observe it getting stronger, as you can the biceps. Therefore, you must rely on the pulse rate, which is an external sign of the heart's condition, since it corresponds exactly to the beat of the heart.

The intensity of a cardiovascular activity may be determined by the response of the pulse rate. How much you increase the heart rate is the critical question. On one hand, if you do not increase it enough, little or no improvement in cardiovascular fitness will occur. On the other hand, exercising too hard too soon may cause extreme discomfort.

Each person has a **maximum heart rate** which should not be exceeded. To determine your maximum heart rate, subtract your age from 220. The Maximal Heart Rate Chart illustrates the maximal heart rate for various ages. You will note that as one becomes older, the maximal heart rate decreases.

To obtain the greatest cardiovascular benefits, the American College of Sports Medicine (ACSM) recommends that the intensity of your training be sufficient to increase your heart rate to 60 to 90 percent of maximum heart rate or at 50 to 85 percent of heart rate reserve. The percent range of your heart rate while exercising is termed the **target heart rate** zone and is the desired level of intensity for most people.

There are two different methods you may use to calculate your target heart rate training zone. One is based on calculating a percentage of your maximum heart rate, while the other is based on a percentage of your maximum heart rate reserve and takes into account your resting pulse rate. Both methods have advantages over the other. For example, while a percentage of the maximum heart rate method is easier to calculate, the maximum heart rate reserve is more personalized since it takes into account your resting pulse rate. Both methods of calculating your target heart rate training zone are described in this section.

Both methods have minimum percentage limits. However, you should always start at a lower percentage if you have not been active for some time or are overweight. Although you will not obtain all of the benefits of aerobic training, some improvement will occur. For example, start at 30 or 40 percent and gradually progress to the 50 or 60 percent range. The ACSM states that individuals starting a cardiovascular fitness program and older adults should take a more gradual approach. They further state that while not all of the benefits of aerobic training will be obtained, many health benefits can be achieved at lower intensities of exercise if more frequent, short (10-minute) sessions make up the intensity shortfall.

Percentage of Maximum Heart Rate

To compute your target heart-rate zone using the percentage of maximum heart rate method, you must first determine your own maximum heart rate (220 – age = maximum heart rate). This value is multiplied by the lower percent at which you wish to train.

As age increases, maximum attainable heart rate decreases, thus affecting the upper and lower levels of the target heart-rate zone.

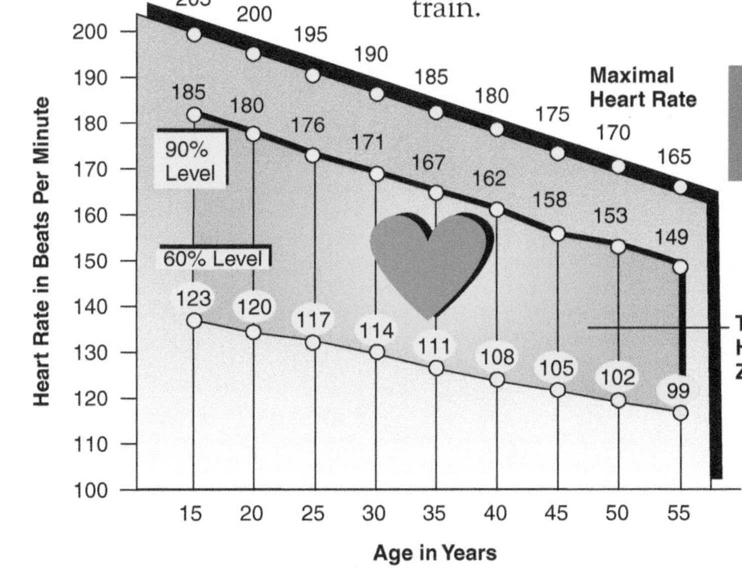

(220 – age) × 60 percent = lower level of target heart rate zone

This formula should be used again to obtain the upper limit of your target heart-rate zone. Ninety percent would be substituted in the formula in place of the 60 percent lower limit.

Below is an example of how Lunetta figured the lower and upper limits of her target heart-rate zone. Lunetta is 14 years old, and her resting heart rate is 70.

Percentage of Maximum Heart Rate Calculation

	Lower Limit	Upper Limit
1. Lunetta subtracted 14 (age) from 220 to obtain her maximum heart rate of 206. 220 – age = maximum heart rate	220 –14 206 MHR	220 –14 206 MHR
2. She decided that 60 percent should be the lower limit of her target heart rate zone and that 90 percent would be a safe upper limit for optimum training effect.	× 60%	× 90%
3. Lunetta multipled step 2 by the value of step 1. It was determined that 123.6 was the lower limit of her target heart-rate zone and 185.4 was the safe upper limit.	123.6	185.4

Percentage of Heart Rate Reserve

To compute your target heart-rate zone using the percentage of heart rate reserve method, you again must first determine your own maximum heart rate (220 – age = maximum heart rate). Your resting heart rate is then subtracted from your maximum heart rate. This value is multiplied by the lower percent at which you wish to train and is added to the resting heart rate.

The previous formula should be used again to obtain the upper limit of your target heart-rate zone. Eighty-five percent would be substituted in the formula in place of the 50 percent lower limit.

[(220 – age) – resting heart rate] × 50 percent + resting heart rate = lower level of target heart rate zone

Percentage of Maximal Heart Rate Reserve

	Lower Limit	Upper Limit
1. Chris subtracted 14 (age) from 220 to obtain his maximum heart rate of 206. 220 – age = maximum heart rate	220 –14 206 MHR	220 –14 206 MHR
2. Using the method described in this chapter, he determined his resting heart rate to be 70, which was subtracted from 206.	–70 RHR 136	–70 RHR 136
3. Chris decided that 50 percent should be the lower limit of his target heart rate zone and that 85 percent would be a safe upper limit for training.	× 50%	× 85%
4. He multiplied step 3 by the value of step 2.	68	122.4
5. Chris then added his resting heart rate.	+70 RHR	+ 70 RHR
6. It was determined that 138 was the lower limit of his target heart-rate zone and 186 was the safe upper limit.	138	185.6

Next is an example of how Chris figured the lower and upper limits of his target heart-rate zone. Chris is 14 years old, and his resting heart rate is 70.

Once the target heart-rate zone is known, you will be able to check the intensity of your exercise by stopping briefly from time to time to count your pulse rate. Many people find it difficult to utilize this information, since they have to count their pulse for 10 seconds and then multiply by 6 for a one-minute count (60 seconds). This may be hard to do if you are swimming in a pool or jogging 2 miles from home. A helpful hint is to use a pencil and paper to divide the lower and upper limits of your target heart rate zone by 6. This will give you a 10-second count that can be easily remembered. For example, if your target heart rate lower limit is 151 and your upper limit is 192, divide both by 6. The 10-second count would be 25 for the lower limit and 32 for the upper limit.

While exercising, if your pulse falls below the lower limit of your target heart-rate zone, you should increase your intensity (speed up your pace). If your pulse goes above the upper limit of your target heart-rate zone, decrease your intensity (slow down your pace).

Time

To achieve all the values of cardiovascular training, you must maintain the target heart rate (60 to 90 percent of your maximum heart rate or 50 to 85 percent of your maximum heart rate reserve) for a minimum of 20 minutes. A beginner may find it necessary to start a program involving less time and progressively increase the length of time of the exercise session. ACSM recommends that if continuous activity cannot be maintained, that you engage in intermittent aerobic activity that last at least 10 minutes and try to accumulate at least 30 minutes or more throughout the day.

To increase the overload, you may choose to increase the pace (intensity) or the distance (time) jogged. For example, after weeks of 20-minute exercise sessions, in which you were steadily increasing your pace (intensity) to keep your pulse in the target heart-rate zone, you might choose to increase your distance (time) and decrease your pace (intensity). Remember, as time is increased, intensity will decrease.

Summary of Cardiovascular Endurance Training Guidelines

Frequency	At least 3 times per week
Intensity	60–90 percent maximum heart rate 50–85 percent maximum heart rate reserve
Time	Minimum of 20 minutes of continuous large muscle group activity

The chart that follows summarizes a typical aerobic exercise session for someone using a percentage of maximum heart rate to calculate his or her target heart rate training zone. As you will note, this individual has a normal heart rate of 70 beats per minute. After a 5- to 10-minute warm-up, the individual gradually increases her heart rate to 130 beats per minute, which is at the lower level of the target heart-rate zone. She slightly increases the heart rate and maintains it within the target heart-rate zone of 124 to 185 beats per minute. This level of activity is maintained for 20 to 60 minutes. At the conclusion of

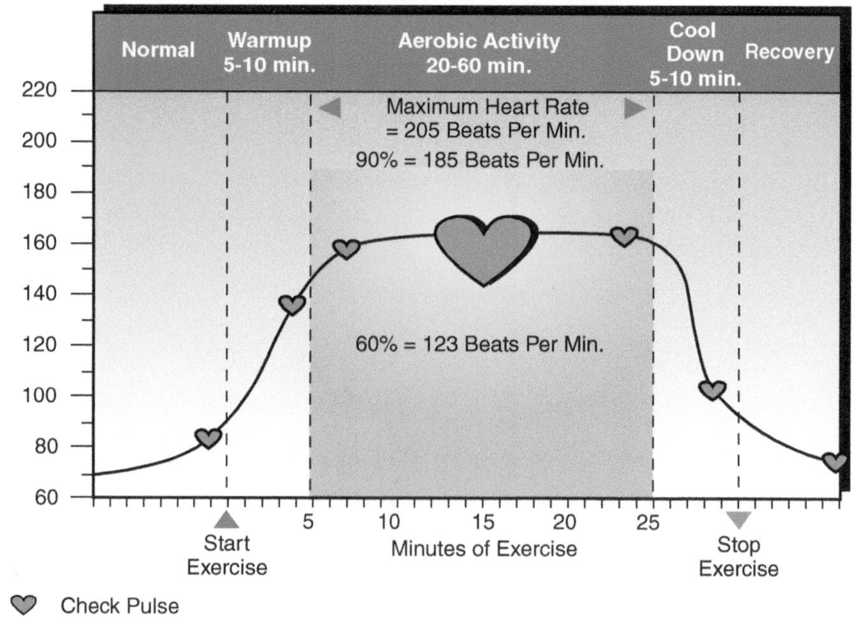

Heart rate during a typical aerobic exercise session

the training period, she begins her cool-down session to gradually reduce the heart rate. After the cool-down, she begins the recovery stage, with the heart returning to its pre-activity level.

Principle of Progression

Since the heart adjusts to the workload you place on it, the overload must be periodically increased in order for improvement to occur. For example, if you begin a regular exercise program that involves jogging 1 mile in 9 minutes, you might find the workout stressful. Your cardiovascular fitness would gradually improve if you continued the 9-minute rate. However, after several weeks of jogging the same distance in the same time, cardiovascular improvement would stop and adaptation would occur. To continue improving your cardiovascular fitness, you would have to increase the stress by jogging a mile in a shorter period of time. This progressive increase in the overload would place additional stress on your cardiovascular system and produce additional improvement.

Corel

Monitoring your pulse will give you an indication whether you need to increase or decrease your intensity.

Remember to observe your target heart rate and recovery heart rate. If while training, your heart rate goes above or below your target heart rate zone, adjustments need to be made. Also, you need to reduce the intensity or duration of your training program if your recovery heart rate is not less than 120 beats per minute 5 minutes after exercising or less than 100 beats per minute 10 minutes after exercising.

Principle of Specificity

Aerobic exercise promotes cardiovascular fitness better than any other type of activity. Aerobic means with oxygen and involves activities that can be performed for at least fifteen minutes without gasping to catch your breath. Examples of aerobic activities include jogging, dancing, swimming, bicycling, racquetball, and soccer.

Anaerobic (without oxygen) activity is performing at a pace, which uses oxygen faster than the body can replenish it. Since this is true, anaerobic exercise can be done only for a short period of time. Examples would be the 200-meter dash or the 50-yard freestyle swimming events. What other events would be considered anaerobic? Aerobic?

Setting Goals for Cardiovascular Improvement

For cardiovascular fitness, substantially less than the health fitness standard may be interpreted as being more than two minutes from the health fitness standard for a mile run/walk. If you fall within this category you may expect rapid improvement initially if you maintain a regular exercise routine. An appropriate cardiovascular goal would be to show improvement in the range from 30 seconds to 5 minutes, depending on how much you are motivated during the test. If you are close, or within two minutes of the health fitness standard, you should set 3-month goals within a range of 15 to 90 seconds. If you exceed the health fitness standard, set improvement goals within a range of 0 to 45 seconds.

Cardiovascular Goal Setting

	Distance from Health Fitness Standard		
	Less	Close	Exceeds
Difference between Test Score and Health Fitness Standard	2 minutes+	0 to 2 minutes	0 or better
Recommended Range for Goals	30 seconds to 90 seconds	0 to 5 minutes	15 seconds

PFP Technology Activity

Create or use an online database to plot your cardiovascular plan based on frequency, intensity, and time. Each session of your workout should be plotted showing days of participation and progression.

PFP Update

How did you do on your cardiovascular fitness test earlier in the semester? This test should have given you an indication of how fit your heart, lungs, arteries, capillary beds, and veins are. Why is it easy to forget about these important organs and structures? You cannot see them. If you could see inside the blood vessels of your heart and arteries, you might be shocked at their poor condition. Your heart is a muscle and just like the other muscles in your body, it needs to be exercised. Include aerobic activities at least three times a week that last 20 minutes continuous, or 10 minute bouts to accumulate throughout the day in your PFP. You will notice an improvement in your energy level and have the added benefit of a healthier heart.

If your family members do not engage in physical activity, you should talk to them. You now have the knowledge about cardiovascular fitness to help get them started . This knowledge can not only help improve their energy levels, but also help them realize how physical activity can combat cardiovascular disease.

Summary

Cardiovascular fitness includes the efficient operation of the circulatory and respiratory systems. These systems improve with use and decline with disuse. Thus, the more active you are, the more energy you will have, and the more your chances of developing cardiovascular disease will decrease.

One important element of cardiovascular fitness is the efficiency of the heart, since it pumps oxygen-rich blood to the muscles. Because your heart is a muscle, it becomes stronger when exercised. Aerobic activities, such as swimming and jogging, will provide a training effect when maintained for a minimum of 15 minutes and performed at least three days per week.

You must rely on your pulse rate to determine the effect of training. By calculating your resting heart rate, target heart rate zone, and recovery heart rate, you will know where to begin, and with careful monitoring during your training session, you will know when to progress.

Having a high level of energy is one of the most important benefits of exercise. Without energy, it is very hard to feel good about yourself. Although following a sound cardiovascular fitness program may not always be easy, the payoff can be most rewarding. Here's to healthy hearts.

Ray Carson

The Wrap-Up

Vocabulary Matching

Match the definitions to the correct term.

1. Pulse

2. Resting heart rate

3. Recovery heart rate

4. Blood pressure

5. Arteriosclerosis

6. Maximum heart rate

7. Target heart rate

8. Aerobic

9. Anaerobic

10. Atherosclerosis

A. a condition in which fatty deposits build up on inner walls of arteries, causing narrowing of arterial passageways

B. energy producing biochemical pathways in cells that do not require oxygen to produce energy

C. heart rate just after exercise

D. a regular throbbing caused by pressure of blood on an artery wall that corresponds to heart beats

E. heart rate that should not be exceeded during exercise

F. 60 to 90 percent of the maximum heart rate

G. the measure of blood force against the walls of the arteries

H. energy producing biochemical pathways in cells that use oxygen to produce energy

I. heart rate just after waking and before getting out of bed

J. hardening of the arteries that occurs in advanced stages of cardiovascular disease

Multiple Choice

Select the most correct answer.

11. Exercising to improve cardiovascular fitness will

A. allow you to exercise longer.
B. increase your energy level.
C. make you feel good.
D. all of the above.

12. Cardiovascular fitness uses which of the following body systems?
A. circulatory and digestive
B. circulatory and respiratory
C. digestive and respiratory
D. respiratory and muscular

13. The number-one killer in the United States is
A. cancer.
B. car accidents.
C. cardiovascular disease.
D. smoking.

14. Which of the following is an example of anaerobic exercises?
A. 100-yard dash
B. bicycling
C. racquetball
D. soccer

15. When you increase the pace of your run, you are increasing:
A. frequency
B. intensity
C. time
D. none of the above

16. In order for jogging to contribute toward the development of cardiovascular fitness, your target heart rate must be maintained for at least
A. 3 minutes.
B. 5 minutes.
C. 10 minutes.
D. 30 minutes.

17. Blood flow in the body follows the pattern of
A. heart to arteries to capillaries to veins.
B. heart to arteries to veins to capillaries.
C. heart to veins to arteries to capillaries.
D. veins to capillaries to heart to arteries.

18. Your friend, who is age 15, wishes to start a jogging program. Using a percentage of maximal heart rate, what would you suggest as a proper starting target heart rate?
A. 123
B. 146
C. 155
D. 178

19. What should your training heart rate be in order to safely develop cardiovascular fitness?
   A. 140 bpm
   B. 60 percent
   C. 95 percent
   D. 190 bpm

20. The intensity of your workout is too difficult if your heart rate has not returned to 120 bpm within how many minutes after exercising?
   A. 2 minutes
   B. 5 minutes
   C. 10 minutes
   D. 15 minutes

Authentic Assessment—Short Response

21. How does cardiovascular fitness allow you to exercise longer?

22. What type of activities are best for developing cardiovascular fitness? Why?

23. You currently can jog 1 mile in 12 minutes, but you have a personal goal of jogging 2 miles in 20 minutes. How would you train to reach your goal?

24. Why should your pulse rate be taken after an exercise session?

25. Review the personal goals you developed in Chapter 3. Did any of your goals focus on improvement of cardiovascular fitness? If not, develop a goal for cardiovascular fitness improvement.

Authentic Assessment—Extended Response

26. **Writing situation:** Linda is 20 years old. Her target heart-rate zone lower limit is 120 beats per minute and his upper limit is 180 beats per minute. After jogging for 20 minutes, she counted her pulse for 10 seconds and obtained a count of 34 beats.

    Directions for writing: If you were Linda, explain what action you should take and why.

27. Writing situation: Larry is 30 years of age and his goal is to improve his cardiovascular fitness and muscular endurance.

Directions for writing: Evaluate the following exercise plans from one to four, based on quality. Number 1 should be the best plan, while number 4 would be the least desirable plan. Briefly explain why you rated the plans as you did.

Name: Cal P. Larry **Age:** 30 **Resting Pulse:** 80
Fitness Goal: Improve cardiovascular fitness and muscular endurance **Blood Pressure:** 130-80

Activity:	Plan A Racquetball	Plan B Rowing	Plan C Soccer	Plan D Wt. training
(F) No. of session per week	2	3	1	4
(I) Target heart rate (10 seconds count)	28–30	22–28	19–24	15–17
(T) Length of session:	15 minutes	20 minutes	30 minutes	10 minutes

8

Muscular Fitness

Photodisc

Objectives

As you read this chapter, look for answers to these key questions:

- What is the difference between muscular strength and muscular endurance?
- How does a weight-training program affect males and females differently?
- What are the three types of fibers found in skeletal muscles?
- How can the training principles be applied to improve muscular strength and muscular endurance?
- What are the primary differences between muscular strength and muscular endurance training?
- What safety practices should you follow when lifting weights?

"The difference between successful people and others is not a lack of strength, not a lack of knowledge, but rather a lack of will."

—Vince Lombardi

V•A•L•U•E

Measurable and noticeable changes in physical appearance result from a well planned muscular fitness program. A well-designed PFP—including muscular fitness—will help to increase strength of muscles, tissue, tendons, ligaments, and bones, decreasing the risk of injury. After the age of 20, individuals lose about one-half pound of muscle per year, primarily due to decreased physical activity. Weight training can help you maintain and even increase your muscle mass. As muscular fitness increases, the effort to complete everyday tasks of carrying your books, cleaning your room, or working in the yard will require less effort.

Chapter Preview

- Muscular Strength and Endurance
- Myths about Weight Training
- Muscle Fiber Composition
- Methods of Developing Muscular Fitness
- Application of Training Principles
- Goal Setting for Abdominal Strength and Endurance
- Goal Setting for Upper Body Strength
- Weight-Training Considerations
- Muscular-Fitness Exercises
- PFP Update
- Summary
- The Wrap-Up

Vocabulary

When you have completed this chapter, you should understand the meaning of these vocabulary terms:

atrophy

slow-twitch fibers

intermediate-twitch fibers

fast-twitch fibers

concentric movement

eccentric movement

isometric exercises

isotonic exercises

isokinetic exercises

resistance

repetition

set

Wellness Connection

Muscular Strength and Endurance

Muscular fitness includes two health-related components of physical fitness: muscular strength and muscular endurance. Muscular strength is the ability of a muscle group to apply a maximal force against a resistance one time. The term *resistance* in weight training simply refers to the weight lifted. Muscular endurance is the ability to repeat muscle movement over a period of time.

To look good and feel good, you must have adequate muscular fitness. Why do two people with the same weight and height but with different amounts of muscle and body fat look different? The person with more muscle looks trimmer because muscle is denser than fat. One pound of muscle takes up less space than a pound of fat. Another reason is that toned muscles prevent protruding in areas such as the abdomen.

Another factor influencing your appearance is good posture. Developing your body's muscles will help you have the strength and endurance to carry your body in an upright position. Good posture makes you look better. Do you know someone who does not stand up straight? Compare that person with someone who does.

Strong muscles not only improve your appearance, they also help you perform physical activity better. Additionally, strong muscles help to reduce fatigue, avoid back pain, and prevent muscle injuries and muscle soreness.

Ray Carson

Myths about Weight Training

Some people may tell you that weight training makes a person muscle-bound or inflexible. Others say muscular fitness is good for men, but unfeminine for women. Still others tell you that muscles will turn into fat if you stop training. Of course, none of these myths are true.

Muscle-Bound Physique

Years ago body builders encouraged men to do exercises that often made them muscle-bound. Such individuals did not perform flexibility exercises or strength training exercises properly. As a result, they lost some of the range of motion in certain joints. Becoming muscle-bound is not a problem when weight-training exercises are performed properly.

Is Weight Training Good for Females?

Those who believe strength training is good for males but not for females are wrong. Females have estrogen, rather than testosterone, as their primary sex hormone. This eliminates the chance of a female developing bulging muscles while training with weights. Females also should not be concerned about dramatic changes in muscle definition, since they have an average of 8 percent more body fat than males, which masks muscle definition. A female can realize all the benefits of weight training without worrying about muscle bulk and definition. Good muscular fitness is just as important for women, as it is for men. Both genders will appear more attractive when physically fit.

Ray Carson

Females will gain many benefits from a muscular fitness program.

Can Muscle Turn into Fat?

A major misconception about weight training is that muscle will turn into fat when you stop lifting weights. Muscle does not turn into fat, nor does fat turn into muscle. Muscle is muscle and fat is fat. What really happens is that muscles **atrophy** or become smaller, when they are not used. Muscle atrophy can easily be seen when an arm becomes thinner after being placed in a cast for several weeks. An increase of fat will occur only if you continue to take in more calories than you burn.

Muscle Fiber Composition

While muscular strength and endurance are closely related, they are separate components of health-related fitness. To understand how to apply the three principles of training to strength and endurance, you must first understand that different muscle fibers are involved in these two health-related components.

GOAL SETTING

Establishing and following a muscular fitness program is essential. This fitness component affects your overall appearance and stamina. Select upper and lower body exercises to add to your PFP. Establish a four-week program with specific goals you would like to reach. To see gains in strength and endurance remember to use the principles of training.

SAFETY AWARENESS

Working out with someone makes it more enjoyable and increases the safety of your workout as you remind each other of rules, procedures, and workout etiquette.

Skeletal muscles are attached to bones by tendons. When they contract or shorten, they produce movement. There are three types of skeletal muscle fibers: slow, intermediate, and fast-twitch. All three types of fibers are found in skeletal muscles. Heredity determines the number of slow, intermediate, and fast-twitch fibers you possess. However, you can improve both the fitness and performance level of each kind of fiber with appropriate exercises.

Slow-Twitch Fibers

Slow-twitch fibers are also called *red fibers* because of the large amount of blood supply directed to them. Such fibers are slow to contract but have the ability to continue contracting for long periods of time. These fibers are best suited for aerobic or muscular endurance activities, since they do not tire easily. Slow-twitch fibers enable individuals to run long distances or repeat muscular tasks many times. It is because slow-twitch fibers contract slowly and do not tire easily that thousands of runners complete the Boston Marathon.

Intermediate-Twitch Fibers

Intermediate-twitch fibers possess a combination of fast and slow-twitch fiber characteristics. Specifically, intermediate-twitch fibers are capable of contracting at a faster speed than slow-twitch fibers, but at a slower speed than fast-twitch fibers. In addition, fatigue occurs much more slowly in the intermediate-twitch muscle fibers that in the fast-twitch fibers.

Fast-Twitch Fibers

Another name for fast-twitch fibers is *white fibers*. These fibers contract quickly, allowing explosive muscular contractions and, therefore, lend themselves more readily to anaerobic, or strength related activities. An example of a person who needs a large number of fast-twitch fibers is a sprinter. This athlete must react quickly to the sound of the starting pistol. Fast-twitch fibers fatigue easily.

Internet Resources

Resistance Training—Georgia State University
http://www.gsu.edu/~wwwfit/strength.html

Online Exercise Diary—American Heart Association
http://www.justmove.org/diary/login.cfm

Progress Chart—Think Quest
http://library.thinkquest.org/12153/pchart.html

Methods of Developing Muscular Fitness

As in strengthening the heart, which has cardiac muscle, a skeletal muscle becomes stronger when it works harder than it has been accustomed to working. Muscle movement against a resistance during training is generally categorized into three major types of actions: concentric, eccentric, and static. Concentric movement, or positive resistance, is when the muscle contracts and becomes shorter. Eccentric movement, or negative resistance, is when the muscle lengthens. ***Static*** refers to a muscle that is contracting against a stationary object, such as a brick wall with no movement.

You should member that muscular strength and endurance result anytime that you recruit muscle fibers to do something beyond everyday activity. Therefore, attention should be given to both lifting and lowering the weight. Both concentric (shortening) and eccentric (lengthening) actions should be incorporated into beginning an intermediate muscular fitness training program. Three types of exercises provide resistance to make the muscle work harder for the purpose of developing muscular fitness: isometric, isotonic, and isokinetic.

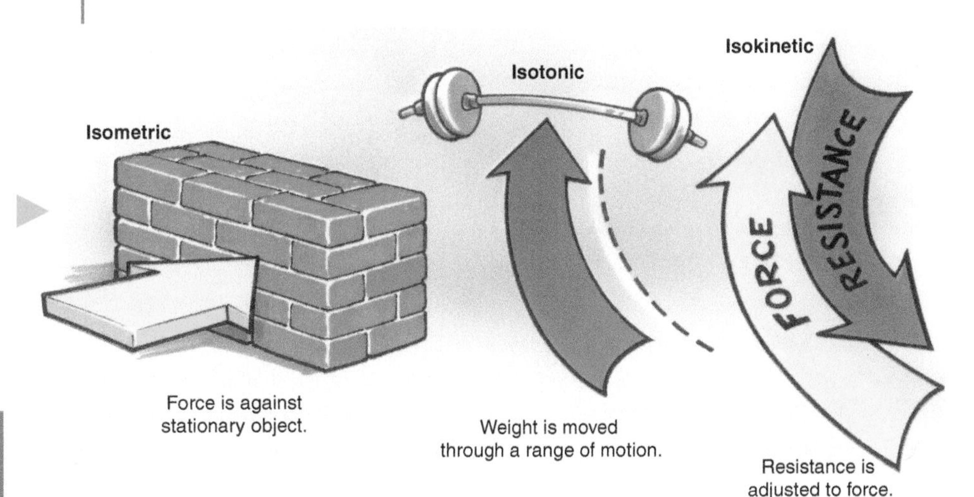

Types of resistance exercises

Ray Carson

Grip strength can be improved through isometric exercises.

Isometric Exercises

In an isometric exercise, you contract, or tighten, your muscles but do not change their length. This is a static contraction because you do not shorten or lengthen your muscle. To perform an isometric exercise you push against a stationary object or against another part of your body that prevents movement. For example, place a tennis ball in your hand and squeeze it as hard as possible for a period of 6 to 8 seconds. Note that there is no movement of the body part (hand) or object (ball) against which the force is exerted.

Strength improvement will result form isometric contraction. However, it is developed only at the position the exercise is performed. Strength is not developed throughout the entire range of movement, which includes many possible positions. For example, if you are performing an isometric arm exercise, you will develop strength only at that specific angle. Your arm goes through many different angles when fully extending and flexing. It would be impossible to exercise all positions effectively using isometric principles. Therefore, these exercises are the least effective in developing strength and endurance.

Isometric exercises can be hazardous for older persons or for those with high blood pressure and other circulatory ailments. Such exercises temporarily impair circulation of the blood and cause the blood pressure to rise. Also, since isometrics provide no movement, muscular endurance and flexibility are not improved.

During isometric contractions, strength is developed only at one fixed position within a muscle's full range of movement.

There are some advantages to doing isometric exercises. They require no special equipment and are useful for people with certain physical disabilities and people confined to a small space. For example, isometrics can be done while sitting at a desk or while riding in a car.

Strength varies according to the angle of the joint.

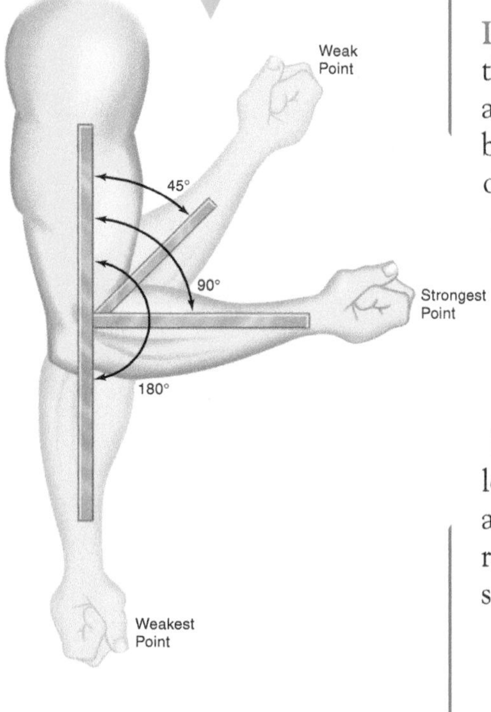

Isotonic Exercises

Isotonic exercises are those in which you shorten and lengthen the muscle through a full range of movement while working against a resistance. The resistance may be in the form of a barbell (weight training) or your own body weight (calisthenics). An isotonic contraction is performed when you lift a glass of water to drink. The biceps muscle on the front of the arm contracts and shortens, causing the elbow to bend. To lower the glass, the biceps muscle relaxes and lengthens. When a barbell is raised and lowered through a muscle's full range of movement, you get the same results.

Ray Carson

Increase resistance by adding weights.

With isotonic exercise, the actual amount of weight the muscle is able to lift varies throughout the range of motion. The heaviest amount of weight lifted will be equal to the capacity of your limb at the weakest joint position throughout the total range of movement. For example, at a 90-degree joint angle you may be able to lift 80 pounds, while at a 160-degree angle you may be able to lift only 40 pounds. The 160-degree joint angle limitation means you will only be able to lift 40 pounds throughout the full range of motion. This amount of weight might not be sufficient to overload the strongest joint position. Despite this drawback, isotonic exercises are excellent muscular fitness developers.

Weight machines with cams provide variable resistance through the full range of motion.

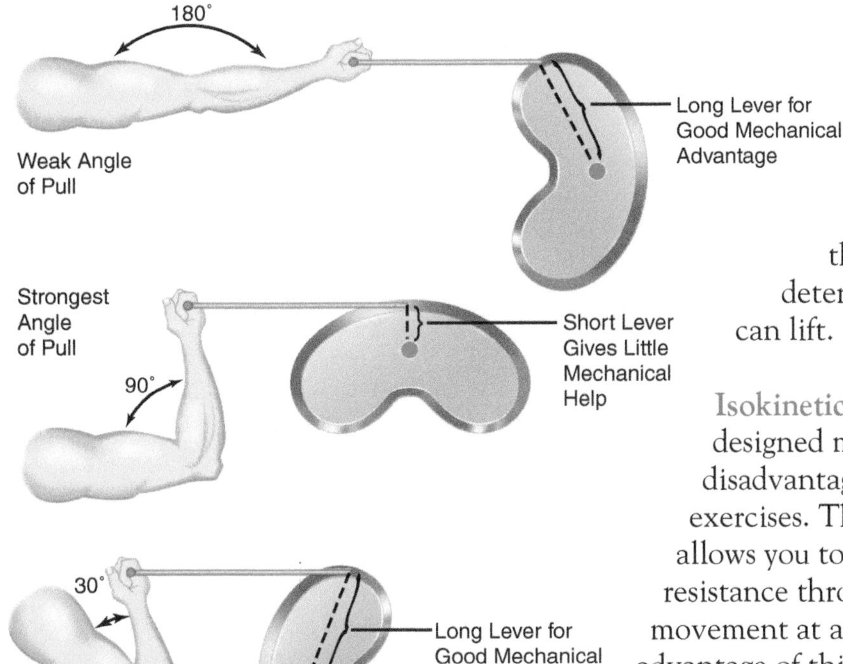

Isokinetic Exercises

A muscle has different levels of strength while moving through a complete range of motion. In other words, the angle at which the muscle is pulling on the bone determines the amount of weight you can lift.

Isokinetic exercises, with the use of specially designed machines, overcome the disadvantages of isometric and isotonic exercises. The isokinetic machine mechanically allows you to overload a muscle with maximum resistance throughout the muscle's entire range of movement at a constant speed. The obvious advantage of this method is that maximum resistance is provided at the stronger angles, while less resistance is provided at the weaker angles.

Currently, there are few truly isokinetic weight-training machines in fitness centers that provide both constant speed and constant resistance. Many fitness centers have variable resistance weight machines which provide varying resistance throughout a complete range of motion. As the cable moves over the irregularly shaped cam, the resistance is adjusted in accordance with the lever characteristics of a specific joint movement.

Application of Training Principles

The type of exercises and equipment you use influences the method in which you apply training principles to muscular strength and endurance development. Since isometric exercises have many disadvantages and isokinetic exercises require expensive equipment not readily available in the home, the application of training principles in this chapter is limited to the use of isotonic exercises.

Recall that fast-twitch fibers allow you to perform strength-related tasks and slow-twitch fibers allow you to perform muscular endurance activities. Intermediate-twitch fibers help you to perform both types of activities. To develop these different types of muscle fibers, you can perform many of the same exercises. The primary difference between muscular strength and muscular endurance training lies in the amount of weight lifted and the number of times it is lifted.

Nutrition Information

Since there is no "perfect food," you must eat a variety of food to get all of the essential nutrients your body needs to be healthy. You should also know there is no perfect supplement to substitute for a balanced diet.

Stress Information

Working out with someone makes it more enjoyable and increases the safety of your workout as each of you can look out for the other. Just as one needs a spotter in gymnastics to help prevent a fall, a spotter is also needed in weight training to assist if a weight falls.

Principle of Overload

To improve muscular fitness, you must deal with three factors. First, you must *stimulate* the muscle. This is accomplished by placing an overload on the muscle, making it work harder than normal. The second factor is *nutrition*. In order for a muscle to grow, it must receive adequate nutrients, which will be discussed in the following chapter. After the muscle has been overloaded and given the necessary nutrients, the muscle must be given time to *rest*, which is the third factor necessary for muscle development.

As in the case with the other health-related components, overload can be placed on the body to increase muscular strength and endurance through the application of frequency, intensity, or time (FIT).

Frequency

Once your muscles have been stimulated by some form of resistance, such as lifting weights, they must be given time to grow. You must spend sufficient time resting between training sessions to allow this growth to occur. Most authorities agree that 48 hours are required. Therefore, muscles should be exercised every other day, not every day.

Some weight lifters prefer to work out every day. They accomplish this by working different muscle groups on alternating days. For example, one day they might work the upper body and the next day work the muscles in the lower body.

Consumer Issues

Eating extra protein will not make you stronger and is a waste of money. When you are active, your body uses its own fat and carbohydrates for fuel. A diet that includes animal and vegetable protein supplies all the body needs to replenish its store. There is no super diet for super performance.

Intensity

The intensity of a weight training program is called the resistance and is determined by the amount of weight you lift. Although you must increase resistance to improve muscular strength and endurance, it is important to remember that the increase must be gradual.

The intensity or amount of weight you can lift to improve muscular strength should be 60 to 90 percent of what you an lift one time. The amount of weight you can lift to improve muscular endurance should be 30 to 50 percent of what you can lift one time. For example, if you can lift 100 pounds one time and wish to improve muscular strength, you should train with a barbell weighing 60 to 90 pounds. If your intent is to improve muscular endurance, you should use a 30- to 50-pounds barbell. It is generally accepted that exercising against a resistance more than 60 percent of your maximum is a form of strength training, and anything less than 60 percent is a form of endurance training. Beginners should always concentrate on endurance training in the early stages. By doing so, you will be able to control the weight, resulting in excellent form and reducing the chances of muscle soreness. Table 8–1 shows a sample workout.

Table 8–1. Sample Workout

Muscular Endurance Development							
		SET	Date				
Exercise	Goal		9–1	9–3	9–5	9–8+	9–10**
Front curl	15 lbs.	1	15/12	15/16	15/20	15/20	20/18
	20 reps.	2	15/12	15/14	15/18	15/20	20/12
		3	15/12	15/14	15/18	15/20	20/12
Muscular Strength Development							
		SET	Date				
Exercise	Goal		9–1	9–3	9–5	9–8+	9–10**
Front curl	40 lbs.	1	40/4	40/6	40/8	40/8	50/6
	8 reps.	2	40/4	40/6	40/6	40/8	50/4
		3	40/4	40/6	40/6	40/8	50/4

*goal achieved for all three sets
**weight increased, repetitions lowered

Time

This refers primarily to the number of times the exercise is performed. A repetition is the completion of a single, full-range movement of the body part exercised. Each time you lift a barbell or do a calisthenic exercise, you are performing one repetition. A group of repetitions performed one after the other is called a set. Usually, a person who is beginning a weight-training program performs three sets of repetitions with at least two minutes of rest between each set. To prevent muscle soreness, beginners should limit themselves to one set and gradually work up to two and three sets.

- *Muscular endurance*—To develop muscular endurance, the resistance (intensity) should be low and the number of repetitions (time) high. Three sets of 12 to 20 repetitions need to be performed to qualify as a muscular endurance exercise.
- *Muscular strength*—Whereas muscular endurance is developed with the use of light weights and many repetitions, muscular strength is developed with the use of heavy weights and few repetitions. Three sets of 4 to 8 repetitions need to be performed for maximum strength gain. Table 8–2 compares endurance and strength in muscular fitness training guideline.

Table 8–2. Summary of Muscular Fitness Training Guidelines

Muscular Endurance	
Frenquency	Every other day for each muscle group
Intensity	Low resistance (30 to 50 percent, 1 RM)
Time	High repetitions (12 to 20 reps, 1 to 3 sets)
Muscular Strength	
Frenquency	Every other day for each muscle group
Intensity	Heavy weights (60 to 90 percent, 1 RM)
Time	Low repetitions (4 to 8 reps, 1 to 3 sets)

Principle of Progression

You now know you must overload muscles to improve muscular strength and endurance. Since your body adapts to lifting the same amount of weight, you must gradually lift more. If you try lifting too much too soon, you run the risk of muscle or joint injury.

You should perform three sets of four to eight repetitions to improve muscular strength. Start with the maximum amount of weight you can lift four times for all three sets. If you cannot lift this amount four times during the third set, decrease the amount of weight. As you make progress and are able to lift the amount of weight eight times for all three sets, add additional weight by 2 to 10 percent and drop your number of repetitions back to four per set. To improve muscular endurance, use the same approach with less weight and more repetitions (12 to 20 per set).

Principle of Specificity

You must overload the specific muscle you want to improve. If you want to increase leg strength, you must do leg exercises. You will not improve your leg strength by doing arm exercises. The more you can target or isolate the muscle you want to improve, the better the results.

To achieve the best results, select the appropriate exercise and place your body and/or body part in a certain position to isolate the muscle. This will force the targeted muscle to do the intended work rather than having the work spread over a number of secondary muscle movers. The standing biceps curl is a good example of how to isolate a muscle group. By standing next to a wall, you can greatly reduce the influence to the legs and hips, forcing the biceps to do the work. This technique results in more strength being gained in the targeted area.

Your weight-training program must be designed to meet your specific needs and goals. You will have to design a specific program to achieve specific results, regardless of whether you are trying to improve strength, add bulk, improve muscle tone, or lose weight.

The ACSM also recommends resistance training that is of moderate intensity, sufficient to develop and maintain fat-free weight. They also recommend at least one set of from 8 to 12 repetitions of 8 to 10 exercises that work the major muscle groups at least two days per week.

Goal Setting for Abdominal Strength and Endurance

Abdominal strength is one of the components of health-related physical fitness that can be improved fairly rapidly, if a person appropriately applies the training principles and the variables of overload. However, this component cannot be improved as rapidly as cardiovascular and flexibility components. Therefore, short-term goals for individuals whose test scores fall within the category of substantially less than the standard should be established carefully. If your sit-up test score is 15 or more below the health fitness standard, you should set 6-month goals to improve from 5 to 15 sit-ups. If your test score falls in the category of "close" to the standard, set your goal for a range of improvement of from 2 to 10 sit-ups. If you "exceed" the health fitness standard, set your goal to improve from 1 to 4 sit-ups. See Table 8–3.

Table 8-3. Goal Setting for Abdominal Strength and Endurance

	Distance from Health Fitness Standard		
	Less	Close	Exceeds
Difference between Test Score and Health Fitness Standard	More than 15	1 to 15	0 or better
Recommended Range for Goals	5 to 15	2 to 10	1 to 4

Goal Setting for Upper Body Strength

Upper body strength is one of the components of health-related physical fitness that can be improved if a person appropriately applies the training principles and the overload variables. Strength components of physical fitness cannot be improved as rapidly as cardiovascular and flexibility components. Therefore, short-term goals for individuals whose test score is initially within the category of substantially "less" than the standard should be established carefully. It is better to set goals low and have to revise them upward than to set them too high and have to revise them downward. If your pull-up test score is zero, or more than 2 below the health fitness standard, you should set 3-month goals to improve 1 to 3 pull-ups. If your test score falls in the category of "close" to the standard, set goals with a range of improvement of 2 to 5 pull-ups. If you "exceed" the health fitness standard, you should set your goal to improve 1 to 3 pull-ups. See Table 8–4.

Table 8-4. Goal Setting for Upper Body Strength

	Distance from Health Fitness Standard		
	Less	Close	Exceeds
Difference between Test Score and Health Fitness Standard	More than 1	1–2	at or better
Recommended Range for Goals	1–3	2–5	1–3

Weight-Training Considerations

Photodisc

Always take precautions to remove the risk of injury.

Regardless of the type of training program, safety should always be a major consideration. When engaging in weight-training programs, you should always take precautions to reduce the risk of injury. One of the most important precautions is to train with a partner, who can serve as a spotter and keep you from being pinned under a weight. You should also take the following precautions.

1. Warm up properly before you begin any physical conditioning program.
2. Concentrate on endurance when beginning a weight-training program. The lighter weights will give you an opportunity to learn how to perform the exercises correctly. The endurance training will prepare your body for higher-intensity strength training.
3. Check barbell plates before you lift to make sure they are properly secured and will not slip off.
4. Keep hands dry for a good grip.
5. Hold the bar or machine handgrips comfortably, since a tight grasp may cause your blood pressure to increase.
6. Exhale when pushing against the resistance (blow the weight up) and inhale when lowering the weight. Holding your breath will cause a dramatic increase in your blood pressure and may damage some blood vessels. Although people argue about the correct way to breathe, the most important consideration is not to hold your breath.
7. Use correct form at all times to prevent injury and to achieve the greatest gains from the exercise. Reduce the weight if you cannot maintain control during the exercise.
8. Keep the weight close to the body when lifting it from the floor to your chest.
9. Space your feet shoulder-width apart to provide balance and to help spread the load of the weight.
10. Keep the back straight, with hips aligned below the shoulders. This will help prevent straining back muscles.
11. Go through the complete range of motion to increase flexibility.
12. Exercise large muscle groups first, then the smaller groups.
13. Perform higher-intensity exercises prior to lower-intensity ones.

14. Exercise muscles on both sides of the joint to ensure muscle balance.

15. Lift the weight on a count of two. Lower it more slowly on a count of four.

16. Always do lifts or exercises in the same sequence from workout to workout. In this way, fatigue will be relatively the same at various points throughout the workout.

17. Do not perform the bench press or other lifts unless spotters are present. If you lose control without a spotter present, you could be pinned under the weight.

18. Avoid a deep-knee bend or full-squat position when performing exercises. You will lessen the chance of knee injury and achieve good results by doing the exercise with one-half knee bends.

Muscular-Fitness Exercises

Shoulders

The following exercises primarily develop the muscles of the shoulder region.

Standing Lateral Raise

Stand erect with feet spread shoulder-width apart. Grasp a 5- to 10-pound dumbbell in each hand with palms inward. Raise the dumbbells sideways to a position directly overhead. Keep the arms straight throughout. Return to starting position and repeat.

Ray Carson

Standing Lateral Raise

Shoulder Shrug

Stand straight, holding the barbell in front of the upper thighs, arms straight, using an overhand grip with hands close together. Shrug shoulders as if trying to touch your ears. Return to starting position and repeat.

Shoulder Shrug

Ray Carson

Upright Rowing

Stand erect, holding the barbell in front of the thighs with overhand grip and hands close together. Pull the bar to chin level while bending the elbows completely, keeping elbows higher than hands. Lower to starting position and repeat.

Upright Rowing

Ray Carson

Arms

The following exercises develop the muscles of the arms and hands.

Push-Ups

Lay face down on the floor and place the hands under your shoulders with the fingers pointing straight ahead. Push your body weight up until the arms are straight. Try to maintain a

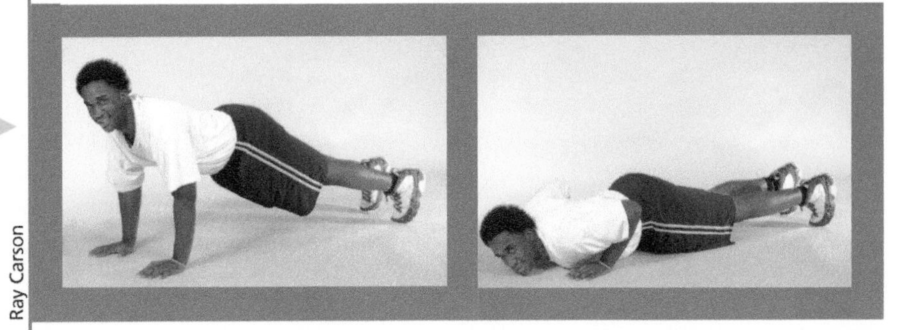
Push-up

Ray Carson

straight line from your shoulders to your heels. Lower your body by bending your arms until they form a 90-degree angle. Additional intensity may be gained by raising one or both legs. The higher the legs are raised (adding body weight), the greater the intensity.

Knee Push-Ups

Lay face down on the floor and place the hands under your shoulders with the fingers pointing straight ahead. Raise upper body off the floor by extending arms until you are supported only by hands and knees. Keep the body in a straight line from the head to the knees. Lower your body by bending your arms until they form a 90-degree angle.

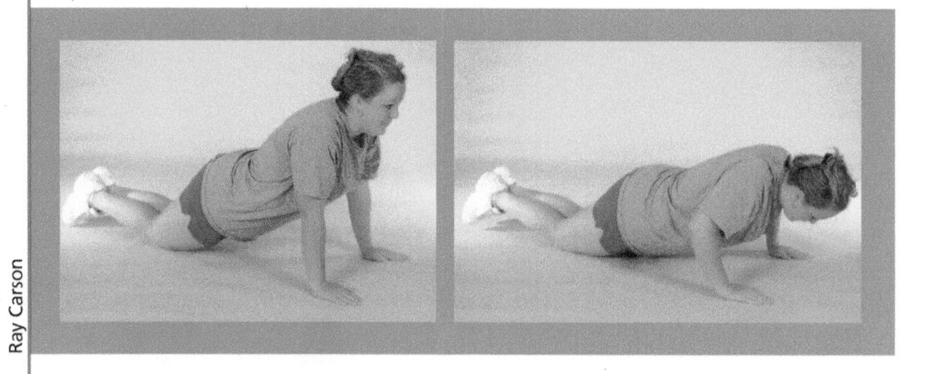

Knee push-up

Ray Carson

Pull-Ups

Grasp a horizontal bar with hands facing away from the body and shoulder width apart. Hang from the bar with extended arms and straight body, Pull chin above the bar without kicking; then lower to starting position. Repeat the movement as many times as possible.

Negative Pull-Up

Step on a chair or bench and assume the pull-up position with the chin above the bar. As you remove the feet from the support, lower your body as slowly as possible.

Front Curl

Hold the bar with palms facing out. Lift weight forward and upward, bending arms completely. Lower to starting position with arms fully extended before repeating. No other motion should be allowed with elbows or back.

Front Curl

Ray Carson

Reverse Curl

Execute in the same manner as a front curl, but use a reverse grip in which the palms face the body.

Reverse Curl

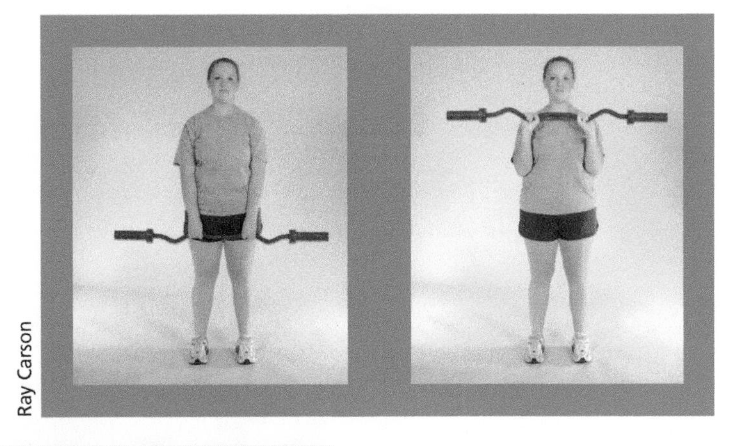
Ray Carson

Two-Arm Press

Ray Carson

Two-Arm Press

Stand erect holding the barbell in front of the chest with palms facing forward while pressing the weight above the head until the arms are straight. Lower the weight and repeat.

Triceps Press

This exercise is the same as the triceps extension except that you use a barbell to exercise both arms. The back should be straight with barbell held overhead and palms facing forward 8 to 12 inches apart. Lower the weight to the neck and repeat.

Ray Carson

Triceps Press

Wrist Curls

Grasp the dumbbell using an underhand grip. Sit and support your forearm on your thigh. Use the other hand to stabilize the wrist doing the curl. Raise and lower the weight by curling hands and wrists.

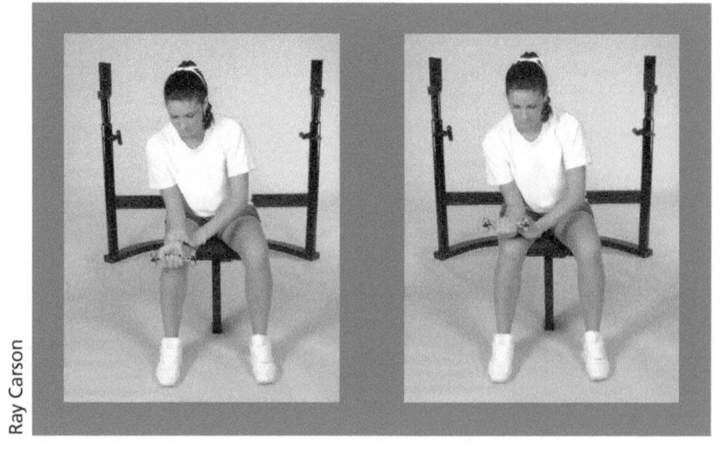
Ray Carson

Wrist Curls

Reverse-Wrist Curl

This movement is performed in the same way as the wrist curl, except that an overhand grip is used.

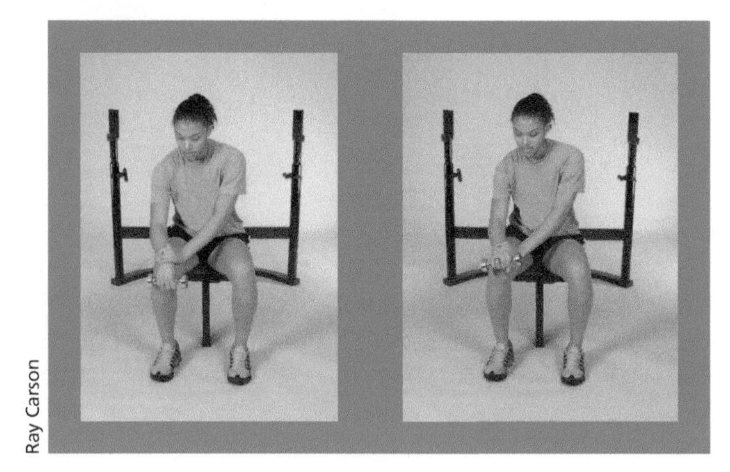
Ray Carson

Reverse Wrist Curls

Chest

The following exercise primarily develop the muscles of the chest region.

Bench Press

Lie face up on the bench. With the arms in the extended position lower the bar to the chest, and return to the extended position. CAUTION: Spotters should always be used for this exercise in case you are pinned under the weight.

Bench Press ▶

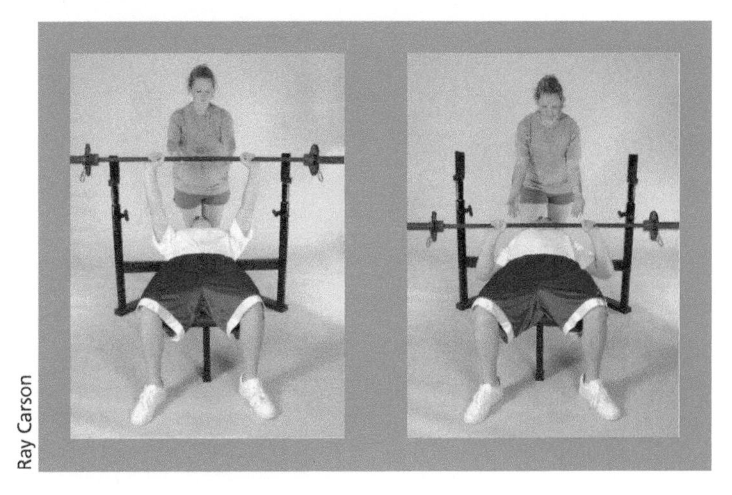
Ray Carson

Flies

Lie face up on the bench with knees bent and feet flat on the floor. Hold a weight in each hand (palms inward). Slowly lower the weights until the arms are parallel to the floor. Keeping the arms straight, raise the weights until they touch above you.

Flies ▶

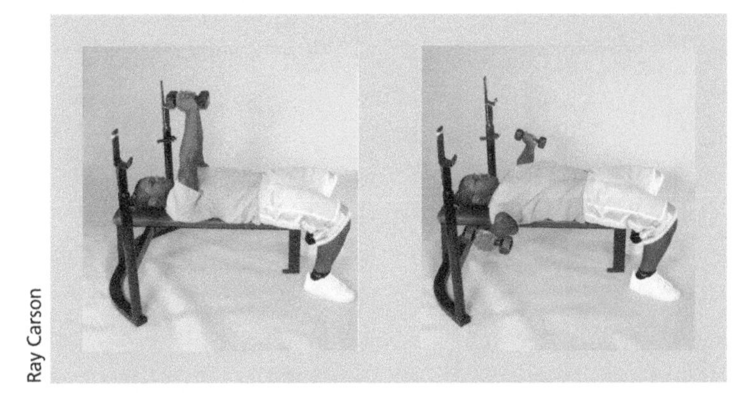
Ray Carson

One-Arm Raising

Place your right hand and right knee on the bench. Lift the weight upward to side of the chest, pause, then lower to starting position. Repeat with the right arm by placing your left hand and left knee on the bench.

One-Arm Raise

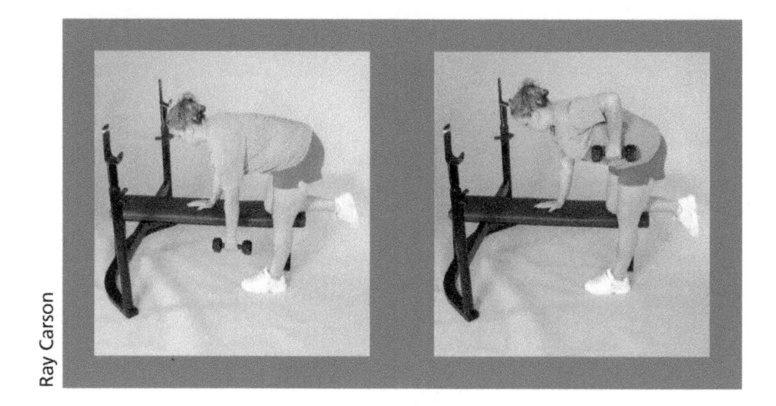
Ray Carson

Back

The following exercises primarily develop the muscles of the back region.

Upper Back Lift

Upper Back Lift

Ray Carson

Lay face down with hands under your chin. Raise your chest off the floor by arching the upper back. Stop when your chest is off the floor. Return to starting position and repeat.

Kneeling Knee Tuck

Kneel with hands placed under the shoulders. Pull the knee of one leg toward your nose, then extend it horizontally. Repeat with the other leg.

Kneeling Knee Tuck

Ray Carson

Abdominals

The following exercise primarily develops the muscles of the abdominal region.

Bent-Knee Sit-Ups (Curl-Up)

Bent-Knee Sit-Up

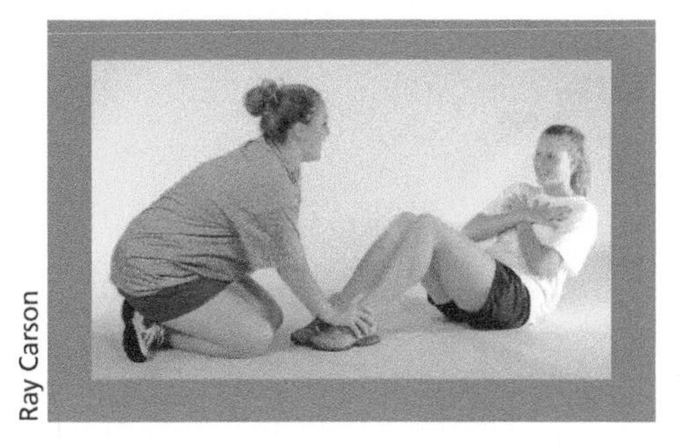
Ray Carson

Lie flat on your back with arms folded across your chest and hands touching opposite shoulders. Bend your knees at a 90-degree angle. Your heels should be 12 to 18 inches from the buttocks. Curl up to a sitting position first with the head, then the shoulders, and finally the back. Uncurl and return to starting position. You may progressively increase the number of repetitions (time) and/or the resistance (intensity) by holding a weight on the chest or by lying head downward on an incline board.

Thighs

The following exercises primarily develop the muscles of the thigh region.

Side Leg Lifts

Lie on your left side and raise your right foot upward. Lie on your right side and repeat with left leg. A freezer bag filled with beans or leg weights may be used to provide added resistance.

Side Leg Lifts

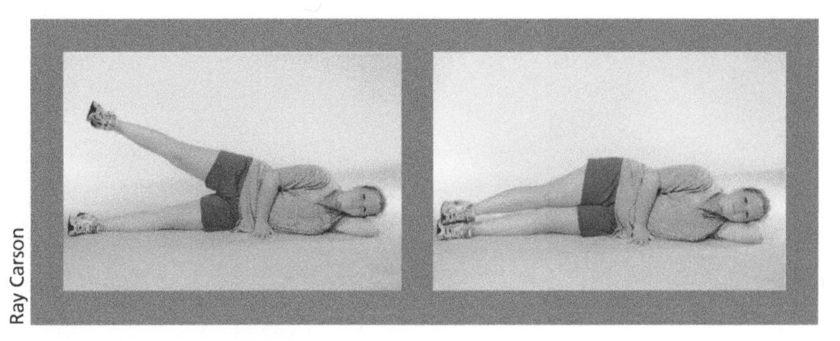
Ray Carson

Half-Knee Bends

Half-Knee Bends

Ray Carson

Beware of doing full squats because knee injury can result. To begin the lift, stand straight with feet parallel and shoulder width apart and with barbell resting across the shoulders.

You may wish to wrap a towel around the bar if it is too uncomfortable on the shoulders. Keeping the back straight, squat to one-half knee bend and return to the starting position. Heels should maintain contact with the floor at all times.

Leg Extension

Sit on the end of a bench with ankles under the padded bar. Extend legs until they are straight and slowly return to the starting position.

Hamstring Curl

Lay face down on a bench with ankles hooked under the padded bar. Flex your knees to a 90-degree angle and slowly return to the starting position.

Calf

The following exercise primarily develops the muscles of the calf region.

Heel Raiser

Stand straight, feet parallel and toes elevated on a board with a barbell resting across shoulders. Supporting yourself on the balls of the feet, raise the heels as high as possible off the floor and then lower the heels to the starting position.

Heel Raiser

PFP Technology Activity

Create or use an online database to plot your muscular fitness plan based on frequency, intensity, and time. Be sure to focus on correct form and muscular endurance when starting your program. Each session of your workout should be plotted showing days of participation and progression.

Muscular Fitness Plan

Date	Frequency	Intensity	Time

PFP Update

What were the results of your muscular endurance test earlier in the semester? Congratulations if you did well. If you did not score as well as you would have liked, you can change the outcome of your next fitness test. You probably set a goal for improving your muscular endurance score for the next test. The key to getting stronger is the proper application of the overload principle and the overload variables that were discussed in this chapter. A good understanding of sets and reps is essential to not only improving your muscular fitness test score in push-ups, but also to improve any muscle group in your body.

Have you included muscular endurance and muscular strength activities in your PFP? One of the best decisions you could make while you are in high school would be to sign up for a weight-training class. If you choose not to, however, there are many ways to work on your muscular endurance and muscular strength at home. For example, if you want to improve the condition of your abdominal muscles, you could do sets of curl-ups several times a week while you are watching TV or perhaps during commercial break times. The bottom line is that you can get stronger and look better if you have a desire to do so.

Major muscles of the human body

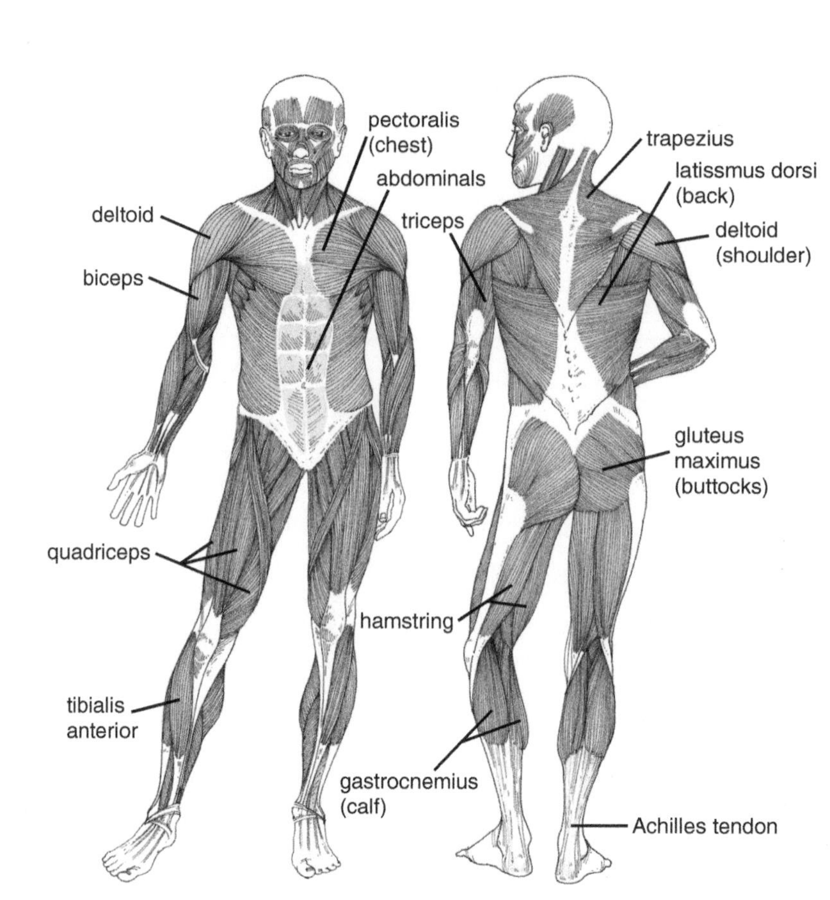

From *Middle School Life Science* by Judy Capra. Used by permission of Judy Capra.

Summary

There are many benefits to be derived from muscular fitness. You not only become stronger and reduce fatigue, you also avoid muscular soreness and injuries.

Both males and females can benefit from muscular strength and endurance exercises. Females need not be concerned about developing bulky muscles because they have different hormones and a larger percent of body fat than males. Remember that fat is fat and muscle is muscle, and muscle can never turn into fat.

There are three types of skeletal muscle fibers. Slow-twitch or red fibers provide the body with the ability to do muscular endurance or aerobic activities. Intermediate-twitch fibers have characteristics of both slow-twitch and fast-twitch. Fast-twitch or white fibers enable the body to do muscular strength or anaerobic activities.

Although muscular strength and muscular endurance are closely related, they are separate components of fitness. The primary difference in training for the two components is in the amount of weight and number of times a resistance if lifted.

Ray Carson

The Wrap-Up

Vocabulary Matching

Match the definitions to the correct term.

1. Atrophy
2. Slow-twitch fiber
3. Intermediate-twitch fibers
4. Fast-twitch fibers
5. Concentric movement
6. Eccentric movement
7. Isometric exercises
8. Isotonic exercises
9. Isokinetic exercises
10. Repetition
11. Resistance
12. Set

A. red muscle fibers that are slow to contract but have the ability to continue contracting for long periods of time

B. shortening of a muscle due to contraction; also called positive work

C. white muscle fibers that contract quickly, allowing explosive muscular contractions

D. the wasting away or decrease in size of a body part, particularly muscle

E. exercises in which one contracts muscles but does not move body parts

F. the completion of a single, full-range movement of the body part being exercised

G. isotonic contractions in which the muscle exerts force while the muscle lengthens; also called negative work

H. muscle fibers that possess a combination of the fast and slow-twitch fiber characteristics

I. exercises in which a muscle lengthens and shortens through its full range of movement while lowering and raising a resistance

J. a group of repetitions performed one after the other

K. the opposition of a force against muscular effort

L. exercises done with special machines that allow for maximum resistance over the complete range of motion

Multiple Choice

Select the most correct answer.

13. Increased muscular fitness is important because it will
- **A.** decrease your flexibility.
- **B.** improve your posture and appearance.
- **C.** make you look big and obese.
- **D.** make you weigh less than a fat person.

14. Which is true about weight training?
- **A.** Females do not need to worry about muscle-bulk and definition.
- **B.** Females, like males, can build large, bulky muscles.
- **C.** Muscle developed during weight training will turn to fat if you stop lifting.
- **D.** Weight training will cause a person to become muscle-bound.

15. Which type of muscle fiber contributes most to muscular endurance?
- **A.** cardiac
- **B.** fast-twitch
- **C.** slow-twitch
- **D.** all of the above

16. Which is a safety consideration for weight training?
- **A.** Concentrate on strength when beginning a program.
- **B.** Go through the complete range of motion to increase flexibility.
- **C.** Smaller muscles should be exercised first.
- **D.** Warm-up is not important.

17. When starting a weight-training program, the emphasis should be on
- **A.** increasing strength.
- **B.** increasing endurance.
- **C.** correct form.
- **D.** both b and c.

18. A group of repeated movements performed continuously with a given weight load is known as a
- **A.** repetition.
- **B.** resistance.
- **C.** set.
- **D.** workout.

19. The reason for limiting your weight-training workout to three sessions per week is
- **A.** people do not have time to train more than three times per week.
- **B.** to give muscles time to rest from intense work.
- **C.** to improve the flexibility of muscle tissue.
- **D.** to permit the cardiovascular system to fully recover.

20. Which of the following would relate to a strength training session?
- **A.** high intensity/low repetitions
- **B.** high intensity/low resistance
- **C.** high repetitions/high resistance
- **D.** high repetitions/low intensity

21. During the lifting phase of weight training, it is recommended that you
- **A.** exhale air.
- **B.** exhale and inhale air.
- **C.** hold your breath.
- **D.** inhale air.

22. The correct progression for someone who can lift 20 pounds for 20 repetitions on all sets is to
- **A.** decrease weight by 5 pounds and increase the number of repetitions to 25.
- **B.** keep weight the same and increase the number of repetitions.
- **C.** increase weight by 5 pounds and decrease number of repetitions per set to a minimum of 12.
- **D.** increase weight by 10 pounds and decrease number of repetitions per set to a minimum of 4.

Authentic Assessment—Short Response

23. Why should females not be concerned about developing bulging muscles?

24. Briefly discuss the differences between isometric, isotonic, and isokinetic exercises. Which ones are you most likely to perform?

25. Explain how the training techniques of muscular strength and muscular endurance development differ.

26. Identify five precautions that will reduce the injury risk of weight training.

27. Review the personal goals you developed in Chapter 3. Did any of your goals focus on improvement of muscular fitness? If not, develop a goal for improvement of your muscular fitness.

Authentic Assessment—Extended Response

28. **Writing situation:** Mike desires to improve muscular strength in his arms. His maximum lift one time is 100 pounds.

Directions for writing: If you were Mike, explain what action you should take and why.

29. **Writing situation:** Your friend has just started a weight-training program. He does not want anyone to see him train, so he trains alone. In addition, he maintains that you are to hold your breath as the weight goes up.

Directions for writing: Explain what advice you would give your friend.

9

Nutrition

Goodshoot

Objectives

As you read this chapter, look for answers to these key questions:

- How did you develop your current nutritional habits?
- What is the relationship of food to health?
- What are the essential nutrients, and why does the body need them?
- What health problems might occur from bad diet decisions about essential nutrients?
- What is the Glycemic index?
- What are trans fats?
- Why is water such an important element of our diet?
- What is the food label, and how can it help you plan a nutritionally balanced diet?
- What is MyPyramid?
- How is the Healthy Eating Pyramid different from MyPyramid?
- How should MyPyramid be used to plan a balanced diet?
- How should you determine your daily calorie requirements?

"You are what you eat."

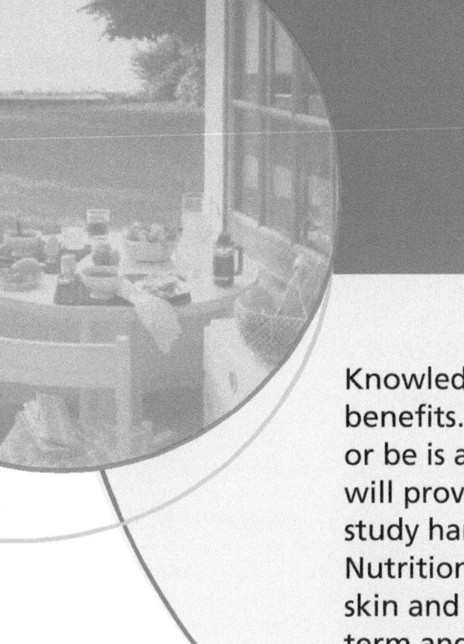

V•A•L•U•E

Knowledge about proper nutrition has many benefits. Everything that a person wants to do or be is affected by nutrition. Proper nutrition will provide you energy to be physically active, study hard, and do well with mental tasks. Nutrition also aids with the appearance of your skin and hair and contributes to both short-term and long-term health. Nutrition has a direct relationship to many of the major health concerns, such as cardiovascular diseases, cancer, and diabetes.

Chapter Preview

- Historical Use of Food
- Acquired Experiences with Food
- Food and Its Relation to Health
- Essential Nutrients
- Healthy People 2010
- The Food Label
- MyPyramid
- The Healthy Eating Pyramid
- Determining Daily Calorie Requirements
- Daily Diet
- PFP Update
- Summary

Vocabulary

When you have completed this chapter, you should understand the meaning of these vocabulary terms:

proteins

amino acids

carbohydrates

Glycemic Index

saturated fats

unsaturated fats

Omega-3 fatty acids

trans fats

HDL

LDL

minerals

fat-soluble vitamins

water-soluble vitamins

antioxidants

basal metabolism

Wellness Connection

Good Nutrition a Must for Students

Both males and females want to have a good physique, beautiful skin, and healthy looking hair. Many teenagers are especially interested in physical fitness and the ability to compete in athletic contests. None of these goals are achievable without good health, and good health cannot be separated from good nutrition. To be in good health means that you feel like doing the things you want to do, such as racing a friend across the pool, skiing on the slopes, or merely getting through a hectic day. When one has plenty of vigor and vitality, second thoughts are not given to the energy required to achieve a desired task. Keeping yourself in a condition that enables you to meet daily situations eagerly is what nutrition allows you to do.

Banana Stock

Historical Use of Food

The original need for food was for survival only. In ancient times, nearly all of the human's day was spent searching for food by hunting, fishing, or scavenging. Later, when we learned to raise and store food supplies, food was used as the centerpiece of social and religious ceremonies. This practice has been carried forward and today food is used during social occasions, fellowship with friends, or as an escape when we are disappointed, sad, or depressed. Many of the ways food is utilized does not contribute to a balanced and nutritional diet and may lead to dietary problems. Today we use food in a variety of ways including supplying our bodies with the essential nutrients.

Acquired Experiences with Food

Why do you choose the foods you eat? Why do you like one food while your best friend likes another? Have you ever stopped to think why you and your family eat the type of food that other people eat, such as food that is popular in another

country? Most people select the type of food they eat with little thought. You may want a pizza or a cheeseburger. Why do you choose them rather than some other food? We eat and like the foods included in our diet for many reasons. The strongest factor is probably our family. We tend to eat and like what our family eats and likes. We have been eating foods our families prepare since birth and have been conditioned to like them without having the opportunity to make decisions about those foods.

Charles Williams

Why do you choose the foods you eat?

In addition to family influences, our friends and our ethnic background are also strong factors that determine the food content of our diets. When you grow older and change your family situation, you will have the opportunity to make your own decisions about what you eat. When you go to college, you will make new friends who like foods that you have never eaten. Your friends will try to get you to taste some foods they like. Perhaps some of your new friends will be from different ethnic backgrounds and will help you develop a broader appreciation of different foods.

Goal Setting

Many people have poor nutritional habits that are difficult to break. Set a goal that you will change a negative habit for one week. Examples of bad habits are, not eating breakfast, drinking an excessive number of soft drinks, eating too many "sweets" or not drinking very much water. Select one that you really want to change and keep a record of your efforts.

Lifestyle also determines what you eat. Are you rushed to get from school to soccer practice, or to a music lesson, or to a game? Think about how a busy lifestyle affects what you eat. Fast foods were developed for people who do not have a lot of time to make their own meals. The microwave is another invention that affects what we eat, allowing us to simply heat up a frozen meal, rather than taking the time in our busy schedule to cook.

Other factors such as; the cost of food, advertisements, region of the country in which you live, and your religious preference all have some influence on the type of foods you eat. You need to be sure that these factors are not influencing you to eat just one type of food. You can hold on to your ethnic or religious traditions and still maintain a balanced diet.

Food and Its Relation to Health

"You are what you eat" is an old saying that may not be too far from the truth. Food and how you relate to it has a great impact on your lifestyle. What do you think of when you hear the word "food?" Perhaps you think of your favorite meal or your favorite snack. Perhaps you think of social events and having fun. Have you ever thought of food as fuel? Food is the fuel that keeps your body going. Food is the energy source for an active, vigorous, and fun lifestyle. If you do not eat enough of this energy source

Photodisc

Nutrition affects the way your hair, teeth, and skin look.

in the right proportions, you may not have the energy needed to enable you to be active.

Too much food leads to health problems associated with being too heavy. If you eat too much food high in cholesterol or other fats, these foods may cause health problems. Health problems may also occur if your diet lacks one or more of the essential nutrients described later in this chapter. Having beautiful skin is a common goal for most teenagers. Many complexion problems are caused by an imbalance of chemicals in the body and a balanced diet may be able to help.

Diets that promote weight loss without establishing sound nutritional practices are considered *fad diets*. Health problems occur with many of the fad diets that you see on television or read about in the newspapers. Individuals have become seriously ill by depriving their bodies of essential nutrients over a long period of time because of a "special diet." No diet can cause a person to lose weight unless the calorie expenditure is greater than the caloric intake. A negative caloric balance forces the body to draw on energy stores for metabolism and jeopardizes health by eliminating essential nutrients. Fad diets that restrict one's dietary intake to only one food, such as eggs or rice, are harmful. No one food contains all of the nutrients necessary for a healthy lifestyle. Even milk, the one nearly perfect food, is low in iron and other nutrients. Good nutritional status requires that the proper balance and quantities of essential nutrients are obtained from a mixed diet of many possible food combinations.

Essential Nutrients

Your body needs certain essential nutrients to function properly. These nutrients are *proteins*, *carbohydrates*, *fats*, *minerals*, *vitamins*, and *water*. An adequate amount of each of these nutrients in your diet is essential for good health and your ability to maintain a balanced exercise program. The food you eat will be the primary source for your essential nutrients. Many people take vitamins and other dietary supplements, but most of us could save that money if we ate a balanced diet.

SAFETY AWARENESS

To avoid poor nutrition, avoid fad diets. Eat a balanced diet, and follow recommendations of MyPyramid for your age and lifestyle.

Proteins

Proteins are the building blocks of the body and are extremely important when you are considering exercise to build muscle. Protein is present in every cell of the body. The most important function of protein is its role in the growth and repair of body tissues. Protein can also supply energy when there are not

enough carbohydrates or fats in the diet. Foods in the meat group are the main dietary source of protein.

Amino Acids

Protein is made up of chemical substances known as amino acids. Amino acids are essential in the digestive process. The body is able to make some amino acids (nonessential) from other food sources, but there are at least eight amino acids (nine in infants) that cannot be manufactured in the body. These are referred to as essential amino acids. *Essential amino acids* must be included in your diet, with meats and animal products being the primary source. Soybeans are also an excellent source of amino acids. If you decide not to eat red meat or animal products, your diet can still be balanced to contain all of the essential amino acids by including a mixture of the right beans, peas, nuts, and seeds. However, this balance is much harder to achieve, and a few vegetarians experience health problems because they are not careful enough about getting the right mixture.

Complete Protein

Complete protein includes such animal products as meat, milk, and eggs. These animal products contain all of the essential amino acids required for a healthy diet. In the United States

Internet Resources

Food and Nutrition Information Center—United States Department of Agriculture
http://www.nal.usda.gov/fnic/

Food Labeling and Nutrition—United States Department of Health and Human Services
http://vm.cfsan.fda.gov/label.html

Eat Five a Day for Better Health—American Cancer Institute
http://www.5aday.gov/

Build a Meal and Nutrition Analysis—Pacific Science Center & Washington State Dairy Council
http://exhibits.pacsci.org/nutrition/cafe/cafe.html

MyPyramid—U.S. Dept. of Agriculture
http://www.mypyramid.gov

and Canada, animal products are a staple food source, and there are few examples of individuals suffering from a lack of protein in their diet. Recent information shows that some forms of animal protein are more healthful than others. Meats high in fat content, many of the red meats, are associated with heart disease when large amounts are consumed. Fish and skinless poultry are much lower in fat content, and have not been found to be associated with heart disease. Milk products, while good sources of protein and calcium, may also be high in fat. Therefore, low-fat varieties of milk products are recommended more than whole-milk products. Additionally, processed meats, such as bacon and lunchmeats, have high sodium and nitrate contents. These are added to preserve the meats, but have shown to be associated with some cancers.

Incomplete Protein

In many parts of the world, the dietary source of protein is plants, nuts, or seeds. Since dried beans and peas, rice, nuts, and seeds do not contain all essential amino acids, they are called incomplete protein. It is not uncommon to see many cases of stunted growth, underweight individuals, slow recovery from illness, lack of vitality, and a lack of muscle tone due to a lack of amino acids. Combinations of foods, however, can be consumed in such a way that all of the essential amino acids are provided. Because nuts and legumes are low in fat and can be good sources of protein when combined appropriately, they are recommended in the diet. If you should decide to become a vegetarian, spend time researching the proper combination of foods so your health is not affected.

Carbohydrates

Carbohydrates serve as the main "fuel" for our active, vigorous lifestyle and are obtained from breads, cereals, fruits, and concentrated sweets. They are the perfect source of energy. The body can use carbohydrates easily and quickly. The body uses them first, before fats or proteins. Many teenagers as well as athletes give up carbohydrates in an attempt to lose weight. When teenagers eliminate carbohydrates, they usually have problems developing strength or muscle bulk even when they

Nutrition Information

Eat abundant helpings of green and orange vegetables to get your daily supply of antioxidants.

Stress Information

Avoid foods that contain sugar and caffeine, such as dark colas, coffee, and chocolate. These foods contribute to your stress level.

are eating a large quantity of protein. In other words, eliminating carbohydrates from the diet forces the body to use protein for fuel, instead of using the protein for bodybuilding.

Starches and Sugars

There are three types of carbohydrates: *starches*, *sugars*, and *fiber*. *Glucose* is blood sugar and is the primary source of energy for the cells of the body. Have you ever been light-headed when you have not eaten for a while? This light-headed feeling could have occurred because you experienced low blood sugar and your brain tissues were hungry because they were deprived of their fuel supply.

Starchy carbohydrates such as bread, potatoes, rice, and cereals provide a good source of energy. Since they take longer for the body to digest, your energy level is maintained for a longer period of time. In addition, they contain a variety of other nutrients including B Vitamins, which are essential for the normal functioning of the body.

Sugary carbohydrates are easier to digest and provide the body with a quick source of energy. Foods providing this type of carbohydrate are called "empty calorie foods," since they are high in sugar and have few, if any other nutrients. Examples of sugary carbohydrates would include soft drinks, candy, pastries, cakes, and cookies. Fruits and fruit juices are the best way of getting additional sugar into your diet because they contain other essential nutrients that the body needs. Be sure to read the food label carefully when buying fruit juices. If the label says orange juice you are purchasing 100 percent juice. If the label states the contents are orange punch or orange drink, you are purchasing a beverage with a high water and sugar content mixed with artificial flavoring and coloring.

Fiber

The indigestible material that makes up the walls of plant cells is known as *fiber*. Fiber is another type of carbohydrate. Fiber is useful in moving waste through the body system and is helpful in lowering the risk of several diseases, including colon cancer. Common sources of fiber include whole grain breads and cereals, fruits, and vegetables. As you increase the fiber content of your diet, you should also increase your fluid intake. However, fiber should not be viewed as the "cure all" of nutrition. Adding fiber to a nutritionally poor diet will not enhance the diet and may even have an adverse effect.

Consumer Issues

Compare serving sizes on food labels so you will not be misled by unjustified advertising claims. Some labels base serving size on one cup and others on a one-half cup.

The Glycemic Index

Recently a new system of classifying carbohydrates has been suggested. This system, known as the **Glycemic Index**, classifies carbohydrates by how strongly and quickly they cause a person's blood glucose level to rise after they are digested. Carbohydrates causing faster and stronger rises in blood glycogen have been linked to heart disease and diabetes. Carbohydrates that have been processed (have had their fiber removed) have higher glycemic levels than do whole-grain foods. Starchy carbohydrates, such as potatoes, also cause blood glucose to rise more quickly than whole grain foods. Even though starches are complex carbohydrates, they should be limited in the diet according to the glycemic index. Examples of high- and low-glycemic foods are listed in Table 9–1. Although it might seem that the glycemic index complicates nutritional advice, the main message is simple. Whenever possible, replace highly refined foods such as white bread, white pasta, and white rice with minimally processed whole grain products such as whole wheat bread, whole grain pasta, and brown rice.

Table 9-1. Carbohydrates and the Glycemic Index

High Glycemic	Low Glycemic
Potatoes	Most legumes
Bananas	Whole fruits
White bread	Whole Wheat, Oats, Bran
White rice	Brown rice
French fries	Bulgar, barley
Refined breakfast cereals	Whole grain breakfast cereals
White spaghetti	Couscous
Soft drinks	
Sugar	

Fats

Fats store twice as much energy as protein or carbohydrates but is not as easy to convert to energy as carbohydrates. In addition to providing energy, dietary fat provides some vitamins that are not provided by other sources. Fats carry fat-soluble vitamins—A, D, E, and K—without fats in the diet the body would not be able to use these vitamins. Some types of fat are better nutritional sources than others. The main factor that determines the healthfulness of fat is the amount and type of cholesterol it contains.

Saturated and Unsaturated Fats

There are two natural types of fat: saturated and unsaturated. Saturated fats are found in animal fats and such vegetable oils as coconut and palm. Saturated fats are usually solid at room temperature and elevate blood cholesterol. Unsaturated fats are usually liquid at room temperature. Vegetable fats are unsaturated fats and are found in margarine, salad dressing, mayonnaise, cooking oils, avocados, olives, and nuts. Recent information regarding unsaturated fats indicates that consuming appropriate amounts actually improves blood cholesterol by lowering "bad" cholesterol (LDL) and elevating "good" cholesterol (HDL) (discussed in more detail later). Unsaturated fats are usually found in liquid form and are categorized into two groups: *polyunsaturated* and *monounsaturated*. Monounsaturated fats are the healthiest form of fats and are found in vegetables.

5 to 9 servings of fruits and vegetables each day
Foods containing omega-3 fatty acids
Vegetable oils instead of solid fats
Nuts instead of proteins high in saturated fat

Chart 9–1

Omega-3 Fatty Acids

Omega-3 fatty acids are a form of polyunsaturated fats. Health and nutrition experts are increasingly recognizing omega-3 fatty acids as having important benefits to one's health. Omega-3 fatty acids are found primarily in oily fish found in cold waters, such as mackerel, salmon, and tuna. However, one type of omega-3 fatty acids can be found in dark green leafy vegetables and vegetable oils.

Health benefits associated with omega-3 fatty acids include the reduction of cholesterol levels and improving hypertension. Omega-3 serves as a natural blood thinner aiding the reduction of the platelet collection in the arteries. Research has also indicated that omega-3 may help improve rheumatoid arthritis, lupus, Raynaud's disease, as well as depression.

Trans Fats

Unsaturated fat is commonly changed through food production to improve the texture of commercially prepared foods. This processing uses unsaturated vegetable oils and through a heating process *hydrogen* is added. This process is called *hydrogenation*, and the resulting fat is categorized as a **trans fat.** Recent information reveals that trans fat actually worsens blood cholesterol more than saturated fats because it increases blood LDL and lowers blood HDL. Trans fats are commonly found in commercially prepared baked foods and fried foods as well as margarine.

Food Sources of Fat

Foods containing fat are divided into two major groups: animal fats and vegetable fats. Both groups of food contain both saturated and unsaturated fat. Animal fats, however, have a high saturated fat content and are found in meat, poultry, milk, cheese, ice cream, butter, and egg yolks. Vegetable fats usually are high in unsaturated fats and are found in cooking oils, salad dressing, mayonnaise, avocados, olives, and nuts. Some plant sources of fat, however, contain high levels of saturated fat. Examples of these are coconuts, coconut oil, palm oil, and palm kernel oil. Trans fats are found in processed foods. Vegetable shortening and stick margarine have high levels of trans fats. Soft tub margarine has a higher level of unsaturated fat, but still contains some trans fat. Vegetable oils that are not hydrogenated do not contain trans fats. For examples of foods containing saturated, unsaturated, and trans fat, read Table 9–2.

There are both good and bad cholesterol. The "good" HDLs are the body's police that help remove the "bad" LDLs from the blood stream.

Cholesterol

Cholesterol is a wax-like fatty substance produced by the body in the liver and helps to build cells. In healthy people, the body produces all of the cholesterol it needs. Animal cells contain

Table 9–2. Percentage of Specific Types of Fat in Common Oils and Fats*

	Saturated	Mon-unsaturated	Poly-unsaturated	Trans
Oils				
Canola	7	58	29	0
Safflower	9	12	74	0
Sunflower	10	20	66	0
Corn	13	24	60	0
Olive	13	72	8	0
Soybean	16	44	37	0
Peanut	17	49	32	0
Palm	50	37	10	0
Coconut	87	6	2	0
Cooking Fats				
Shortening	22	29	29	18
Lard	39	44	11	1
Butter	60	26	5	5
Margarine/Spreads				
Imperial 70% Soybean Stick	18	2	29	23
Fleischmann 67% Spread, Corn & Soybean Tub	16	27	44	11
Shedd's Country Crock 48% Spread, Soybean Tub	17	24	49	8
Promise 60% Tub, Sunflower, Soybean, and Canola	18	22	54	5

*Values expressed as percent of total fat; data are from analyses at Harvard School of Public Health Lipid Laboratory and U.S.D.A. publications.

cholesterol; therefore, when you eat animal products high in saturated fats such as meat, cheese, and eggs, you consume additional cholesterol. Cholesterol is transported throughout the body in the blood stream with excess amounts stored on the walls of the blood vessels. Excessive amounts of cholesterol in the circulatory system require storage and result in blocked arteries that limit blood flow to the brain and heart.

HDL and LDL

There are both "good" cholesterol and "bad" cholesterol. The good type is called HDL (high-density lipoprotein) while the bad type is LDL (low-density lipoprotein). Scientists believe that the good HDL helps remove the extra cholesterol from artery walls while the bad LDL leads to the build-up of cholesterol on the artery walls. Cholesterol levels of greater than 180 to 200 places a person in danger of developing blocked blood vessels. Although the total amount of cholesterol in the blood is related to health dangers, the real concern is the ratio of HDL to total cholesterol. That ratio is determined by dividing the HDL value into the total cholesterol value. Our goal should be to have a ratio of 3.8 or lower for females and 4.0 or lower for males. For example, if a person's total cholesterol was 180 and the HDL was 50, the ratio would be 3.6. This would be considered good. Another person could have the same total cholesterol (180), but a lower HDL (40) producing a ratio of 4.5. This would be considered high and unhealthy.

The amount of total cholesterol in the body is closely related to diet, heredity, and regular vigorous exercise. It is believed that regular vigorous exercise and heredity are the major factors in determining the amount of HDL that you have in your blood. HDL helps remove cholesterol from the blood, so you want to do everything possible to develop HDL. You can increase the ratio of HDL to LDL by exercising and decreasing your intake of saturated fats.

Minerals

When someone says your body needs **minerals**, you probably think of minerals found in the ground. In truth, the minerals needed by the body are absorbed from the ground. This occurs when we eat plants or animals that have eaten the plants.

There are 20 *essential minerals* present in the body that are used in body functions. Each of these is needed (in very small amounts) or serious deficiency and diseases may occur. Like vitamins, minerals have no calories and provide no energy. They are important in regulating various bodily functions. Adequate mineral intake is necessary for good health. In general, those who eat a sound diet do not need a mineral supplement. Excessive mineral intake can be harmful.

Calcium and *phosphorus* are used for the development of bones, teeth, and muscles. They are also used in the work of the muscles and the nervous system. Milk is a food rich in calcium.

Iron combines with protein to form hemoglobin, an essential element of the blood. Good sources of iron are meats, green leafy vegetables, apricots, prunes, and whole-grain and enriched cereals.

Iodine is essential for proper functioning of the thyroid. This mineral is available in iodized salt, seafood, and in fruits and vegetables grown in soil along seacoasts.

Potassium helps to maintain heartbeat, water balance, nerve transmission, and the breakdown of carbohydrates and proteins. A banana is an example of a food high in potassium.

Sodium is a mineral that helps the body maintain a proper balance of body fluid. It plays a major role in nerve transmission, cardiac function, and normal metabolism. However, excessive amounts of sodium may lead to abnormal fluid retention, which is related to hypertension. A balanced diet normally provides all of the sodium that you will need.

Vitamins

Vitamins are organic, chemical substances found in very small amounts in food. You only need small amounts for normal growth and maintenance of the body. They do not supply energy but aid in utilization and absorption of nutrients. For example, the body requires vitamins in order to use carbohydrates, fats, and proteins for energy. Several vitamins work in combination for a specific body reaction. The absence of one of these needed vitamins prohibits the reaction from occurring. One vitamin cannot be substituted for another. All vitamins are dissolvable. Some are soluble in fat and some in water.

Photodisc

Many people waste money on vitamin supplements. A balanced diet provides the required vitamins for most people.

Fat-Soluble Vitamins

Some vitamins can be stored in fat deposits of the body and are called **fat-soluble vitamins**. It is critical that you do not take large supplemental doses of these vitamins, since an oversupply stored in the body could cause toxicity. The most important fat-soluble vitamins include Vitamin A, D, E, and K.

Table 9-3. Vitamins

Water-Soluble Vitamins		
Vitamins	Use	Source
B_1 Thiamine	Changes glucose into energy or fat.	Whole-grain or enriched cereals, yeast, legumes, wheat germ, nuts, liver
B_2 Riboflavin	Essential in metabolism of carbohydrates, fats, and proteins. Transports hydrogen, helps keep skin healthy	Green leafy vegetable, whole-grain or enriched cereals, liver, milk, cheese, eggs, fish
B_6	Essential in metabolism of amino acids and carbohydrates	Wheat bran and germ, whole grains, vegetables, yeast, liver, kidneys, fish, meat
B_{12} Cyano-cobal-amin	Production of red blood cells and supports normal growth	Eggs, milk, liver, meat
C Ascorbic Acid	Aids in healing wounds, protects against infection, maintains healthy blood vessels, helps with the formation of connective tissue	Citrus fruits, vegetables such as tomatoes, cabbage, broccoli, potatoes, peppers
Folacin (folic acid)	Essential for the production of RNA and DNA and normal red blood cells	Green vegetables, nuts, orange juice, liver
Niacin	Maintenance of body tissues, energy production, helps body utilize carbohydrates, to synthesize fat, hydrogen transport	Yeast, wheat germ, liver, kidney, eggs, fish
Pantothenic Acid	Breakdown and synthesis of carbohydrates, fats, and proteins—also synthesis of some adrenal hormones	
Fat-Soluble Vitamins		
Vitamins	Use	Source
A	Healthy teeth and eyes, utilization of calcium and phosphorus in bone development, growth of body cells	Green vegetables, carrots, milk and other dairy products, animal liver
D	Essential for proper development of bones and teeth, absorption and uses of calcium and phosphorus	Produced in the skin from ultra-violet rays in sunlight, fish oils, beef, butter, eggs, milk
E	Contributes to protection of red blood cells, works against oxidation in the cells, and contributes to longevity	Green leafy vegetables, whole grains, yellow vegetable oil
K	Essential for blood clotting and regulating blood calcium levels	Spinach, cabbage, tomatoes, eggs, liver

Water-Soluble Vitamins

Many vitamins that our body requires for proper functioning dissolve in water and, therefore, cannot be stored in the body tissue. When the body takes in more than it can use immediately, the extra vitamin is excreted in the urine. These vitamins must be contained in our diet on a regular basis. You should be careful in food preparation because water-soluble vitamins dissolve in the liquid used in food preparation. If you throw away those liquids, you will lose the vitamins. You should limit the amount of water used in cooking and then try to incorporate that liquid into the meal. Overcooking also destroys water-soluble vitamins in foods.

Antioxidants

Antioxidants are a special group of vitamins that help protect the body from cell damage and may help repair cells if damage occurs. Antioxidants aid in preventing cell damage from such diseases as cancer, atherosclerosis, and premature aging. Antioxidants include vitamin C, vitamin E, and beta-carotene. They are found in green or orange foods such as carrots, squash, spinach, and green, leafy vegetables.

Consumer Concerns Regarding Vitamins

Advertisements in the media push the idea that multi-vitamin pills and mineral concentrates could benefit almost everyone. They state this claim in order to make up for the lack of nutrients in modern processed foods or the lack of time for eating three balanced meals a day. The truth is that the body cannot store many vitamins, and any taken in excess will simply be excreted in the urine. If the ones that can be stored are taken in large doses, illness may result. Good health cannot solely be gained from a bottle of vitamins.

Balanced Approach to Vitamins

The best approach to providing the body with the proper amount of vitamins is by eating a balanced diet. If a person is deficient in a particular vitamin, a balanced diet may not correct the situation and supplements may then have to be taken. In such cases a physician should be consulted.

Water: An Essential Element

Water is essential for your body and makes up about 65 percent of your weight. Although you might not think of water as a nutrient, it is essential for the normal functioning of the body. You can live longer without food than without water, for water is the primary component of blood and tissue fluids.

Water carries dissolved waste products from the body, helps digest food, and carries nutrients throughout the body. It is also critical to temperature control. When you perspire heavily, you lose some of your body's mineral and water content. Heat illness can result if you fail to drink enough water before, during, and after strenuous activities. Remember that you need to drink a cup of water every 20 minutes when you are exercising to avoid heat-related problems. Everyone should drink approximately 2 quarts of water a day.

Healthy People 2010

Healthy People 2010 provides nutritional goals for the nation:

- Increase the proportion of adults who are at a healthy weight.
- Reduce the proportion of adults who are obese.
- Reduce the proportion of children and adolescents who are overweight or obese.
- Increase the proportion of persons aged 2 years and older who consume at least two daily servings of fruit.
- Increase the proportion of persons aged 2 years and older who consume at least three daily servings of vegetables, with at least one-third being dark green or orange vegetables.
- Increase the proportion of persons aged 2 years and older who consume at least six daily servings of grain products, with at least three being whole grains.
- Increase the proportion of persons aged 2 years and older who consume less than 10 percent of calories from saturated fat.
- Increase the proportion of persons aged 2 years and older who consume no more than 30 percent of calories from total fat.
- Increase the proportion of persons aged 2 years and older who consume 2,400 milligrams or less of sodium daily.
- Increase the proportion of persons aged 2 years and older who meet dietary recommendations for calcium.

- Reduce iron deficiency among young children and females of childbearing age.
- Increase the proportion of children and adolescents aged 6 to 19 years whose intake of meals and snacks at school contributes to good overall dietary quality.

The Food Label

In order to ensure that you have a nutritionally balanced diet, appropriate decisions must be made when shopping for food. In an attempt to aid consumers to make the best nutritional decisions, the federal government requires producers to place a standardized food label on all food products.

The food label makes it easier for consumers to make comparisons and quickly determine the specific nutritional value of each product. When making comparisons check the serving size first. One cereal may list a serving size of 1 cup, while another may list 1/2 cup serving size. The label looks the same on all food products, contains the same information, and provides that information in a standardized form. The food label includes a number of requirements that were not always included on previous food labels. The chart, Nutrition Facts, identifies features of the food label.

Health Claims and Legal Definitions

The food label also provides information on those topics, such as nutrients, that reflect current health concerns. In order to provide Americans with information they need to make healthy nutrition choices about foods and dietary supplements, the Food and Drug Administration (FDA) review health claims before they appear in food labeling.

The regulations prohibit using these claims for one nutrient if the food also contains other nutrients that undermine its benefits. While it is true that a jelly doughnut is high in fiber, it is also high in fat. Therefore, it cannot be claimed that a jelly doughnut should be part of a healthy diet.

Approved Health Claims That Meet Significant Scientific Agreement

- Calcium and Osteoporosis
- Dietary Lipids (Fat) and Cancer

HOW TO READ A FOOD LABEL

1. Serving Size
Serving size and number of servings in the container is given in easily understood measures. This makes it easier to compare similar products and know the serving sizes are basically identical.

2. Calories and Fat
The total number of calories per serving and the amount of fat per serving is provided.

3. Percent Daily Values
The percent Daily Values for key ingredients is based on a standardized daily diet of 2000 calories. This section of the label helps the consumer determine the foods that are high or low in the required daily nutrients.

4. Vitamins and Minerals
Provides information about four important vitamins and minerals: Vitamin A, Vitamin C, Calcium, and Iron.

5. Suggested Daily Value
The bottom portion of the panel presents the Daily Value that should be consumed. Figures for a 2000 and 2500 diet are provided for comparison.

Nutrition Facts

Serving Size 1 cup (228g)
Serving Per Container 2

Amount Per Serving

Calories 250	Calories from Fat 110
	% Daily Value*
Total Fat 12g	**18%**
Saturated Fat 3g	**15%**
Trans Fat 1.5g	
Cholesterol 30mg	**10%**
Sodium 470mg	**20%**
Total Carbohydrate 31g	**10%**
Dietary Fiber 0g	**0%**
Sugars 5g	
Protein 5g	
Vitamin A	4%
Vitamin C	2%
Calcium	20%
Iron	4%

*Percent Daily Values are based on a 2,000 calorie diet. Your Daily Values may be higher or lower depending on your calorie needs:

	Calories:	2,000	2,500
Total Fat	Less than	65g	80g
Sat Fat	Less than	20g	25g
Cholesterol	Less than	300mg	300mg
Sodium	Less than	2,400mg	2,400mg
Total Carbohydrate		300g	375g
Dietary Fiber		25g	30g

Chart 9–2

- Dietary Saturated Fat and Cholesterol and Risk of Coronary Heart Disease
- Dietary Non-carcinogenic Carbohydrate Sweeteners and Dental Cavities
- Fiber-Containing Grain Products, Fruits and Vegetables and Cancer
- Fruits and Vegetables and Cancer
- Fruits, Vegetables and Grain Products That Contain Fiber, particularly Soluble Fiber, and Risk of Coronary Heart Disease
- Sodium and Hypertension
- Whole Oat Foods to Make Health Claim on Reducing the Risk of Heart Disease
- Soy Protein and Risk of Coronary Heart Disease

Prior to the current labeling law, producers could use the terms *low, high,* and *free,* but the meaning could vary from one product to another. These terms must now meet legal definitions:

- *High*—it must contain 20 percent or more of the daily value for that nutrient.
- *Reduced, less, fewer*—it must contain 25 percent less of a nutrient or calories than the regular food item.
- *Fat free*—it must contain only a tiny or insignificant amount of fat, less than 0.5 grams (1/8 teaspoon) per serving.
- *Low fat*—it must contain no more than 3 grams (3/4 teaspoon) per serving.
- *Lean*—it must contain less than 10 grams (2 and 1/2 teaspoons) of fat per serving and less than 4 grams (one teaspoon) of saturated fat and 95 milligrams of cholesterol per serving.
- *Extra lean*—it must contain less than 5 grams (1 and 1/4 teaspoon) of fat, 2 grams of saturated fat (1/2 teaspoon), and 95 milligrams of cholesterol per serving.
- *Light/lite*—it must contain one-third fewer calories or half the fat of the original.
- *Sugar free*—it must contain less than 0.5 grams per serving.
- *Cholesterol free*—it must contain less than 2 milligrams of cholesterol and 2 grams or less of saturated fat per serving.
- *Low cholesterol*—it must contain 20 milligrams or less and 2 grams or less of saturated fat per serving.

Calculation of Fat, Carbohydrate, and Protein Calories

The average daily fat consumption in the American diet is about 37 percent of the total caloric intake, which greatly increases the risk for chronic diseases such as cardiovascular disease, cancer, diabetes, and obesity. Less than 30 percent of total calories should come from fat. Of the energy nutrients, carbohydrates and protein both supply the body with 4 calories per gram, while fat provides 9 calories per gram.

One way to monitor the amount of fat in your diet is to look on the food label to see how many fat grams are in a serving. As already stated, each gram of fat equals nine calories. Multiply the grams of fat by 9 and divide by the total number of calories in a serving. Multiply this number by 100 to determine the percent of calories from fat. For example, if a food label lists a total of 150 calories and 13 grams of fat, the fat content is 78 percent of the total calories. Nutritionists recommend that only 30 percent of your total daily caloric intake come from fat. See Chart 9–3 for a calculation example.

Chart 9–3. Calculation of Percent Fat Calories
Formula:
Percent of fat calories = (grams of fat × 9)/ calories per serving × 100
Example:
One beef hot dog has: 13 grams of fat per serving 150 total calories per serving
Therefore:
13 grams × 9 calories per gram = 117 calories 117 / 150 × 100=78% fat*
*This means the 78 percent of the calories from one beef hot dog come from fat.

You could also figure the percent of protein and carbohydrate calories provided by a certain food using this formula. By reading the label you can determine the total grams of fat, protein, or carbohydrate and substitute in the formula accordingly. Since fat provides more than twice the amount of calories per gram (9) than carbohydrate (4) and protein (4), it is recommended that you eat more carbohydrates. By using this simple formula, you will have useful information on which to base your food selections and decrease the amount of fat in your diet.

MyPyramid

MyPyramid is a simple guideline to help you select foods for proper nutrition. Proper nutrition means that an individual's diet supplies all of the essential nutrients necessary to carry out the body's normal processes of growth, repair, and maintenance.

The amount of carbohydrates, fats, and proteins contained in our diet is measured in calories. A calorie is the unit of measure for the potential energy that the body can obtain from a certain amount of food. A chemical reaction must take place for a calorie of carbohydrate, fat, or protein to become energy. Limiting calorie consumption and increasing physical activity has become very important since two-thirds of Americans are overweight or obese, and more than one-half get too little physical activity. The 2005 Dietary Guidelines place a stronger emphasis on calorie control and physical activity.

The United States Department of Agriculture (USDA) and the Department of Health and Human Services released the new Dietary Guidelines in 2005 through a joint effort. The Dietary Guidelines are a foundation of the Food Guidance System. The

Chart 9–4

Anatomy of MyPyramid

One size doesn't fit all

USDA's new MyPyramid symbolizes a personalized approach to healthy eating and physical activity. The symbol has been designed to be simple. It has been developed to remind consumers to make healthy food choices and to be active every day. The different parts of the symbol are described below.

Activity
Activity is represented by the steps and the person climbing them, as a reminder of the importance of daily physical activity.

Moderation
Moderation is represented by the narrowing of each food group from bottom to top. The wider base stands for foods with little or no solid fats or added sugars. These should be selected more often. The narrower top area stands for foods containing more added sugars and solid fats. The more active you are, the more of these foods can fit into your diet.

Personalization
Personalization is shown by the person on the steps, the slogan, and the URL. Find the kinds and amounts of food to eat each day at MyPyramid.gov.

Proportionality
Proportionality is shown by the different widths of the food group bands. The widths suggest how much food a person should choose from each group. The widths are just a general guide, not exact proportions. Check the Web site for how much is right for you.

Variety
Variety is symbolized by the 6 color bands representing the 5 food groups of the Pyramid and oils. This illustrates that foods from all groups are needed each day for good health.

Gradual Improvement
Gradual improvement is encouraged by the slogan. It suggests that individuals can benefit from taking small steps to improve their diet and lifestyle each day.

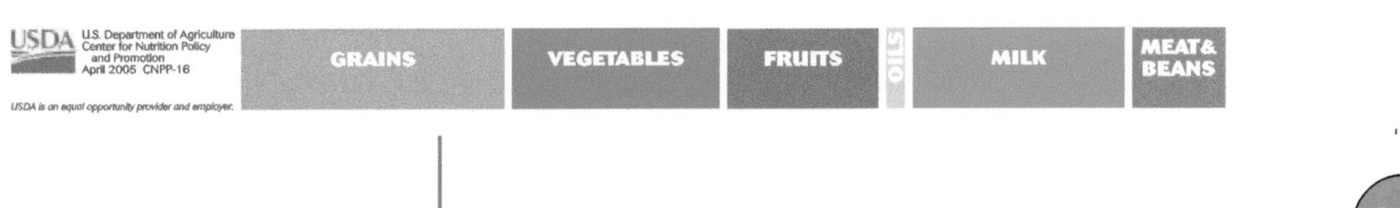

intent of the initiative is to present the science of dietary guidelines in a consumer-friendly form that helps the American public to be healthier by applying the information to their own lives. The Food Guidance System updates the Food Guide Pyramid, which was released in 1992 and makes recommendations on what and how much to eat.

Not only do the new guidelines encourage one to make better food choices, but they also emphasize the need for one to limit calorie consumption and live a more active lifestyle. Note the new guideline recommendations of varying your choices within each food group on page 206. These measures along with the physical activity guidelines presented in Chapter 8 will help you reduce the growing problem of obesity.

Physical activity is important for a healthy body image and increases fitness levels. The recommended amount of daily physical activity is 30 to 60 minutes of moderate to vigorous activities. This goes above and beyond daily activities, such as household chores or walking through the mall. Moderate to vigorous activities include aerobics, fitness walking, jogging/running, swimming, and active sports such as soccer, tennis, or basketball.

MyPyramid takes into account the amount of a person's daily physical activity. An athlete will have a high caloric intake, whereas, a sedentary person will have a low caloric intake. Your age, gender and physical activity will determine the number of servings per food group a person will intake on a daily basis.

Table 9-4 indicates the daily calorie needs for individuals 14–18 based upon their activity levels. Sedentary is defined as those who participate in physical activity less than 30 minutes a day. Moderate activity is defined as those who participate 30–60 minutes a day in physical activity. Those who participate 60 minutes or more in physical activity are classified as active.

MyPyramid categorizes food into six food groups according to the nutrients they contain. Since some nutrients are needed in greater amounts than others the number of servings from each food group varies. The six food groups are shown below.

Table 9-5 provides a sample serving size for each food group. Appendix H gives the size of a serving for a variety of foods in each food group and their caloric content.

Along with exercise, eating a variety of foods based on MyPyramid has proven to be an effective way to assist

Table 9-4. What is Your Calorie Level? MyPyramid Food Intake Calorie Levels for Ages 14 to 18

Activity Level	Males			Activity Level	Females		
Age	sedentary	mod. active	active	Age	sedentary	mod. active	active
14	2000	2400	2800	14	1800	2000	2400
15	2200	2600	3000	15	1800	2000	2400
16	2400	2800	3200	16	1800	2000	2400
17	2400	2800	3200	17	1800	2000	2400
18	2400	2800	3200	18	1800	2000	2400

Table 9-5. Sample Serving Size

Grains
1 slice of bread
1/2 cup of cooked rice or pasta
1/2 cup of cooked cereal
1 ounce of ready-to eat cereal

Vegetables
1 cup of raw, or cooked vegetables
2 cups of leafy raw vegetables

Fruits
1 piece of fruit or melon wedge
1 cup of juice
1 cup of canned fruit
1/2 cup of dried fruit

Milk
1 cup of milk or yogurt
1 1/2 to 2 ounces of cheese

Meat and Beans
2 1/2 to 3 ounces of cooked lean meat, poultry or fish
Count 1/2 cup of cooked beans, or 1 egg, or 2 tablespoons of peanut butter as 1 ounce of lean meat

Oils
Limit oils, especially if you need to lose weight

individuals in reaching and maintaining their ideal body weight. Individuals, who need to gain weight or lose weight and those involved in an extremely vigorous exercise program, may need to modify the recommended size of each serving. Athletes may wish to add servings from the food groups that will provide additional calories from carbohydrates. See Table 9-4.

MyPyramid Food Groups

Examples of foods included in each group are listed below:

Grains

Grains—Enriched breads and cereals are our major energy source, since they contain large amounts of carbohydrates. This group also furnishes our body with the most fiber and provides vitamins and minerals. You need to eat more servings per day from this group than any other food group. Half of your daily intake of grains need to be whole grains. Examples are oatmeal, brown rice, and whole wheat bread or pasta. A one-ounce serving is equal to a slice of bread or a biscuit or muffin about the size of a yo-yo, 1 cup ready to eat cereal, or 1/2 cup cooked cereal, rice, or pasta.

Vegetable s

Fruits

Milk

Meat and Beans

Oils

Vegetables—The vegetable group includes a large variety of foods from plants. Vegetables are a good source of fiber and the major source of vitamins and minerals. One serving of a dark green or deep yellow vegetable should be eaten each day as it provides vitamin A. One serving is equal to two cups of raw leafy vegetables or one cup cooked or raw vegetables. Another way to look at this is to imagine a portion about the same size of a baseball equaling a one-cup serving.

Fruits—Fruits are a good source of fiber and a major source of vitamins and minerals. Citrus fruit provides an excellent source for vitamin C. Since vitamin C is a water-soluble vitamin and cannot be stored in the body, one piece of citrus fruit or glass of juice should be consumed daily. One piece of medium sized fruit counts as one serving. One cup (baseball) of cut up fruit and one cup of 100% fruit juice counts as a serving. Fruit punches and drinks are not included in this group.

Milk—Foods in this group come from animals or animal products and are good sources of protein, calcium, iron, and zinc. When looking at the nutritional value of milk products, it is interesting to note that the only difference between whole milk and two percent milk is the fat content. Eating low fat cheese, sour cream, and ice milk will reduce the amount of fat consumed and lessen the possibility of cardiovascular diseases. An eight-ounce glass of milk or eight-ounce cup of yogurt counts as one serving. A two-ounce piece of cheese is equal to one serving. Visualize a piece of cheese the size and thickness of two domino game pieces equaling one serving.

Meat and Beans—This food group is the major source for protein and iron essential for the growth and repair of body tissues, but it is also a major source of fat. You should select foods from this group that have a lower fat content. For example, fish and poultry have a lower fat content than beef or pork. It is also recommended that you eat small portions consisting of two or three ounces per serving. This would be a piece of meat about the size and thickness of a deck of cards.

Oils—The yellow band, oils is very narrow. It is so narrow because oils are very high in calories and should be limited so that only the essential fatty acids are received. The daily allowance for teens is about 5 to 6 teaspoons. Oils are fats at room temperature, which make them liquids. They come from plants as well as fish. Examples are: canola, corn, olive, and sunflower. Oils from plant sources limit cholesterol and saturated fat intake. Saturated fats are from solid fats at room temperature, which includes fat from: butter, stick margarine, meat and poultry fat. Remember, when choosing oils that the saturated and trans fat will tend to raise cholesterol levels, increasing risk of heart disease.

Discretionary Calories—A section in MyPyramid has been allocated for discretionary calories. These calories represent a number of calories left over after you have eaten the proper amount from the food groups. The more active you are and the better food selections you make from low fat food, then the more discretionary calories you have to expend.

A truly balanced daily diet does not eliminate any of the first five food categories. If you are short of servings from one of the food groups on a regular basis, you may not be getting enough of the nutrients supplied by that group. It is essential that you eat a variety of foods in order to obtain all of the nutrients needed.

Although the basic food groups included in the MyPyramid contain a variety of possibilities, many individuals fail to take advantage of the variety. The point to remember is that you can eat a balanced diet and still make highly individual food choices.

Determining Daily Calorie Requirements

The daily calorie requirements for each person are different. How many calories a person requires to support daily body functions depends on two factors: body mass and amount of physical activity. The greater the body mass, the more calories required to support that body mass. The same is true for level of physical activity: the more active you are, the more calories required to support your body. If a construction worker and a secretary have the same body size, the construction worker will require more calories just to maintain and support daily activities.

Basal Metabolism

Basal metabolism is the amount of energy required to simply maintain your body at rest. This rate of metabolism is reduced with age. Therefore, caloric intake to support basic metabolism should be reduced with age. Basal metabolism is usually estimated as 1 calorie per kilogram of body weight per hour. To determine basal metabolism convert your body weight from pounds to kilograms. One kilogram is equal to 2.2 pounds. Suppose that Juan weighs 140 pounds or 63.64 kilograms (140 divided by 2.2). To determine how many calories he needs to eat just to maintain his body at rest, he has to multiply his body weight in kilograms (63.64) by 24 hours. This amounts to 1,527 calories (63.64 × 24) needed to maintain the basic functioning of his body, without considering his daily physical activity. See Chart 9–5.

Chart 9–5. To Determine Basal Metabolism Requirements

Step 1	Convert body weight to kilograms 140 (body weight) / 2.2 = 63.64 kg
Step 2	Kilograms of body weight by 24 hours 63.64 (kg) × 24 (hrs.) = 1527 calories

Caloric Needs for Daily Activities

To determine the calories required to support his daily activities in addition to his basal metabolism, or his nonsleeping activities, John should use Table 9–6 and Table 10–1. The figures in those two tables represent the number of calories above basal metabolism required to perform certain types of daily activities. Table 9–6 lists the calories burned in routine work and Table 10–1 lists the calories burned in various sports activities. To estimate the number of calories required to support daily activities in addition to basal metabolism, estimate the number of hours you spend performing different types of activities included in the tables. First, multiply the number of hours for each type of activity times the number of calories required per hour, and then add the total number of calories for all activities. This method is further explained in Chapter 10.

Daily Diet

Your daily diet should be based on MyPyramid. If your daily activities include a lot of physical activities, such as athletics, you might want to add one or two servings of the bread, cereal, rice, or pasta group, all of which are high in carbohydrates. If you are very active, you may also want to add one or two servings from the fruit and the vegetable food groups. It is important to remember that when you are no longer in sports competition, you should reduce your servings to meet the normal guidelines for your age group, since you no longer need the extra calories.

Table 9–6. Energy Expenditures for Various Activities

Daily Activities	Calories per 1/2 Hour	Daily Activities	Calories per 1/2 Hour
Cooking	40	Making beds	60
Dressing	40	Marketing	40
Driving car	25	Mowing lawn (hand mower)	93
Dusting	40	Office work	38
Eating	15	Sawing or chopping wood	150
Ironing (standing)	23	Sitting or doing quiet seated work	15
Gardening	68	Standing	20
		Washing floor	65

Keep a Diet Log

The first step in evaluating your daily diet is to keep a daily diet log by writing down everything you eat and drink. The best method is to keep the diet log for one week, since your lifestyle is likely to be similar from week to week. If you keep a diet log for a few days, it may indicate a higher or lower caloric intake than you really have over a long period of time. For example, if you kept a diet log only for three or four days during the week but did not include the weekend, your caloric intake would be low because the pizza you had with friends over the weekend would not have been included.

Photodisc

Good nutrition contributes to a happy, active lifestyle.

Once you have completed the diet log, you are ready to evaluate your eating patterns. First, look to see if you included the first five food groups of MyPyramid and if you ate the suggested number of servings from each group. You should not be too critical of yourself if you did not meet the recommended number of servings for a specific day. However, you should average the recommendations over the period of a few days. Next, estimate the number of calories you ate each day. Use Appendix E to determine the caloric content of the foods included in your diet. Now compare your estimated daily output and your estimated daily intake. If your intake is greater, check to see where you could cut extra calories. If your output was greater, check to see if you had enough servings from the bread and cereal group, or if you were short on servings from the milk group. How to adjust your diet, whether you want to gain weight or lose weight and still maintain good nutrition, will be discussed in Chapter 10.

Good Nutrition Helps You Look Good and Feel Good

Eating a diet that contains the required number of servings recommended by MyPyramid with a sufficient number of calories to maintain a desired weight is important. A proper diet will go a long way toward giving you the figure or body build, complexion, and glossy hair that will make you look good and feel good.

PFP Technology Activity

To log your daily food intake, go to *www.MyPyramid.gov* and click on MyPyramid tracker. Indicate your activity level and enter the foods you have eaten. Save the information to your PFP file and/or print it our for your PFP notebook.

PFP Update

You may have included the health behavior of eating better as one of your PFP goals for this course. By this time, you have probably made various improvements in your pursuit of this goal.

Be strong in your commitment to put the best possible fuel in your body. Doing anything less will guarantee the fact that you will not feel as good, look as good, or perform near your potential. Be the best you can be. One suggestion: If you or some of your friends are having problems with nutritional habits, work together and set some group goals related to sound eating practices.

Summary

You are what you eat. This may be a cliché, but it is true. Teenagers and adults who look good and feel good and who lead active lifestyles usually eat a sound nutritional diet. The nutritional habits of most people are developed from family, ethnic background, and lifestyle. Many of these habits may not be the best for you. The effects of poor eating habits are not immediately visible. Just as consuming extra calories will lead to creeping obesity, poor nutrition over a period of time will lead to health problems.

Your body requires the essential nutrients to function properly and stay healthy. These nutrients include proteins, carbohydrates, fats, minerals, and vitamins. However, there are also some health concerns related to these essential nutrients, like cholesterol and essential amino acids, so it is not just the amount you eat from each of the six food groups in MyPyramid.

Corbis

The Wrap-Up

Vocabulary Matching

Match the definitions to the correct term.

1. Proteins
2. Carbohydrates
3. Trans fats
4. Saturated fats
5. Unsaturated fats
6. HDL
7. LDL
8. Minerals
9. Fat-soluble vitamins
10. Water-soluble vitamins
11. Glycemic index
12. Basal metabolism
13. Vitamins
14. Antioxidants

A. essential nutrients needed by the body in small amounts to prevent deficiencies and diseases

B. a nutrient that helps control growth and maintain body functions

C. fats found in animal products

D. vegetable oils that have been hydrogenated

E. type of fat that leads to buildup of cholesterol on artery walls

F. vitamins that can be stored in fat deposits in the body

G. essential nutrients needed for growth and repair of body tissues

H. type of fat that helps remove excess cholesterol from artery walls

I. carbohydrates rated by how strongly and quickly they affect blood glucose

J. the amount of energy required to maintain the body at rest

K. fats found in plant sources

L. vitamins that dissolve in water and that cannot be stored in body tissues

M. the essential nutrients that are the body's primary source of energy

N. vitamins that help protect the body from cell damage

Multiple Choice

Select the most correct answer.

15. The nutritional practices of teenagers are most influenced by
- **A.** age and religious beliefs.
- **B.** age and region of the country.
- **C.** family and friends.
- **D.** friends and region of the country.

16. Nutrients considered to be "building blocks" for body development are
- **A.** carbohydrates.
- **B.** fats.
- **C.** minerals.
- **D.** proteins.

17. Individuals who do not eat meat might choose to eat other protein-rich foods such as
- **A.** dried beans.
- **B.** peanut butter.
- **C.** soybeans.
- **D.** all of the above.

18. What nutrients are considered to be the fuel for body activities?
- **A.** carbohydrates
- **B.** fats
- **C.** minerals
- **D.** proteins

19. The type of carbohydrate that is useful in moving waste through the body system is
- **A.** cholesterol.
- **B.** fiber.
- **C.** starch.
- **D.** sugar.

20. ____________ helps remove extra cholesterol from artery walls while ____________ leads to build up of cholesterol on the artery walls.
- **A.** Fiber;HDL
- **B.** Fiber;LDL
- **C.** HDL;LDL
- **D.** LDL;HDL

21. What is a high source of cholesterol?
- **A.** bread–cereal group
- **B.** fruit group
- **C.** meat–poultry–fish–bean group
- **D.** milk–cheese group

22. What carries dissolved waste products from the body, helps digest food, and carries nutrients throughout the body?
- **A.** fat
- **B.** minerals
- **C.** vitamins
- **D.** water

23. The Glycemic Index is a system of classifying
- **A.** carbohydrates.
- **B.** cholesterol.
- **C.** fats.
- **D.** protein.

24. The purpose of keeping a daily diet log is to
- **A.** determine if all food groups are represented in your diet.
- **B.** determine the number of calories you are eating.
- **C.** evaluate your eating patterns.
- **D.** all of the above.

Authentic Assessment—Short Response

25. Describe how you would use a diet diary to evaluate your diet.

26. Plan a balanced diet for one day using MyPyramid.

27. Using your personal three-day diet diary, analyze your eating habits using both MyPyramid and the Healthy Eating Pyramid.

28. Why are minerals and vitamins considered essential nutrients?

29. Calculate the daily caloric requirements for an active teenager of your choice.

Authentic Assessment—Extended Response

30. **Writing situation:** Tom and Trent were both on the football team. Tom also was on the basketball team following the football season. Both boys maintained the same diet over the school year. By the time spring break arrived, Tom was still fit and his appearance was good. Trent was a little out of shape and had put on considerable weight.

Directions for writing: Briefly explain why the two boys experienced different weight gains.

31. **Writing situation:** Your friend read about a diet that discourages consumers from eating carbohydrates.

Directions for writing: Based on the information in the text, would you agree or disagree with the anti-carbohydrate diet? Why/why not?

Authentic Assessment—Extended Response

30. **Writing situation:** Tom and Trent were both on the football team. Tom also was on the basketball team following the football season. Both boys maintained the same diet over the school year. By the time spring break arrived, Tom was still fit and his appearance was good. Trent was a little out of shape and had put on considerable weight.

Directions for writing: Briefly explain why the two boys experienced different weight gains.

31. **Writing situation:** Your friend read about a diet that discourages consumers from eating carbohydrates.

Directions for writing: Based on the information in the text, would you agree or disagree with the anti-carbohydrate diet? Why/why not?

10

Body Composition and Weight Control

Photodisc

Objectives

As you read this chapter, look for answers to these key questions:

- What are the characteristics of the three classifications of body types?
- How do you determine how much of your body weight is fat and how much is lean body mass?
- What medical problems are associated with excessive body fat?
- Why are fat children and fat teenagers likely to become fat adults?
- What is the difference between being overweight and obese?
- What three methods can a person use to lose weight?
- Why is permanent weight control best achieved by a combination of diet and physical activity?

"It is not what you are, it's what you can become."

—Frederick Hatfield

V•A•L•U•E

It is estimated that 34 million adults are obese (20 percent above desirable weight). Excess body fat has been linked to high blood pressure, heart disease, diabetes, arthritis, and certain forms of cancer. For these reasons, we all need to be concerned about our weight. Some weigh just the right amount; others need to gain a few pounds, while others need to lose weight. Whatever your goals, you should understand the importance of good nutrition and physical activity in keeping your weight under control.

Chapter Preview

- R_X for Looking Good and Feeling Good
- Body Types
- Body Composition
- Methods of Measuring Body Fat
- Importance of Weight Control
- Weight Loss, Weight Gain, and Weight Maintenance
- Caloric Cost of Physical Activity
- Permanent Weight Control Methods
- Goal Setting for Body Composition
- Eating Disorders
- Weight-Control Misconceptions
- PFP Update
- Summary
- The Wrap-Up

Vocabulary

When you have completed this chapter, you should understand the meaning of these vocabulary terms:

somatotype
endomorph
mesomorph
ectomorph
body composition
lean body mass
overweight
obese
ideal body weight
creeping obesity
anorexia nervosa
bulimia
spot reduction

Wellness Connection

Rx for Looking Good and Feeling Good

Today people are becoming more concerned about their physical appearance. There is a greater awareness of diet and physical activity than ever before. This can be seen by the growth in businesses such as weight reduction centers, aerobic dance studios, fitness centers, and an endless number of fitness and weight-control products.

The goal for many is to appear as healthy and attractive as possible. Looking good and feeling good about yourself are important personal goals.

Corbis

Body Types

It is important for you to know why you appear as you do. Body types describe differences that go beyond weight and height measurements in individuals. For example, two individuals of identical weight and height may be very different in terms of bone structure, muscle structure, and amount of body fat.

Your body type is called a **somatotype**. There are three basic classifications of somatotype: endomorph, mesomorph, and ectomorph. An **endomorph** is a rounder, heavier somatotype. A **mesomorph** is a muscular somatotype. An **ectomorph** is a lean, slender somatotype. Very few people are pure endomorphs, mesomorphs, or ectomorphs. Some people have characteristics of all three body types. Most people are a combination of two types.

You inherit your body type from your parents and grandparents. This means you are born with a tendency toward a certain basic body type. Gaining weight is harder for individuals with ectomorphic characteristics. Staying lean is more difficult for individuals with endomorphic characteristics. You may desire to weigh more or less than you do or even look like a superstar.

These goals might not be healthy or realistic. Do not set yourself up for disappointment. Even though heredity influences what your body looks like, what you eat and how much physical activity you participate in can play important roles in determining your overall appearance.

How much you weigh is not as important as your actual body composition.

Photodisc

You can easily see how much you weigh by getting on a scale. But what does your weight consist of? Is it mostly muscle? Is it fat? Is it bone? Your body weight is a combination of all three. Body composition is the ratio of fat to muscle, bone, and other tissues that compose your body. Recall that body composition is one of the health-related components of physical fitness, along with flexibility, cardiovascular fitness, muscular strength, and muscular endurance.

Lean Body Mass versus Body Fat

Lean body mass is muscle tissue and other nonfat tissue such as bones, ligaments, and tendons. Body fat results from stored calories that have not been burned up. The distribution of your lean body mass and body fat can change, depending on how active you are, how much you eat, and how fast you are growing.

Determining your body composition involves measuring your percentage of body fat as precisely as possible. By knowing the percentage of body fat, you can determine the percentage of lean body mass. For example, if a person weighs 140 pounds and has 20 percent body fat, then 28 pounds of the weight is fat (140 lbs. × 20% = 28 lbs.). The other 80 percent, or 112 pounds, is lean body mass.

GOAL SETTING

Keep a journal of everything you eat and drink for three days and conduct an analysis of your daily caloric input and food groups. Use MyPyramid to help with your evaluation.

Height and Weight Charts Can Be Misleading

People review standard height and weight charts to see how much they should weigh. The ranges on height and weight charts represent average weights and can be misleading. They do not tell you how much of your weight is lean body mass and how much is body fat. For example, a person who does not exercise regularly could be in the acceptable range according to height and weight charts, but have excessive fat. On the other hand, a muscular person might be considered overweight according to a height and weight chart, yet have very little body fat. A point to remember is that muscle mass weighs more and takes up less space than the same amount of fat tissue.

Many people have the mistaken belief that their body weight is crucial. How much you weigh is not as important as your actual body composition. Weighing yourself cannot be used to determine your percentage of body fat and lean body mass. Therefore, it is important to periodically measure your body fat and make sure that most of the weight you are gaining is lean body mass.

Safety Awareness

Weigh yourself only once a week at the same time of day. Your weight goes up and down from day to day. It might be discouraging if you weigh yourself too often. This misleading information may cause you to skip meals, eliminate certain foods, or experiment with fad diets. These decisions may prove to be hazardous to your health. Remember that muscle weighs more than fat. Learn how to evaluate the percentage of body fat rather than relying on body weight.

Overweight versus Obese

Overweight and *obese* are words often used interchangeably. However, they do not mean the same. In order to obtain your proper or ideal body weight, it is important to understand the meaning of these terms.

Overweight people are those who exceed their desirable body weight by 10 percent, according to height and weight charts. However, height and weight charts do not tell you how much of your body weight is fat. You can be overweight on height and weight charts and still have an acceptable level of body fat. Remember that muscle weighs more than body fat and takes up less space.

Obese people are those who have an excessive amount of body fat. You can be obese without being overweight. It is not how heavy you are but, rather, how much excess body fat you have that is important to your health and appearance.

Ideal Body Weight

Ideal body weight is the amount you would weigh if you had an appropriate percentage of body fat. It has also been described as the weight at which you look good and feel the most comfortable. It is the healthiest weight for your body.

The proper or ideal percentage of body fat varies with age and sex. The chart illustrates acceptable ranges of body fat. A person should try to stay below the upper limits given in the chart. A person at the lower limit would be described as lean.

Age	Males	Females
up to 30	9%–15%	14%–21%
30–50	11%–17%	15%–23%
50 and up	12%–19%	16%–25%

As you can see, the ideal weight for your body is an individual and personal matter. There is no single ideal body weight for people with the same body size and shape. For example, an athlete might weigh more than others of his age and height, but the extra weight is in the form of muscle, not fat. On the other hand, a person who does very little physical activity might weigh as much as the athlete, but have too much body fat.

Methods of Measuring Body Fat

How much of your weight is fat can be measured by a variety of methods including underwater weighing, skinfold measurements, and body circumference measurements. Body mass index (BMI) provides information on the appropriateness of your weight relative to height. BMI does not provide an estimate of how much of your weight is fat.

Underwater Weighing

Underwater weighing is the most accurate means for testing body fat. However, it requires specialized, costly equipment and highly trained individuals to operate the equipment. This method requires a large water tank or swimming pool. First, the person is weighed in a chair that has a scale attached. The chair is then submerged into a tank of water and weight is recorded again.

The individual submerges totally for underwater weighing.

Skinfold Measurements

Another method for assessing body fat is to measure skinfold. This technique as described in Chapter 2 utilizes an instrument called a *skinfold caliper* to measure a fold of skin and its underlying layer of fat at key locations on the body. Approximately half of your body fat is located deep within your body. The other half is found underneath your skin between the skin and muscles. The diagram below shows how a skinfold caliper measures the thickness of a fold of skin and its underlying layer of fat. Special computations provide your percentage of body fat based on the various measurements of skinfold thickness.

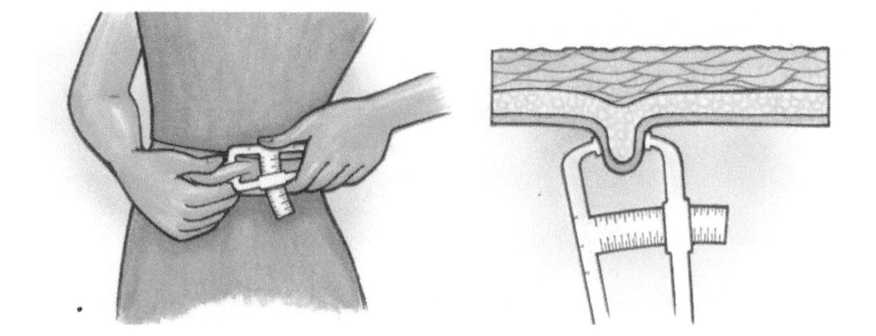

Drawing illustrates location of fat under the skin and how a caliper is used to measure the thickness of a skinfold.

Body Circumference Measurements

The least accurate method for determining percentage of body fat is the measurement of body circumference. This method uses the circumference of selected body parts plus your weight. A cloth measuring tape and a scale are the only equipment needed for this method. Special computations provide your percentage of body fat.

Internet Resources

Menu Planner—National Institute of Health
http://hin.nhlbi.nih.gov/menuplanner/menu.cgi

Packing Your Lunch—Centers for Disease Control and Prevention
http://www.bam.gov/fit4life/eatPowerPacking.htm

Controlling Your Weight—National Institute of Health
http://www.nhlbi.nih.gov/health/public/heart/obesity/lose_wt/control.htm

Portion Control—National Institute of Health
http://hin.nhlbi.nih.gov/portion/

Calculate Body Mass Index—National Institute of Health
http://www.nhlbisupport.com/bmi/bmicalc.htm

Body Fat Lab—Shape Up America
http://www.shapeup.org/bodylab/frmst.htm

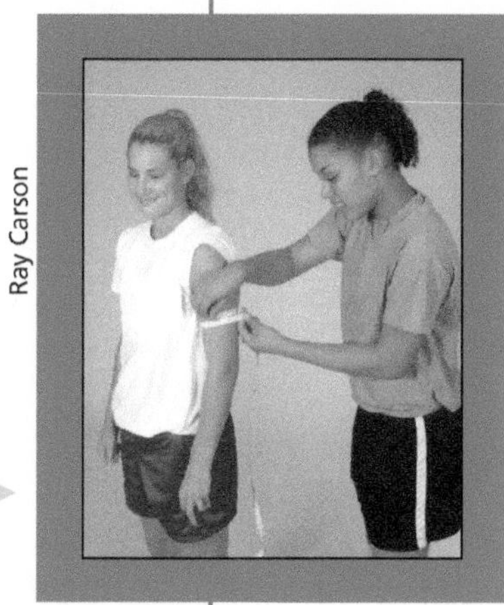

Ray Carson

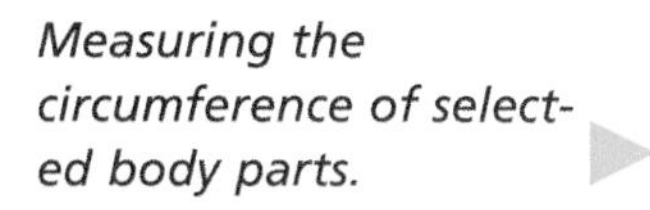

Measuring the circumference of selected body parts.

Body Mass Index

The body mass index provides an indication of the appropriateness of your weight relative to your height. BMI is determined by dividing the body weight measured in kilograms by the height measured to the nearest meter squared (weight (kg)/height (m)2). An easy formula is used to convert your weight to kilograms and your height to meters. Please note that BMI does not indicate the percent of body fat.

Importance of Weight Control

Obesity is a major public health problem in the United States. There has been a dramatic increase in the prevalence of obesity among children and adolescents in the past 20 years. It is estimated that more than one in five U.S. children and adolescents are overweight. It is believed that this is due to a higher standard of living, increased mechanization, more leisure time, less physical activity, insufficient knowledge about weight control, and a lack of motivation in regard to weight control.

Nutrition Information

Eat five fruits and vegetables a day. Diets rich in fruits and vegetables help reduce the risk of stomach, lung, mouth, colon, and esophageal cancer by as much as 30 to 40 percent. Additionally, they are low in calories.

Stress Information

For stressful situations when you get the urge to munch, carry some low-calorie snacks in your backpack. Fresh fruit, raw vegetables, or a granola bar would be a good choice.

Excess Fat Is Unhealthy

Although some body fat is necessary, it is now an accepted medical fact that excess fat is bad for your health. Research shows that American men who are obese have a life expectancy that is 20 percent shorter than men of average weight. Obese women have a life expectancy that is 10 percent shorter than women of average weight. People with excessive fat have a greater likelihood of developing medical problems. Health hazards from excessive fat include these:

- breathing difficulties
- kidney disorders
- diabetes
- surgical risk

- cancer
- pregnancy problems
- high blood pressure
- less resistance to infections
- heart disease
- shortened life expectancy
- stroke

Excess body fat is not only unhealthy, it also keeps you from looking, feeling, and performing as well as you can. Feeling good about your weight and understanding how to obtain and maintain your proper or ideal body weight are important goals in personal fitness.

Vulnerable Stages for Fat Cell Growth

There are three major time periods in your life when fat cells are primarily formed: (1) during the last month of fetal development, (2) during the first year of life, and (3) during the growth spurt of adolescence. Your total number of fat cells becomes permanently established once you reach adulthood.

Goodshoot

You can maintain your ideal body weight throughout life with regular physical activity and good nutrition.

Limit Fat Cells Now

When adolescents and children grow fatter, an increase in the size of existing fat cells and an increase in the number of fat cells occur. When adults grow fatter, only an increase in the size of existing fat cells occurs.

Fat children and fat teenagers are more likely to become obese adults because they have developed more fat cells. These extra fat cells make it easier to become obese. Weight control is more difficult for individuals who have extra fat cells. However, with adequate physical activity and proper diet, people with extra fat cells can achieve and maintain their ideal body weight.

Creeping Obesity

As people reach adulthood, they usually start to gain weight. Excess calories add up day by day, month by month, and year by year. People do not become overweight or obese overnight, but over a period of time. The slow gaining of fat over a period of years is called creeping obesity.

An excess of 10 calories per day beyond what you need over a year results in one additional pound of fat. After 10 years you will have gained 10 pounds and will begin to experience what is referred to as middle-age spread. Maybe you have noticed this occurring in your parents or their friends. If there is an excess of 100 calories (one slice of bread) per day for one year, the weight gain is 10 pounds. This translates to one dress size larger for women. Over a 5-year period, the dress size creeps from a size 6 to a size 14.

The average weight gain for Americans between the ages of 25 and 55 is 30 pounds. Since an increase in age is usually accompanied by a decrease in the basal metabolic rate and a decrease in physical activity, the weight gained is more likely to be fat tissue than muscle tissue.

Creeping obesity does not have to happen. You can maintain your ideal body weight throughout your life with regular physical activity and good nutrition.

Weight Loss, Weight Gain, and Weight Maintenance

A calorie is a measure of energy the body is able to produce from food. Each pound of weight is equivalent to approximately 3,500 calories. To gain a pound, you must take in and store 3,500 calories. To lose a pound, you must burn off that number of calories.

To reach your ideal body weight, you must balance what you eat (caloric intake) against what your body uses (caloric output). Weight loss or weight gain can be achieved by (1) changing caloric intake, (2) changing caloric output, or (3) a combination of the two.

Consumer Issues

Claims that a supplement allows you to eat all you want and lose weight effortlessly are incorrect. To lose weight, you must lower your calorie intake or burn more calories by increasing physical activity. Most medical and nutritional experts recommend doing both.

To have a weight loss or weight gain you must unbalance your caloric intake or output. To maintain weight you must balance your caloric intake and output.

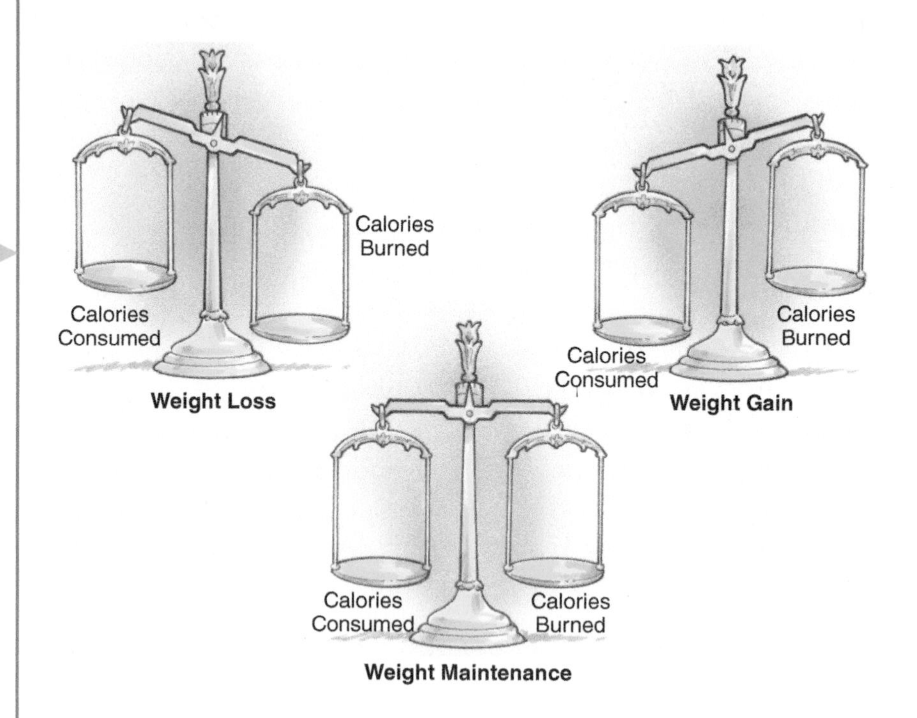

Weight Loss

You must unbalance your caloric intake or output to have a weight loss. To lose a pound a week (1 pound = 3,500 calories), you could do one of the following:

1. Eat 500 calories less each day than your average daily caloric output.
2. Add physical activity each day in an amount that would be equal to burning 500 calories.
3. Do a combination of 1 and 2, such as eating 250 calories less per day and engaging in physical activity that would be equal to burning 250 calories per day. Biking 30 minutes would burn 250 calories. Drinking two less sodas or leaving the butter and sour cream off your baked potato would reduce caloric intake by 250 calories.

Weight Gain

You must also unbalance your caloric intake or output to gain weight. To gain a pound a week (1 pound = 3,500 calories), you could do one of the following:

1. Eat 500 calories more each day than your average daily caloric output.
2. Reduce your physical activity each day by an amount that would be equal to burning 500 calories.

3. Do a combination of 1 and 2, such as eating 250 calories more and reducing your physical activity by an amount that would be equal to burning 250 calories.

Weight Maintenance

To maintain weight, your average daily caloric intake should be the same as your average daily caloric output. In other words, you have to consume as many calories as your body burns.

Caloric Cost of Physical Activity

You use up calories when you engage in physical activity. How many calories you use during any activity depends on the intensity at which you perform the activity, the length of time you perform it, your skill level, and your body weight.

Your weight has an effect on the number of calories burned.

Photodisc

Think of ways you could increase physical activity throughout the day. Take the stairs rather than the elevator, park farther away from the building, or walk rather than drive to your destination, if it is close.

The approximate caloric cost of various activities is shown in the Estimated Caloric Cost of Selected Activities chart. To calculate the caloric cost for a given activity, take the number of calories burned per minute per pound and multiply it by your weight and the number of minutes the activity is performed. For example, a 120-pound individual running at a rate of 6 miles per hour (10 minutes/mile) would burn 284 calories during a 30-minute period.

0.079	×	120	×	30	=	284
calories/minute/pound		weight		minutes		calories

The best kinds of activities for losing weight are those that burn the most calories per minute. Such activities include bicycling, running, swimming, basketball, soccer, handball, racquetball, and cross-country skiing. Table 10–1 gives the estimated caloric cost of many activities.

The first column of numbers provides an estimate of the number of calories burned per minute per pound of body weight for selected activities.

Corel

Archery

Corel

Bicycling

Corel

Cross-country skiing

Photodisc

Hiking

Table 10-1. Estimated Caloric Cost on Selected Activities

The first column of numbers provides an estimate of the calories burned per minute per pound of body weight for selected activities. The three weight classification examples provide a estimate of the number of calories burned in the various activities during a 30-minute period.

Activity	Cal/min/lb	100 lb	140 lb	180 lb
Archery	.034	102	143	184
Badminton:				
moderate	.039	117	164	211
vigorous	.065	195	273	351
Baseball:				
infield/outfield	.031	93	130	167
pitching	.039	117	164	211
Basketball:				
moderate	.047	141	197	254
vigorous	.066	198	277	356
Bicycling:				
slow (5 mph)	.025	75	105	135
moderate (10 mph)	.05	150	210	270
fast (13 mph)	.072	216	302	389
Bowling	.028	84	118	151
Calisthenics	.045	135	189	243
Canoeing:				
2.5 mph	.023	69	97	124
4.0 mph	.047	141	197	254
Dancing:				
slow	.029	87	122	157
moderate	.045	135	189	243
fast	.064	192	269	346
Fencing:				
moderate	.033	99	139	178
vigorous	.057	171	239	308
Fishing	.016	48	67	86
Football (tag)	.04	120	168	216
Golf	.029	87	122	157
Gymnastics:				
light	.022	66	92	119
heavy	.056	168	235	302
Handball	.063	189	265	340
Hiking	.042	126	176	227
Hill Climbing	.06	180	252	324
Horseback Riding:				
walk	.019	57	80	103
trot	.046	138	193	248
gallop	.067	201	281	362

Photodisc

Horseback riding

Photodisc

Racquetball

Photodisc

Swimming

Photodisc

Tennis

Table 10-1. *continued*

Activity	Cal/min/lb	100 lb	140 lb	180 lb
Jogging: 4.5 mph (13:30 min/mi)	.063	189	265	340
Judo	.087	261	365	470
Karate	.087	261	365	470
Mountain Climbing	.086	258	361	464
Racquetball	.069	207	290	373
Rowing:				
moderate (2.5 mph)	.036	108	151	194
vigorous	.118	354	496	637
Running:				
6 mph (10 min/mi)	.079	237	332	427
10 mph (6 min/mi)	.1	300	420	540
Sailing	.02	60	84	180
Skating:				
moderate	.036	108	151	194
vigorous	.064	192	269	346
Skiing (snow):				
downhill	.059	177	248	319
cross country	.078	234	328	421
Soccer	.063	189	265	340
Squash	.07	210	294	378
Stationary Running: 70-80 counts/min	.078	234	328	421
Swimming (crawl)				
20 yards/min.	.032	96	134	173
45 yards/min.	.058	174	244	313
50 yards/min.	.071	213	298	383
Table Tennis:				
moderate	.026	78	109	140
vigorous	.04	120	168	216
Tennis:				
moderate	.046	138	193	248
vigorous	.06	180	252	324
Volleyball:				
moderate	.036	108	151	194
vigorous	.065	195	273	351
Walking:				
slow	.023	69	97	124
moderate	.032	96	134	173
fast	.044	132	185	208
Water Skiing	.053	159	223	286
Weight Training	.05	150	210	270
Wrestling	.091	273	382	491

The three weight classification examples provide an estimate of the number of calories burned in the various activities during a 30-minute period.

Permanent Weight Control Methods

Achieving and maintaining your ideal body weight can be realized through three methods: (1) diet, (2) physical activity, or (3) a combination of diet and physical activity. The combination of proper diet and physical activity is the best way to achieve and maintain your ideal body weight. One advantage of the combined method is that neither food reduction nor the increase in physical activity needs to be as severe as when either is practiced alone. Another advantage is that weight loss is mostly fat, not lean tissue. However, this is not true when you attempt a weight-reduction program by dieting without physical activity. When you lose weight by this method, lean tissue is lost, along with fat. Dieting alone also slows down your metabolism, which makes fat loss more difficult and can cause fatigue. Physical activity speeds up metabolism, burns calories, and decreases body fat. Another important advantage of combining diet and physical activity is the improvement of flexibility, cardiovascular fitness, muscular strength, and muscular endurance.

Eating Smart

Eating smart is important to achieving and maintaining your ideal body weight. Smart eating habits help you look good and feel good, have plenty of energy for school work and leisure activities, and keep your body healthy now and in the future.

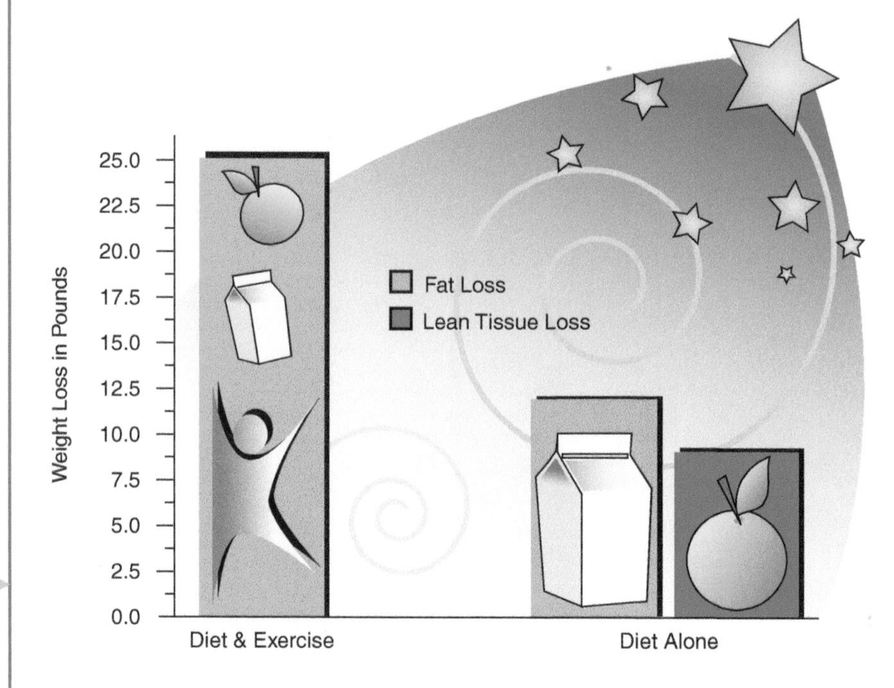

A combination of dieting and exercise will cause more fat to be lost. Dieting alone will result in a loss of lean tissue, as well as fat.

Eating smart is not difficult. It simply means being knowledgeable about the amounts and kinds of food you eat. The following recommendations will help you eat smart.

Eat smart! Build a better meal.

Instead of . . .	Try . . .
Fried Chicken Breast with Skin	Baked Chicken Breast without Skin
French Fries (6 oz)	Baked Potato with Margarine (1 pat)
Cole Slaw (3 oz)	Cooked Carrots (3 oz)
Whole Milk (1 cup)	Skim Milk (1 cup)
Vanilla Ice Cream (4 oz)	Vanilla Non-Fat Frozen Yogurt (4 oz)
Total	**Total**
Calories: 1079	**Calories:** 760
Fat: 49 gm*	**Fat:** 10 gm*
Saturated Fat: 20 gm	**Saturated Fat:** 2 gm
Cholesterol: 241 mg	**Cholesterol:** 150 mg
*41% calories from fat	*12% calories from fat

1. Increase your consumption of fruits, vegetables, pastas, breads, unsweetened cereals, and grains such as barley, wheat, oats, cornmeal, and rice.
2. Reduce your consumption of red meats such as beef, pork, and lamb.
3. Increase your consumption of chicken, turkey, and fish.
4. Eat foods that are broiled or baked rather than fried. Frying doubles the number of calories in foods. A broiled chicken leg has 45 calories and a fried chicken leg has 90.
5. Reduce your consumption of high-fat foods such as eggs, butter, whole milk, ice cream, and all fried foods. Switch to nonfat or low-fat milk and cheeses.
6. Reduce your consumption of high-cholesterol foods such as bacon, sour cream, hot dogs, hamburgers, luncheon meats, and gravies.
7. Reduce your consumption of foods containing a lot of sugar, such as pastries, candies, honey, jams, jellies, syrups, most desserts, and sweetened cereals.
8. Reduce the number of sodas, juices, and other sweetened drinks you consume. Drink water or sugar-free beverages when you are thirsty.

9. Reduce your consumption of table salt and foods high in salt, such as potato chips, crackers, condiments, pickles, and canned fish.

10. Eat less, but more often. Have a small, healthy snack such as carrot sticks, pretzels, or fruit between meals. Adding a healthy snack will help you eat smaller portions during mealtime.

11. Eat a combination of five fruits and vegetables daily. They are low in calories and are filling.

12. Avoid prepackaged diets. Trading meals for canned shakes is not a good idea.

13. Never eliminate a food group in an attempt to lose weight. A variety of foods in a rainbow of colors is essential for staying healthy.

14. Do not give up all of your favorite foods, just eat less than you usually do.

15. Reward yourself for losing each 5 pounds with a movie, new CD—anything but food.

Following these guidelines does not mean that you should never eat a hamburger or french fries. These recommendations should be used as a guide to help you become more aware of what foods you eat.

Eating smart means looking at your diet as a giant balance sheet. When you eat foods that may not be nutritionally good for you, balance your diet with foods that are nutritionally better. For example, if you eat bacon and eggs for breakfast, eat a fruit salad for lunch.

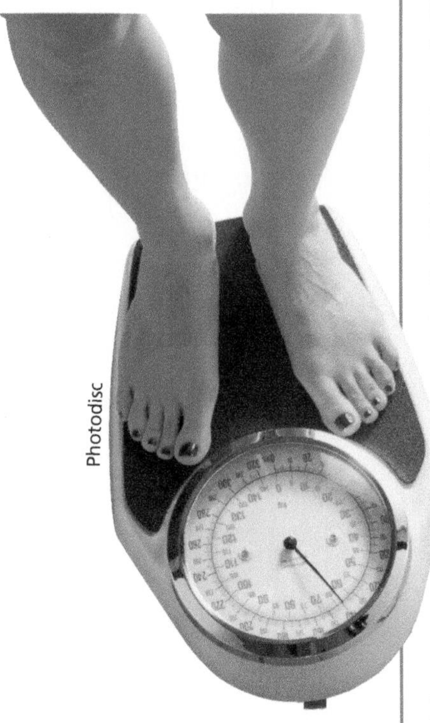

Photodisc

It is recommended that you lose no more than 1 or 2 pounds per week.

Long-Haul Concept

Weight loss is usually permanent if it is done gradually. It is recommended that you lose no more than 1 to 2 pounds per week. This is called the *long-haul approach* to weight reduction.

Being overweight is not the real problem. Bad habits that lead to being overweight are the problem. It is important that you develop proper eating and physical activity habits, which will help ensure that you keep the weight off once your ideal body weight is reached. Your goal should be to get it off and keep it off, using the long-haul concept. Or better still, never put on

the extra weight. Most people look their best and feel their best both physically and mentally when they maintain their ideal body weight.

The following behavioral modifications can be beneficial when you are trying to lose or maintain your weight:

1. Keep a record of what, when, and where you eat. Look for a pattern of bad habits, such as eating candy when you are upset. You are more likely to be successful if you try to modify one bad habit, rather than tackling two or three at a time.
2. Avoid eating while reading or watching television. A whole bag of potato chips can be consumed before you know it.
3. When eating snacks, do not eat out of the bag. Rather, pour out a small amount into a bowl. Remember, 10 potato chips are equal to 100 calories.
4. Eat breakfast every day. Those who skip this meal usually snack before lunch, eating less nutritious food and more calories than if they had eaten breakfast.
5. Drink a glass of water before you sit down for a meal. The water will help your stomach feel fuller.
6. Eat slowly by chewing your food well. If you eat small portions and are still hungry, wait 20 minutes. It takes this long for the stomach to transmit a signal to the brain that it is full.
7. Get moving. You may not need to give up calories, as much as you need to be physically active. If you think you have to be an athlete or play a team sport to be active, you are wrong. Find ways to be active during the day. Instead of instant-messaging your best friend, meet him at the park for frisbee golf. Walk or bike to school, jog, and move the remote and portable telephone so you are moving to adjust the television or answer the telephone.
8. Ask your mom and dad to help you by making dietary or lifestyle changes that would benefit everyone in your family.

Goal Setting for Body Composition

Body composition is a health-related component of physical fitness that must be improved slowly over a long period of time. Short-term goals for individuals whose skinfold measurements are initially within the category of substantially less than the standard should be established carefully and revised as success is achieved. Remember that changes in body composition should be accomplished by changing eating and physical activity habits, not by going on drastic diets. If your skinfold measures are 10 millimeter or more below the health fitness standard, you should set 3-month improvement goals to improve from 2 to 15 millimeter. If your test score falls in the category of close to the standard, you should set goals with a range of improvement from 1 to 10 millimeter. If you exceed the health fitness standard, you should set you goal to improve from 1 to 3 millimeter. Improvement here should be interpreted as either gain or loss. See Table 10–2.

Table 10–2. Body Composition

	Distance from Health Fitness Standard		
	Less	Close	Exceeds
Difference between Test Score and Health Fitness Standard	More than 10 mm	1 to 10 mm	0 or better
Recommended Range for Goals	1 to 15 mm	1 to 10 mm	1 to 3 mm +/–

Eating Disorders

Eating disorders involve serious disturbances in eating behavior, such as extreme and unhealthy reduction of food intake or severe overeating. Many experience feelings of distress or extreme concern about body shape or weight, which may lead to over-training. Eating disorders frequently develop during adolescence or early adulthood, but some reports indicate their onset can occur during childhood or later in adulthood. The main eating disorders are *anorexia nervosa* and *bulimia*.

Unfortunately some people become so obsessed with the fear of being overweight that they refuse to eat normally. Unusual eating habits develop, such as avoiding food and meals, picking out a few foods and eating these in small quantities, or weighing and portioning food. This disorder is called **anorexia nervosa**. Anorexics have distorted body images. They see themselves as overweight even though they are dangerously thin. They often look like walking skeletons. People suffering from anorexia nervosa can starve to death or die from severe vitamin and mineral deficiencies.

Some people have recurrent episodes of binge eating, followed by purging—self-induced vomiting, misuse of laxatives, diuretics, and enemas, and excessive exercise—to avoid gaining weight. This disorder is called **bulimia**. These repeated actions can cause serious medical problems. Because purging follows the binge-eating episodes, people with bulimia usually weigh within the normal range for their age and height. People with bulimia often perform the behaviors in secrecy, feeling disgusted and ashamed when they binge, yet relieved once they purge.

Anorexia nervosa and bulimia are very serious eating disorders. People suffering from these disorders need both medical and psychological advice. If you know someone who has one of these disorders, encourage them to seek help.

Weight-Control Misconceptions

Because of the emphasis placed on weight control in our society, some misconceptions have developed about physical activity and weight control. The following misconceptions are most common.

Corel

You can lose fat over the long haul by engaging in physical activity regularly.

Exercise and Fat Loss

Some people believe that participating in physical activity will not help them lose weight because of the time it takes to burn 3,500 calories through exercise. This myth comes from those who say it takes 8 1/2 hours of playing tennis, 11 1/2 hours of walking, or 7 hours of splitting wood to lose 1 pound of fat. The impression is that such physical activity has to be done during one long session. You cannot lose a large amount of weight quickly by exercising. You can lose fat over the long haul by engaging in physical activity regularly. Jogging for 20 minutes a day, 7 days a week, over a 1-year period will allow you to shed more than 20 pounds.

Spot Reduction

There is a widely held myth that exercising the muscles in a particular area of the body will remove fat from that area. This is called **spot reduction**. There is no truth to the idea that you can reduce in specific areas of the body. Exercising will only tone up or strengthen the muscles in a specific area.

Increased Appetite

Another myth is that an increase in physical activity automatically creates an increase in appetite. Mild to moderate physical activity will in fact decrease the appetite of most people.

Glandular Problems

A popular myth is that excessive fat is caused by glandular problems. In reality, only a small percentage of people have glandular problems that make it difficult to control fat.

PFP Technology Activity

Using a Web-based or software menu planner, develop a weekly menu to help you reach your body composition goals. After you have created the healthy menu, print it out and put it in your PFP notebook.

PFP Update

Your personal fitness program will play a crucial role in helping you with your weight control program. Set short-term goals. Don't expect to lose or gain 20 pounds in 2 weeks. Keep a record of your progress. Here are some tips to help you get started.

- Develop a specific plan based on the results of your body composition assessment.
- Set short-term and long-term realistic goals. Post your goals on the refrigerator door.
- Keep a log to record your progress and be sure to keep it up to date.
- Include periodic measures of weight and percent body fat.
- Update your PFP as you progress.
- Choose activities that will help you meet your goals and that you will enjoy.
- Enlist the support and company of your friends and family.
- Reward yourself periodically for a job well done.

While nutrition plays a critical role in maintaining weight, another factor, and perhaps an even more important one, is physical activity. Your PFP will play a critical role in helping you feel good or better about yourself if you build nutrition goals and physical-activity goals into your lifestyle.

Summary

The results of numerous research studies indicate that teenagers are heavier than ever before. Some researchers are predicting that this trend is going to create a population of adults who are more and more likely to have various diseases that had their origin in young people who were either overweight or obese.

Heredity plays a role in your physical appearance. Your genetic makeup determines your body type. There are three basic classifications of body type: endomorph (stocky), mesomorph (muscular), and ectomorph (thin).

Body weight is made up of body fluids, lean body mass, and body fat. This is called body composition. Height and weight charts can be misleading because they do not indicate how much of your body weight is lean body mass and how much is body fat.

Weight gain is not always bad. Excessive fat is what should be avoided. Several methods are used for determining the percentage of body fat. Measurements taken with a skinfold caliper are reliable and easy to use. An acceptable percentage of body fat for the average person your age is from 9 to 15 percent for males and from 14 to 21 percent for females.

Weight control is a major health problem. Fat children and fat teenagers are more likely to become fat adults. Excessive body fat can contribute to a number of health problems, including high blood pressure, heart disease, stroke, diabetes, and kidney disorders, as well as reduced self-image.

Weight loss or gain can be achieved by (1) changing caloric intake; (2) changing caloric output; or (3) a combination of the two. To maintain weight, your caloric intake (what you eat) should be the same as your average daily caloric output (what you burn up). A combined program of proper nutrition and regular physical activity best achieves permanent weight control.

Photodisc

The Wrap-Up

Vocabulary Matching

Match the definitions to the correct term.

1. Somatotype
2. Endomorph
3. Mesomorph
4. Ectomorph
5. Body composition
6. Lean body mass
7. Overweight
8. Obese
9. Ideal body weight
10. Creeping obesity
11. Anorexia nervosa
12. Bulimia
13. Spot reduction
14. Eating smart

A. exceeding desirable body weight by 10 percent
B. a large soft, bulging body and a pear-shaped appearance
C. gaining fat very slowly over a period of years
D. having an excessive amount of body fat
E. obsessed with the fear of being overweight that they refuse to eat normally
F. body type
G. ratio of fat to muscle, bone, and other tissues that compose your body
H. a solid, muscular, and large-boned physique
I. exercising a particular area of the body to remove fat from that area
J. a slender body and slight build
K. amount you should weigh if you have an appropriate percent of body fat
L. part of the body made up of muscles, bones, ligaments, and tendons
M. use of laxatives, self-induced vomiting, and strenuous exercise to avoid gaining weight
N. choosing non-fried foods that are low in fat and carbohydrates

Multiple Choice

Select the most correct answer.

15. Height and weight charts can be misleading because
  A. they are established for people more than 20 years of age.
  B. they do not tell you how much of your weight is lean body mass and how much is body fat.
  C. weight scales are not accurate for all people.
  D. all of the above.

16. The most accurate method of determining the percentage of body fat is
  A. electrical impedance.
  B. measurement of body circumferences.
  C. skinfold measurements.
  D. underwater weighing.

17. The method to measure body fat requiring the use of calipers is
  A. electrical impedance.
  B. measurement of body circumferences.
  C. skinfold measurement.
  D. underwater weighing.

18. Which health hazard is related to excessive body fat?
  A. heart disease
  B. high blood pressure
  C. surgical risk
  D. all of the above

19. How many calories is each pound of body weight equivalent to?
  A. 2,500
  B. 3,000
  C. 3,500
  D. 4,000

20. The most effective way of achieving permanent weight loss is by
  A. increasing calories burned.
  B. reducing calories consumed.
  C. a combination of A and B.
  D. taking steroids.

21. Which activity would contribute least to weight loss?
  A. golf
  B. jogging
  C. soccer
  D. wrestling

22. The advantage of the combined diet and physical activity method for permanent weight control is

A. that neither food reduction nor the increase in physical activity needs to be as severe as if either were practiced alone.
B. that weight loss is mostly fat, not lean tissue.
C. the improvement of the health-related components of fitness.
D. all of the above

23. In a weight loss program, it is recommended that you lose no more than

A. 1 to 2 pounds per week.
B. 3 to 4 pounds per week.
C. 5 to 6 pounds per week.
D. 7 to 8 pounds per week.

24. Which statement about weight control is true?

A. Exercise will increase appetite.
B. Exercise will not help weight control.
C. Selected exercises will help remove fat from particular areas of the body.
D. None of the above are true.

Authentic Assessment—Short Response

25. Why are height and weight charts not very useful standards?

26. What is the difference between actual body weight and ideal body weight?

27. Explain why many adults and youth in the United States are overweight.

28. Explain how you would lose weight, gain weight, or maintain your weight.

29. Why is the combination of sound nutrition and regular physical activity the most desirable method for permanent weight control?

Authentic Assessment—Extended Response

30. Writing situation: Interview an adult in each of the following age groups: 20s, 30s, 40s, 50s, and 60s. Ask them the following regarding their weight:

How has it changed with age? Have they had any health problems associated with weight gain?

Directions for writing: Illustrate your findings in a chart or graph. Summarize and draw conclusions from the information collected.

31. Writing situation: Because of the emphasis placed on weight control in our society, some misconceptions have developed about physical activity and weight control.

Directions for writing: Describe several of the most common misconceptions about weight control.

11

Stress

Corel

Objectives

As you read this chapter, look for answers to these key questions:

- What is stress, and why do some of your peers react differently to a specific situation than you?
- What are the common sources of stress?
- What are the physiological effects of stress on the body?
- How do positive stress and negative stress affect your emotions and how you behave?
- How is stress related to various diseases, such as cardiovascular diseases?
- How are sleep and stress related?
- What are the components of a stress management program?
- What are stress diversion activities and how are they helpful?
- What are negative coping techniques and why should you avoid them?

"Most people are about as happy as they make up their minds to be."

—Abraham Lincoln

V•A•L•U•E

Knowledge about what stress is, what causes stress, and how you can manage your stress has many benefits. Good stress management will allow you to do better on those important tests or presentations in school, and it will allow you to perform better in pressure packed sporting events. Good stress management will also allow you to improve the quality of personal relationships, with a special person, your brothers and sisters, and your parents. Since stress is a contributor to such major health problems as cardiovascular diseases, good stress management will provide you an added defense against such health problems.

Chapter Preview

- The Importance of Understanding Stress
- What Is Stress?
- Case Study: Sammy's Story
- What Causes Stress?
- How Does Your Body Physically React to Stress?
- How Do You Mentally React to Stress?
- How Do Positive and Negative Stress Affect You Differently?
- Sleep and Stress
- Developing a Stress-Management Program
- Stress-Diversion Activities
- Negative Coping Techniques You Should Avoid
- Summary
- The Wrap-Up

Vocabulary

When you have completed this chapter, you should understand the meaning of these vocabulary terms:

stress

positive stress (eustress)

negative stress (distress)

stressor

homeostasis

fight-or-flight response

general adaptation syndrome

stimulus

adrenaline

time management

positive coping strategies

stress-diversion activities

negative coping techniques

Wellness Connection

The Importance of Understanding Stress

It is not unusual that teenagers do not understand stress and how it affects them. They do not know about stress and its causes, or how to deal with new or different sources of stress. Most people, adults as well as teenagers, do not understand or are not even aware of stress and the consequences of negative stress. Those who are aware of stress think of it only as negative. If teenagers and parents understood stress, they could help each other.

Corbis

What Is Stress?

Photodisc

Feelings of loneliness are common. We all need friends to talk to and share with.

Stress is the nonspecific response of the body to any demand made upon it and may vary from one individual to another. Good things (a good grade on a test) or bad things (getting cut from a team) may both cause you stress. Therefore, stress can be either good or bad, depending on how you and your body react to the specific demand.

If stress results from something good and you react to it in a positive manner, the stress is good. Good stress, or **positive stress**, is called **eustress**. If stress is caused by something bad or if you react to a given situation in a negative manner, the stress is bad for you. Bad stress, or **negative stress**, is called **distress**.

Individuals React Differently to Stress

Different people react to the same demand differently. Some people may receive negative stress when the teacher calls on them in class, while others receive positive stress from having the opportunity to answer questions in class. Therefore, you can see that stress is specific to each individual. How you react to a specific demand might be different from the reaction of your friends or classmates. This does not mean that you are abnormal. It just means that you are an individual.

Case Study: Sammy's Story

The school year was only 2 weeks old, but Sammy was already frustrated, confused, and lost. He felt as if he was drowning. Sammy was in the ninth grade at Midway High School, and he didn't know anyone. During the summer, he and his family had moved to Midway from a smaller town. The middle school he had attended last year was small, and Sammy knew all of the students and teachers. He received personal attention in his classes that enabled him to do well and receive excellent grades. He was also active in after-school activities, and was particularly good in athletics. . . .

During these first 2 weeks at Midway High, Sammy did not find or experience any of the positive things that made him enjoy school in the past. The classes were large and the teachers were too busy to give students individual attention. The football coach had discouraged him from coming out for the team because he was too small, didn't know the system, and would have trouble adjusting. . . .

Sammy did not know anyone, and no one knew him. The school was very large, very crowded, and, it seemed to Sammy, very noisy. It seemed that all of the other students had their own peer groups, with no room for new people. Students smoked openly at Midway, popped pills, and drank alcohol. Half of the students spent most of the time high on one drug or another. In fact, these were the only students who showed any interest in him, and they had freely offered him different types of drugs. Although he always turned them down, he found himself thinking that if he accepted their offer just once, maybe he would make friends and be accepted. But that thought scared him. Could he accept only once? . . .

At home, Sammy's family was just as confusing. Everyone had his or her own problems adjusting to new jobs, new friends, new everything. There did not seem to be the time or the interest to listen to Sammy's problems at school. His mother had passed it off as a period of adjustment. Sammy felt himself withdrawing. He was floating through school, and at the end of the day he could not remember any details. He only remembered an increasingly desperate feeling.

Goal Setting

Pick one positive coping strategy each week to focus on to be included in your Personal Fitness Plan to prevent or reduce the stress in your daily life.

What's Wrong with Sammy?

Sammy is experiencing stress from many sources. He does not understand what is happening to him. He has never heard of stress or the causes of stress. He does not know what coping strategies (techniques of dealing with stress) are or how to use them. If Sammy does not receive help with his stress soon, it is likely he will begin protecting himself by using whatever means are easy or available to him. Withdrawal, negative behavior, and drug abuse are all unconscious and common reactions to stress. Sammy's new life has him in a pressure cooker, and the pressure is building. Sammy needs help or the pressure will build to a point of explosion. The help Sammy needs may be the friendship of people, or it may be the knowledge of what is happening to him and how he can deal with it in a positive manner.

What Causes Stress?

Situations that cause stress are referred to as stressors. Nearly everything is a stressor, creating either positive stress (eustress) or negative stress (distress). Every activity encountered stresses you, with each activity creating a different degree of stress. Some of these activities cause you negative stress, and some cause you positive stress. You may experience positive stress, while your best friend may experience negative stress from the same activity because you are different individuals.

Stockbyte

Nearly everything can be a stressor, whether positive or negative.

Extreme heat and cold temperatures cause the homeostasis (internal balance) of your body to be upset. This is a negative physical stressor that requires a physical response. However, extreme temperatures can also cause mental stress.

The death of a person who is close to you requires both a physical and a mental response. The death of a family member may even be a positive stressor. For example, death may occur after the person has been ill for a long time.

Potential Causes of Stress

Many potential sources of stress bombard you every day. These might include family relationships, schoolwork, peer groups, discrimination, injury, sickness, or fatigue. These stressors can generate both positive stress and negative stress. How you handle or react to these stressors determines their effect on you and your lifestyle.

SAFETY AWARENESS

Try to schedule a moderately active physical activity after events that are stressful to you. This will help the body burn the additional adrenaline that the stressful situation created.

Are All Changes Stressors?

Yes. Even pleasant changes in your daily routine can cause stress. This type of stressor does not cause as great a stress as a bad change, but the body still needs to make an adjustment and use up some of its energy reserve. An example of this is a summer vacation or a holiday season. Many people feel physically tired at the end of their vacation, even though it was enjoyable. This fatigue is caused by the body using up its energy reserve to make all of the adjustments to changes in its normal routine. A good change (vacation) does not create as much negative stress as a bad change (death in family, divorce). But if you are not aware that the situation is stressful, you may let it affect you negatively and ruin your vacation.

Internet Resources

Stress Test and Ways to Reduce Your Stress
http://www.changeourminds.com/stress.html

Stress Busters
http://stressrelease.com/strssbus.html

NIH—For the Public
http://www.nimh.nih.gov/publicat/index.cfm

Major Stressors Come in Many Forms

Major changes in your life are the real negative stressors for which you need to plan coping techniques in order to handle them positively. Sammy's family moved, a change that frequently creates a great deal of negative stress in all family members. This is true even if such a move is caused by something positive, such as a promotion that requires a parent to move to another city.

Photodisc

Moving away to college is a major change and usually causes a great deal of negative stress, even if the long-term results may be positive.

If a family like Sammy's is required to move, an adjustment in the behavior of all family members should be expected. This change in behavior occurs even though the move is due to a positive reason. If the move is regarded as a negative situation, the emotional response will be even greater. Children often think a family move is negative because they have to move away from friends and a comfortable, secure environment. Although all family members are expected to act in a calm, mature manner, some may in fact feel anger and resentment toward other members of the family or their employers. Children frequently let this kind of resentment against their parents build.

If the threat of stress caused by the move is managed in an appropriate manner, the resulting response will be positive rather than negative. But if no satisfactory way can be found to cope with the stress, those involved will feel increasingly angry and resentful. This continued build-up of stress would cause a weakening of the body systems.

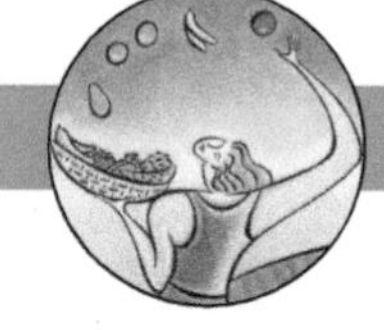

Nutrition Information

Reduce the amount of sugar and caffeine in your diet from dark colas, chocolate, and coffee, especially prior to a major test or other event that may be stressful to you.

How Do You Physically React to Stress?

Your body responds physiologically in exactly the same manner to both positive and negative stress. The body's response to a specific stressor occurs in a sequence of three steps, or stages. This sequence is known as the general adaptation syndrome. The *first stage* is the alarm stage. The body makes an immediate response to a stressor, anticipating change and perceiving change as a danger or an emergency. During the *second stage*, the body learns, or tries to learn, to adapt to the stressor, or it goes through a stage of resistance. The *third stage*, exhaustion, occurs when the body uses up the energy reserves required for coping with stress.

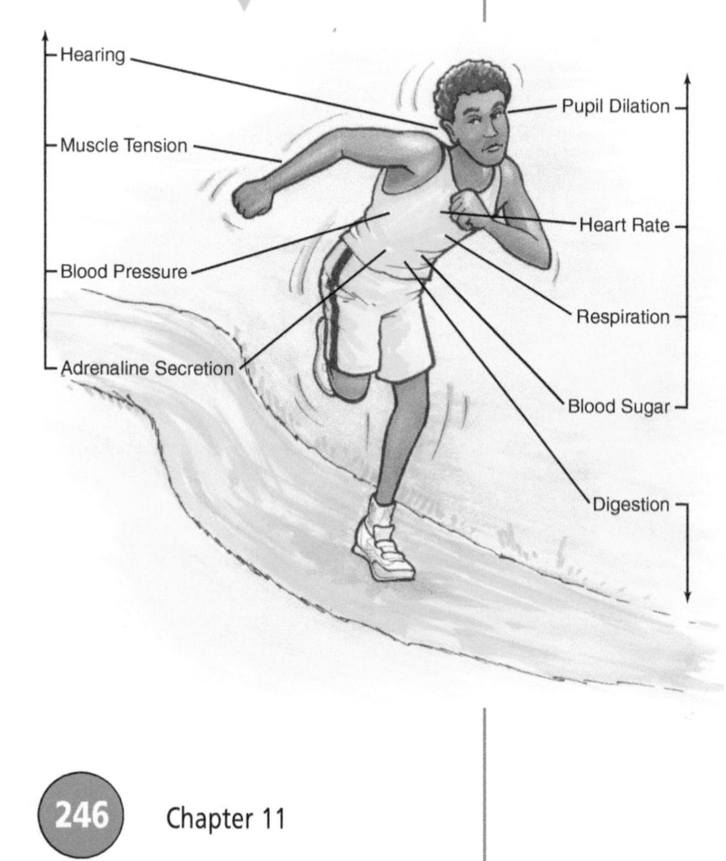

The "fight-or-flight" response causes many changes to occur in the body. These changes are the same for both positive and negative stress.

Fight-or-Flight Response

Initiation of the alarm stage occurs when the body receives a stimulus, such as one of your parents yelling at you for not carrying out the garbage. This stimulus immediately activates the nervous system that releases adrenaline into the body. Adrenaline is the chemical that gives you energy to perform physical acts in an emergency. By increasing the supply of adrenaline, the body moves into the fight-or-flight mode. The fight-or-flight response is the natural protective technique of your body. Every stressor, whether positive or negative, causes the same thing to happen in your body. The amount of adrenaline released depends on the strength of the stimuli and your previous experience with that stressor.

The release of additional adrenaline causes body functions to change. The more important changes include the following:

- Blood circulation is increased to provide your brain, lungs, and muscles with more nutrients (fuel for energy).
- Nutrients (energy supplies) in the blood are increased.
- Muscles are strengthened to respond to the fight-or-flight response.
- Breathing becomes more rapid to give you more oxygen.
- Your senses become more alert; for example, the pupils of your eyes dilate to sharpen vision.

Stress Information

Practice relaxation techniques that can be used when you experience a conflict during physical activity, such as taking ten deep slow breaths, counting backwards from ten, or thinking of a pleasant memory.

Other Responses

The degree to which stress affects you physically is also determined by what you are doing when you receive the stimuli from a stressor and the additional adrenaline is released. If you are physically active when the adrenaline is released, it is easier for you to deal with the stress because the exercise burns up the additional supply of adrenaline and allows body functions (such as heart rate and blood pressure) to return to normal. This will not happen if you are sitting. When sitting, the body reacts to the stressor in the very same manner that it would if you were active, except that the adrenaline is not burned up quickly. The adrenaline remains in the body for a long period of time, keeping body functions at an unusually high level. If your blood pressure is frequently elevated by stress and not subsequently lowered by exercise, you could develop high blood pressure.

How Do You Mentally React to Stress?

You respond to stress both physically and mentally. Your mental response usually involves such emotions as happiness, joy, fear, and anger. The mental or emotional changes you exhibit in response to a stressor actually control how you respond physically. If the emotions caused by your stressor are strong enough, you will undergo a change in behavior.

The psychological (mental) changes in behavior that occur due to an emotional response to stress can be classified as follows:

- *Rationalizing:* making up reasons why the situation turned out the way it did, rather than the way it should have
- *Projecting:* blaming someone else for your own fault
- *Compensation:* over-reacting to make up for a feeling of inadequacy
- *Avoidance:* refusing to act on a situation

Although they are common, these forms of behavior are not considered healthy. If such behaviors are not corrected, they can lead to more serious mental disturbances.

How Does Positive and Negative Stress Affect You Differently?

As you know by now, stress has both positive and negative effects. The way you respond to the stress, both physically and mentally, determines whether the immediate and long-term effects of stress will be positive or negative.

Positive Stress (Eustress)

Stress affects you in a positive manner every day. It can provide you with the energy and motivation to accomplish things you want to do or have been demanded of you. Positive stress makes you more creative, alert, assertive and dedicated to a task. Positive stress keeps you from becoming bored and fatigued with your daily tasks. By helping you resist fatigue and boredom, positive stress will make you feel good about yourself. It makes you alert and happy, not nervous or uptight. Your peers view you as feeling good about yourself.

Banana Stock

Stockbyte

Positive stress makes you alert and happy, not nervous or uptight.

Negative Stress (Distress)

Too much stress can have a negative effect and can interfere with schoolwork, home life, and your relationship with your peers. It can even lead to health problems over an extended period of time. The effects of negative stress can pile up on you. They act on you in combination, not as individual stressors. Sammy had many different stressors affecting him. He had to deal with the total effect of all stressors. If you are in a situation like Sammy, and you reach the point where you cannot deal with the accumulated effect of all the stressors, you are suffering from a condition commonly called *burnout*.

The effect of negative stress (distress) can be set at three different levels. Each level has different symptoms and is more serious than the previous one.

- *Level 1:* This level is least severe. The symptoms include short periods of irritability, fatigue, worry, and frustration.
- *Level 2:* The symptoms for this level are similar to the symptoms for level one, but they last as long as 2 weeks or more.
- *Level 3:* This level is the most serious. If you are experiencing stress at this level, you may have minor health problems, such as frequent colds, headaches, dizziness, or diarrhea.

The conditions at level 3 can develop into severe health problems requiring medical assistance if they go unattended. These conditions include high blood pressure, asthma, panic attacks, ulcers, and diabetes.

Sleep and Stress

Individuals' need for sleep varies, and changes with age. As one grows older, less hours of sleep are required. Young children and teenagers require more time than adults do in the deepest stages of sleep. It is during this time that the growth hormone is secreted. The constant interruption of these deep stages of sleep could, therefore, affect your growth and development.

Adequate sleep is a positive stress management strategy. The latest research indicates that you need 8 to 9 hours of sleep each night. The brain emits a sleeping chemical and if you are getting less than the necessary 8–9 hours of sleep, you are sitting in a classroom first period with brain chemicals signaling it is nighttime. Sleep is food for the brain, and even mild sleepiness can affect performance. Students who participated in the research study who slept only 6 1/2 hours earned Cs and Ds, while students who got the most sleep made As and Bs. Earning good grades will help you have a positive self-concept, another buffer against stress. A proper amount of sleep will help you have energy to face the stressors you will face the next day.

Consumer Issues

Advertising attempts to sway your opinion on health and fitness purchasing decisions. Some advertisers want you to have a negative feeling about yourself. You are then led to believe that you will be much happier if you just buy one of their products.

However, stress can seriously alter your sleeping patterns. How sleeping patterns are changed will depend on you and the stress that you are experiencing. Many times, teenagers may be stressed out by an important upcoming event, such as a key sporting contest, major exam, or a concert. This often results in your inability to get to sleep or stay asleep for a long period of time. Stress may also cause you to spend more time than normal sleeping. This situation is usually brought on by long-term stress, like family or parents always arguing or a disrupted social relationship. Sleep would then become a form of avoidance.

Developing a Stress-Management Program

What should you do about negative stress? You need to develop your own stress management program in order to resist the consequences of negative stress. This program should include strategies that can be grouped into three sets: building up your resistance to negative stress, developing techniques for avoiding negative stress, and developing positive coping strategies that will help you deal with the distress you cannot avoid.

Photodisc

Develop your own stress-management program in order to resist the consequences of negative stress.

Developing Resistance to Stress

These strategies to help you resist stress include improving your level of fitness, getting an adequate amount of sleep, and developing a sound nutritional diet.

Get Fit

The first part of a good stress management program is to work at developing a greater energy reserve. This can be done by maintaining a high level of physical fitness. This will give you greater energy and help keep you from becoming fatigued as the demands of the day begin to wear you down. We all become more irritable and susceptible to minor stressors when we are tired.

Get Enough Sleep

An adequate amount of sleep and a high fitness level will help you have sufficient energy to resist stressors that you will face each day. Remember, as you become fatigued, you become more irritable and therefore more susceptible to stress.

You Are What You Eat

Proper diet is also part of your fitness and stress-management program. A proper diet will help you look good and feel good. Certain aspects of your diet may increase your susceptibility to

stress. Sugar and caffeine are two components of most people's diet that are high stressors. Chocolate, colas, coffee, and tea have high concentrations of caffeine and should be avoided after lunch. Many prepared foods have high levels of sugar. You should attempt to limit your intake of these items. Limiting your intake will help keep you from becoming irritable, uptight, and unable to cope with even minor stressors.

Developing Strategies for Avoiding Stress

There are things that you can do to avoid stress, or not let a situation cause you negative stress. The main things to remember are: don't worry about little things, set realistic goals, and start a time-management program.

Do Not Worry about Little Things

Respond to minor stressors in a positive manner.

Goodshoot

The first step in developing a stress management plan is to stop fighting things that usually cause you a lot of negative stress. You need to allow simple or minor demands on the body (minor stressors) to pass without concern. Such minor stressors might be what happens to you when you drive a car (someone cuts in front of you), spill a glass of milk (the responses of family), or meet new people (they are probably as nervous as you are). You need to learn to respond to these minor stressors in a positive way.

If you do not respond to minor stressors in a positive manner, your irritation level will build up to a point where you will be unable to deal with the impact of a major stressor in a reasonable manner. You do not want to use up your daily energy reserve on these minor stressors.

Set Goals

Wise and effective goal setting, as discussed in Chapter 3, is also an important aspect of successful stress management. This is true whether you are dealing with school, work, leisure time, or your social life. Many people become frustrated and burned out from being involved in too many activities where there is little satisfaction or the expectations are unreasonable. Unreasonable expectations may mean too little is expected (you become bored) or too much is expected (you become frustrated). Get involved in a variety of activities that will challenge you. If you have a positive attitude and put forth a good effort, you can experience success. These types of activities are positive stressors. However, do not get involved in activities that are beyond your abilities, or in so many different activities that you do not have time to devote the effort required to be successful. Getting in over your head, so that failure is almost a certainty, is a negative stressor.

Practice Time Management

Learning to organize your time, or **time management**, is an important stress-management technique. Having too many demands made on you is a common cause of negative stress. Therefore, do not get involved in too many activities. Learn to say no. Get involved in activities that are challenging, within your abilities, and within your time limit. Time management may involve setting time schedules that you follow, regardless of what may come up: a specific time to do homework, a time for physical activity, and a time to watch television. Another technique is keeping a priority list of things that need to be accomplished each day. The pressure of time is a major stressor for most people. How well you manage your time will determine how well you manage the stress in your life. See Table 11–1.

Table 11–1. Sample Time Usage Log

Track usage of time for one week.			
Day	**Activity**		**Time**
10-3	Dressing for school		7:00–7:25
10-3	Breakfast		7:25–7:50
Summary of Time Wasted			
Time	**Activity**	**Should have. . .**	**How to Avoid**
10-3	Watching TV	Exercised while watching	Select priority shows to view
10-3	Video Games	Updated PFP	Limit playing time

Developing Positive Coping Strategies

The next step in building your stress-management program should be the development of **positive coping strategies** to be used in dealing with stressors you cannot avoid.

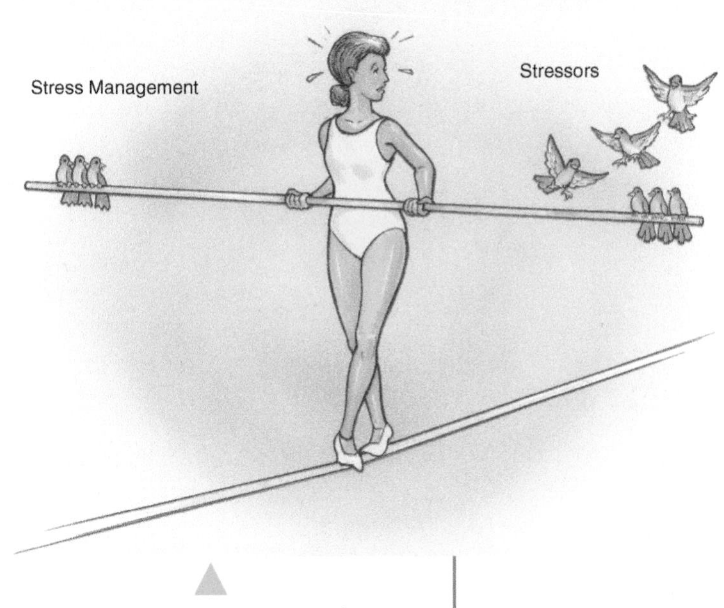

You must keep your stress scale balanced.

Each person must have his or her own coping techniques. What is a stress release for your best friend might be a stressor for you.

Seek Temporary Relief

The first approach to coping with distress is to get some temporary relief. You may do this through exercise, yoga, or just plain daydreaming. There are a number of relaxation techniques that are very helpful. Learn at least one relaxation technique and practice it daily. Alternating the way you breathe is all it takes sometimes to make you feel better.

1. As you slowly inhale, silently count to five. As you slowly exhale, count to five.
2. Balloon breathing is a technique where you imagine that your stomach is a small balloon. When you inhale through your nose, pretend that you are bringing air through your bellybutton, inflating the stomach. Slowly exhale through your nose, allowing the air to leave through your bellybutton.

Practice Self-Talk

When you become angry during a competitive sporting event, learn how to use self-talk to bring the anger under control. You will soon realize that some phrases bring special meaning to you, whereas they may not have the same interpretation to others. Here are some examples of phrases you might use:

- Is it worth getting upset about?
- Focus on the behavior, not the person.
- Just as I have the right to my opinion, so do others.
- Getting angry never solves anything.
- Do not do something you will regret tomorrow.
- It's not worth dealing with.
- Will I remember this next week, month, or year?

Recognize Early Symptoms of Stress

A second approach to developing coping techniques is learning to recognize the early symptoms of stress. You can learn how you physically respond to stress and how to use those physical responses as an early warning of negative stress. If you find your jaw or facial muscles becoming tired, you might be reacting to stress by clenching your teeth. This physical symptom, once identified, can be used as a warning signal that you need to take a short break. Other common physical symptoms include tight neck muscles, eyestrain, shoulder or back stiffness, and increased heart rate. Do you recognize any of these symptoms in yourself?

Identify Stressful Situations

Another important step in developing positive coping strategies is identifying common stressful situations and defining how you normally respond to them. Once you have done this, you can modify your reaction or concentrate on replacing your usual response with a more positive response, or coping strategy.

Support Groups Are Helpful

At times, you will be faced with stressful situations that you cannot handle by yourself. In those situations, you will need a support group, people with whom you can talk about a particular stressor. Developing a variety of support groups, such as parents, friends at school, teachers, coaches, or counselors, can be very helpful, regardless of what caused you to become uptight or tense. There will be things you may not feel comfortable talking to your parents about, but you may feel free to discuss them with a peer or a physical education teacher. The more support groups you develop, the better you will feel.

Stockbyte

You cannot cope with stress by yourself. You need support groups, such as good friends, school teachers, or family members.

Progressive Relaxation

Progressive relaxation is based on the theory that you do not realize that your muscles are tensed. Therefore, if you consistently tense a muscle and then focus on relaxing that muscle you will become less tense and more relaxed. Start with your toes and move all the way up your body by tensing and relaxing sets of muscles.

You start progressive relaxation by lying down or sitting in a comfortable position. Close your eyes and be quiet. Tense the toes and hold for approximately 10 seconds. Gradually let go of the tension until the toes go limp. Repeat the same technique with various muscle groups until you have reached the shoulder muscles.

Stress-Diversion Activities

Stress-diversion activities are either active or passive activities that help you reduce or divert stress. You should especially try to fill your leisure time with activities that are vigorous enough to provide some of the training effects discussed earlier. These types of activities will provide you two benefits: (1) they burn up the extra adrenaline caused by stressors to prepare you for the fight-or-flight response, which allows physiological functions (heart rate, blood pressure, breathing rate) to return to normal following the exercise; (2) they improve your level of fitness, preventing you from becoming easily fatigued, which enables you to better cope with negative stressors.

Some activities help you to reduce or divert stress.

Photodisc

Quiet, passive activities are also good stress-diversion activities. These types of activities help you forget about stressors that are bothering you. Watching television, reading a book, or listening to music may all be good stress-diversion activities if they help you relax and focus on positive things.

Remember, what is stress diversion for your friend might be a stressor for you. If you are highly competitive and concerned with winning or losing, any competitive game or activity might be a stressor. If this is the case, you need to pick a noncompetitive activity as your stress-diversion activity.

Positive coping techniques can be summarized in the following list:

1. High level of physical fitness
2. Proper diet
3. Awareness of your reaction to distress
4. Awareness of common stressors
5. Relaxation techniques
6. Involvement in challenging activities
7. Support groups
8. Time management

Negative Coping Techniques You Should Avoid

Negative responses, or **negative coping techniques**, are those responses you use to ease or disguise the symptoms of stress. These techniques are harmful not only to you but also to the people around you. Most of these negative techniques can be grouped into four categories: excessive emotion, impatience, avoidance, and use of drugs and alcohol.

Being Overemotional

A common reaction to negative stress is an overemotional one, particularly when your feelings, ego, or self-esteem are threatened. Stress causes a fight-or-flight response. Most of the time it is not appropriate for you to fight physically and you cannot run away, so the fight-or-flight response becomes an emotional attempt to protect yourself or your self-esteem. A common response to criticism is to charge emotionally, "it's not my fault." This type of response is particularly common when the accumulated pressure of a large number of negative stressors begins to wear you down, fatigue you, or cause you to become more irritable. Many times people become emotional and blurt out negative statements they really do not believe or even want to say. These negative comments may hurt the feelings of people or generate emotional responses from them. Practice a number of positive coping strategies as a way of helping yourself avoid this negative technique.

Impatience

You may become impatient with yourself or with others. Impatience may occur when you become involved in activities in which your abilities are not challenged or in activities that are far too difficult. You may also experience impatience when you become involved in too many activities. Proper goal setting and appropriate selection of activities are important if you are going to offset the threat of impatience.

Avoidance

Although avoiding certain stressful situations is a positive coping technique, there are times when withdrawal or avoiding a stressor is not good. If you are afraid to talk with strangers and avoid such stressful situations, you may not meet or get to know that boy or girl with whom you really would like to become acquainted. By avoiding that stressful situation, you are limiting your peer group and negatively affecting your lifestyle choices.

If talking in class is very stressful to you, you may choose to avoid that stressor by not volunteering or, when called on, saying you do not know. This may not be appropriate if your grade is partly determined by your participation in class. Avoiding this stressor is also negative, since you are not learning to handle this situation properly. It is important that you learn to deal with this problem because all people, from time to time, find themselves in a situation in which they need to talk with or in front of peers. Depending on their occupations, some people need to do this more than others. If you choose to avoid this situation and never learn to deal with it, you will place limits on yourself in social situations and in your job. To avoid speaking in front of groups may be viewed as negative. This practice has even kept people from accepting good jobs for which they were qualified. You should not let a stressor control your lifestyle choices.

Drugs and Alcohol

The fourth category of coping strategies is the use of drugs or alcohol. Some adults have a couple of drinks every day to relax after work. Drugs and alcohol can cause physical and mental problems, be habit forming, and may cause an individual to lose efficiency and motivation. Exercise and relaxation techniques work better and have the double benefit of relaxation and increasing resistance to stress. Drugs and alcohol only cover up your stress and lower your resistance to stress.

PFP Update

We all experience stress from many sources. You may feel stressed from school, friends, family, or dating. If stress is not handled properly, you can feel tired, angry, frustrated, and upset with friends and family. Your performance in school can be affected as well. You have learned various ways to handle stress positively in this chapter. Take a few minutes and decide which coping techniques you wish to use to reduce the stress in your life. If you have included physical activities in your ongoing PFP, you are already taking an action step to control your stressors. Physical activity is probably the best way to decrease the stress in your life; however, the other methods discussed in the chapter are excellent, too. Make a decision—set a goal related to stress management and develop a strategy to reach it and include it in your PFP.

PFP Technology Activity

After completing a Web-based stress inventory, write a one-page summary, analyzing your stress level and how you will "de-stress" your life. When finished, save the information to your PFP file and/or print out the results and place it in your PFP notebook along with your stress management plan.

Summary

Stress is the nonspecific response of the body to any demand made upon it. Stress may be either good or bad. Many factors cause stress. What causes stress for you may not cause the same reaction in your friend.

Nearly everything you encounter is a stressor; some are positive and some are negative. All changes cause stress, even the pleasant ones, but major changes cause the major stressors.

The body's response is the same for both positive and negative stress. Responses to stress will be both physical and mental. Many of these changes can have serious effects if left unattended.

In order to deal with stress, you need to develop a strong stress-management program. This program should allow you to build your resistance to stress, develop strategies that will allow you to avoid some stressors, and develop positive coping strategies for the stress that you cannot avoid. Also, being involved in challenging activities will help you handle your stress. Active and passive stress diversion activities may also help you cope with stressors.

The use of negative coping techniques can be dangerous. Negative methods of dealing with stress only cover up the effects of stress and do not deal with the stressor. Emotional outbursts, impatience, avoidance, or the use of drugs or alcohol are all negative coping techniques.

Photodisc

The Wrap-Up

Vocabulary Matching

Match the definitions to the correct term.

1. Adrenaline
2. Coping techniques
3. Stress-diversion activities
4. Fight-or-flight response
5. Homeostasis
6. Negative stress
7. Time Management
8. Positive stress
9. General adaptation syndrome
10. Stimulus
11. Stress
12. Stressors

A. eustress
B. distress
C. things that cause stress
D. a signal to your body that a change has happened or is about to happen
E. chemical in the body that gives you added energy
F. learning how to organize your day
G. your body's response to a specific stressor which occurs in 3 stages
H. the ways that you deal with stress
I. your body's nonspecific response to a demand made upon it
J. the body's response to negative stress
K. shielding from or reflecting the effects of stress
L. internal balance or biological balance of the body

Multiple Choice

Select the most correct answer.

13. The first step to managing stress is to
- **A.** avoid the source of your stressors.
- **B.** identify your stressors.
- **C.** improve dietary behaviors.
- **D.** learn time-management skills.

14. Which of the following statements is correct?
- **A.** Changes in your life will only cause stress if they affect you negatively.
- **B.** Stress is always present.
- **C.** Your body will react differently to positive and negative stress.
- **D.** Your response to stress is only physical, not mental.

15. The term used when someone puts off doing something that should be done is
- **A.** avoidance.
- **B.** coping.
- **C.** fight-or-flight.
- **D.** procrastination.

16. Which food(s) may cause you to be more irritable and less able to cope with minor stress?
- **A.** caffeine
- **B.** chocolate
- **C.** sugar
- **D.** all of the above

17. Which would not be a cause of stress?
- **A.** death in the family
- **B.** good grades
- **C.** peer groups
- **D.** none of the above

18. During the "fight-or-flight" mode, which is true?
- **A.** Digestion improves, heart rate, blood pressure, and blood sugar increase.
- **B.** Hearing and vision improve, heart rate and blood pressure increase.
- **C.** Heart rate and blood pressure increase, blood sugar decreases.
- **D.** Vision becomes blurred, heart rate and blood pressure increases.

19. Negative stress (distress) could
- **A.** help you resist fatigue.
- **B.** interfere with your schoolwork.
- **C.** keep you from being bored.
- **D.** make you alert and happy.

20. You are better able to handle stress if

A. you are physically active.
B. you are physically passive.
C. you eat foods high in sugar.
D. your body functions remain normal.

21. A negative coping technique is one that

A. could be harmful to other people.
B. could be harmful to you.
C. eases or masks stress.
D. could be all of the above.

22. Identifying common stressful situations and defining how you normally react

A. is not a good idea; you should look at the future instead.
B. will allow you to modify your responses.
C. will cause distress to increase.
D. will only increase your negative stress.

23. Which is true about goal setting as it relates to stress management?

A. Getting in "over your head" will positively challenge you.
B. Goals that are easy to reach will not cause stress.
C. Realistic goals are never difficult to obtain.
D. Unreasonable expectations mean that goals are too difficult.

24. A good stress-management program should consider

A. diet.
B. physical activities.
C. relaxation techniques.
D. all of the above.

Authentic Assessment—Short Response

25. Identify and discuss the different stressors that Sammy is facing.

26. Describe the negative coping strategies Sammy could use in dealing with his stress.

27. Discuss how you could identify stressful events and how you could better cope with those events.

28. Discuss the benefits of exercise to stress diversion.

29. Identify common situations where someone may use avoidance when it is a negative coping technique.

Authentic Assessment—Extended Response

30. **Writing situation:** Reshard has just been elected president of the senior class. Mary was elected president of the junior class. Both had wanted to be president of their classes. Reshard began to worry and have doubts. He would have to run meetings, organize projects, and meet with faculty and administrators. What if he didn't do a good job, or if his classmates didn't give him support? What if he failed? The more Reshard thought the more the pressure built inside him. Mary's position is more demanding than Reshard's, primarily because the juniors are responsible for the prom. She is excited and enthusiastic about the challenge ahead of her.

Directions for writing: What type of stress are Reshard and Mary experiencing? Suggest positive coping strategies for the person with whom you more closely identify.

31. **Writing situation:** You have just been elected as your class president.

Directions for writing: Would your response be more like Reshard or Mary? Explain why.

12

Consumer Issues

Photodisc

"You can't always judge a book by its cover."

Objectives

As you read this chapter, look for answers to these key questions:

- What influences people to buy certain products?
- What is the most powerful tool in combating consumer fraud?
- What are examples of unsound and worthless fitness products?
- How can a fitness center be evaluated?
- Why are advertisements claiming fast weight reduction and spot reduction fraudulent schemes?
- What are anabolic steroids and why should they be avoided?
- How can teenagers combat false advertising claims?

V • A • L • U • E

Consumers are constantly bombarded with advertisements urging them to buy certain products. On the surface, this sounds all right until an analysis of health and fitness products reveals the fact that many of the claims are false and misleading. Knowledge gained from this chapter will help ensure that you will not waste your money on products related to health and fitness.

Chapter Preview

- You the Consumer
- What Influences Your Buying Decisions?
- Have You Been Ripped Off?
- Spot Reduction: The Big Myth
- False Advertising
- Exercise Gadgets and Gimmicks
- Fad Diets and Weight-Loss Drugs
- Anabolic Steroids
- Evaluating Fitness Centers
- Personal Trainers
- Understanding Web Sites
- Selecting Fitness Equipment for Your Home
- PFP Update
- Summary
- The Wrap-Up

Vocabulary

When you have completed this chapter, you should understand the meaning of these vocabulary terms:

consumer

advertising

fraudulent

diuretics

edema

anabolic steroids

personal trainer

Wellness Connection

You the Consumer

What do you have in common with your neighbors and grandparents, with entertainers and professional athletes? All of you are consumers. A **consumer** is a person who buys goods and services. As a consumer, you have many choices. You can choose what to buy, where to buy, and when to buy. You can also choose to get the best value for your money. By making wise purchasing decisions, you can become a satisfied consumer.

Corbis

Each year teenagers spend billions of dollars on clothing, music, magazines, athletic gear, and many other items. In fact, teen spending power is so large that many companies cater only to the teen market. After studying this chapter, you will be better prepared to make wise decisions about spending your money on items, brand names, and services related to physical fitness and health.

What Influences Your Buying Decisions?

What influenced your buying decision when you bought your last pair of jeans? Did you buy the same brand you bought before? Did you buy the brand advertised in the latest issue of your favorite magazine? Or was your decision influenced by the brand your friends were wearing?

Influence of Peers

You are probably influenced by friends when you buy certain items or brand names. You enjoy the feeling of belonging to a group and naturally like to do what your friends are doing. While it is fun and natural to follow the crowd, it is important to be sure you are buying what is best for you. When buying an item, ask yourself the following questions:

- Am I buying a fad item that is popular today but will soon be out?

Goal Setting

Set a goal of being a knowledgeable consumer. Critically evaluate what is being said about health and fitness products to see if misleading information is being presented to convince you to buy them.

Photodisc

Many people waste money on useless products they see advertised on television.

- Am I getting the best value for my money?
- Am I spending twice as much money for a name-brand item?

Influence of Habit

Buying decisions are frequently influenced by buying habits. You might think that other brands are inferior if you have the habit of always buying name-brand items. You might be missing excellent bargains if you shop at only one store. Try to fight off the tendency to be a consumer snob.

Influence of Advertising

Advertising can have a powerful influence on your buying decisions. Businesses spend more than $230 billion each year to reach the 105 million U.S. households. This translates to an average of $2,190 per household. It is estimated that $13 billion is spent by corporations to influence youth. **Advertising** is found in all types of media that surround you every day. Whatever the form, advertising offers many advantages and lets consumers know which products or services are available. It lets people know about sales, and it introduces new products, along with the benefits of those products. There are also disadvantages to advertising. Sometimes it encourages people to buy things they do not need. It can also be misleading. For example, some ads make exaggerated claims in regard to your physical activity needs.

Some experts believe that television commercials damage young people's self-esteem by portraying people in almost supernatural ways. Do not allow such commercials to convince you that you are neither attractive, nor witty, nor physically capable when compared to people seen in television ads. This is exactly what the advertisers hope for because the products in the commercials then appear to be the solution for people not feeling good about themselves.

Have You Been Ripped Off?

Do you like to get ripped off? The obvious answer to this question is NO. Although this is true, many people appear ready to buy any product that has some promise of helping them look and feel better. Teenagers are no different, as they have a strong desire to look as good as possible. Americans as a whole spend billions of dollars every year on questionable products. All of us have been victimized by false advertisements at one time or another, but teenagers are an extremely susceptible group because they have little information and less experience as consumers. Because of this, many companies advertise almost anything that promises to help teenagers look more attractive.

Knowledge Is the Key

Knowledge is probably the only way to combat false advertising. It does not take much knowledge to be able to spot unethical or worthless claims. You must beware of any treatment, device, or product that is being promoted to make your body more attractive. You need to be especially leery of products or treatments promising amazing results in a very short time. Your body cannot be reshaped overnight.

Safety Awareness

Drugs that suppress the appetite are of little value and can be habit forming. These drugs may also cause unhealthy side effects such as dizziness, depression, constipation, insomnia and increased heart rate.

Are You a Knowledgeable Consumer?

Physical fitness consumers must be knowledgeable in order to get the greatest benefit from their money. Knowledge is the key to consumer power—your power! You must be able to determine which advertisements are sound and which are unsound. People selling unsound products do not want you to be knowledgeable about the real effects of their products. They would much rather have you believe what you see, hear, or read about the thousands of products on the market. The end result is that they make money, and the uninformed consumer finds very little satisfaction from the products because few of the promised results actually happen.

Spot Reduction: The Big Myth

Many people want to lose pounds in one area of the body, such as the stomach or thighs. To lose these pounds, people look to advertisements that promise fast and easy results in spot reduction if they purchase a certain product.

The misconception that fat can be reduced or removed from one specific area of the body is probably the most obvious denial of established knowledge about the way the body responds to exercise. It has been shown through research that spot reduction is impossible. Many people still hold to the idea that exercising an isolated part of the body, where the fat has accumulated, trims fat from that specific area. This is simply not true. There is no known means by which fat may be broken down and lost from just one part of your body. If this were true, many people would do what was necessary to trim unsightly fat from their stomachs, hips, or thighs.

Many exercise gadgets, devices, and programs are based on the misconception that, if muscle groups beneath the fat are used, the fat will go away. The most prevalent example of this is the

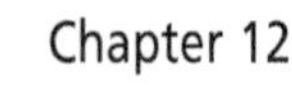

belief that sit-ups reduce fat on the stomach. Ask 10 of your friends how they would reduce the fat on their stomachs and, in all probability, 9 out of 10 will answer by saying, "Sit-ups." It is also commonly believed that stretching exercises can be used to get rid of fat in a specific spot. Some of these exercises serve a very useful purpose, but that purpose is not the reduction of fat from a specific part of the body.

False Advertising

Wouldn't you agree that this advertisement is very impressive from the standpoint of sounding easy to do? Imagine! All you have to do is lie down and relax. The rest of the advertisement, a full-page ad not included here, uses such phrases as "will unleash unused powers of your subconscious mind," "ignite natural fat burners," "launch an attack on stubborn bulges," "break down the fat on thighs, stomach, and hips," "shrink the size of your stomach," and finally "get rid of your hunger." Typically, the reader's attention is drawn to the glamorous woman shown in the ad. The final bait thrown out to tempt the buyer is a statement such as: "If you just send in $29.95 plus $6.00 shipping charge, plus tax, you will receive a DVD which will guarantee beautiful results, and you can be just as attractive with little effort."

Photodisc

"Just lie back, relax. You can lose as much weight as you want and never gain any of it back."

Nutrition Information

A weight-control misconception is that if you increase your physical activity, your appetite will automatically increase. The truth is mild to moderate exercise will actually decrease the appetite of most people.

Tips on Identifying False Advertising

Following are a few more tips to help you recognize unsound advertisements.

- Beware of testimonials. Have you ever wondered why so many people offer testimonials for various products? You are right if your answer is money. The people who make the testimonials are paid by the companies who make the products. Are there good testimonials? Sometimes, but you must read or listen carefully to their claims. You should also be wary of friends who talk about products that have helped them lose fat in just 3 days, or some similar claim.

- The offer generally involves a special gift for fast action. If it sounds too good to be true, it probably is.
- The location of the ad or the time of the commercial may be another tip-off. An unsound ad is usually placed in the back of a magazine. Commercials promoting unsound products or programs are often on late at night when the rates are less.
- Is it likely that one product can do everything? No! One product cannot do everything, although it is easy to find advertisements that make this claim.
- Ignore claims that an exercise machine or device can provide long-lasting, easy, "no-sweat" results in a short time. These claims are false: You can't get the benefits of exercise unless you exercise.
- Be skeptical of testimonials and before-and-after pictures from "satisfied" customers.

In this country, people are allowed and even encouraged to start small businesses that provide services to others. They need to advertise to promote the sale of their services, but a few get greedy for quick money and make exaggerated claims about their products. The claims for these products are referred to as being fraudulent because the product does not accomplish what is claimed.

Internet Resources

Consumer Information—U.S. Department of Agriculture
http://www.nal.usda.gov/fnic/consumersite/nutrition.htm

Commercialism—Center for a New American Dream
http://www.newdream.org/

Consumer Action Campaign—Center for Science in the Public Interest
http://www.cspinet.org/

Selecting Home Equipment—American College of Sports Medicine
http://www.acsm.org/health+fitness/productpurchase.htm

What You Can Do to Combat False Advertising

You may wonder how you can stop false advertising if government agencies are slow and at times ineffective. There are things that you can do as an individual or in a group (teens) to combat false advertising. Many people who are trying to

make a living from the sale of useless products assume that teenagers are not smart enough to filter through the big words and fancy promises and recognize that certain products are worthless. They are in for a surprise!

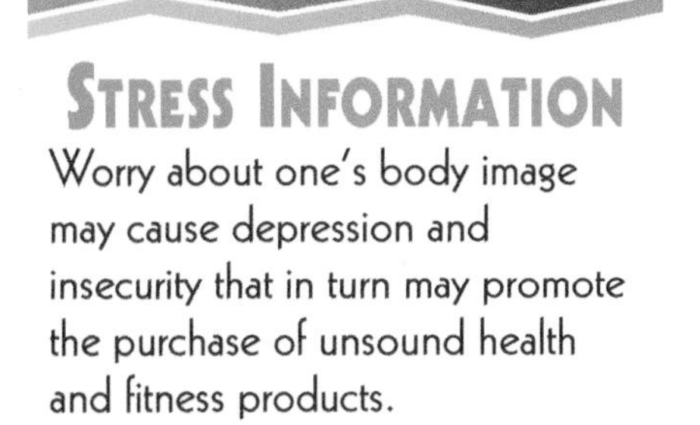

STRESS INFORMATION

Worry about one's body image may cause depression and insecurity that in turn may promote the purchase of unsound health and fitness products.

If you want to become an advocate for teenage consumerism, take these steps if you believe a product is not what it is supposed to be.

1. Tell all of your friends about the advertisements and ask them to write or call the editor of the particular magazine explaining why they think the advertisement is misleading or falsely advertised. You will have a lot more influence if there are 20 calls or letters as compared to just yours.
2. If you bought something locally, complain as soon as possible. This increases the chance of a satisfactory settlement.
3. Call your local Better Business Bureau, and explain why you believe the advertising for a particular product is fraudulent.
4. Contact the merchant by phone, who sold you the product or service and be prepared to answer any questions he/she may have. Clearly present your problem, and make sure you have relevant information on hand including: a description of the item model and /or serial number, receipt, billing statement or cancelled check.
5. If the telephone call is unsuccessful, go to the merchant in person and ask to speak to the manager or supervisor.
6. If the above steps result in failure, it is time to put your complaint in writing. Complaint letters are important because a business may ignore a complaint, if it is not in writing.

Goodshoot

Become an advocate for teenage consumerism.

Everyone wants to look and feel as good as possible. However, there are no easy methods to accomplish these goals. Neither pills nor diets nor secret formulas will do the trick. The Federal Trade Commission and the Food and Drug Administration are unable to effectively regulate the sale of fraudulent weight-reducing schemes, since companies are not required to provide evidence of their beneficial claims prior to public sale of their products.

Be a smart shopper! Control your money carefully, and remember that the knowledge you have gained from this chapter is power in your pocket. Use it wisely. Ignorance will get you in trouble.

Exercise Gadgets and Gimmicks

Approximately 18 million consumers purchase products from infomercials annually. The Federal Trade Commission reports that a number of companies selling equipment through infomercials use questionable tactics to get customers to buy their products.

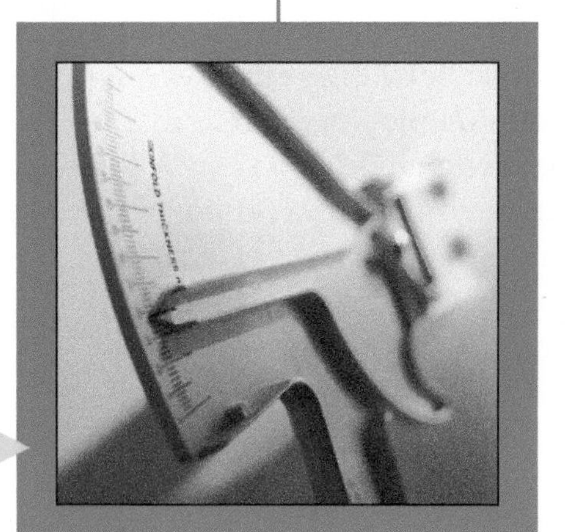

Many products advertised have no effect on weight loss.

The following are just a few examples of unsound exercise gadgets and gimmicks.

- The electric muscle stimulator is designed for use in physical therapy, not in a fitness club. Such devices cause a mild electric current to go to a muscle and make it move. Such devices are not designed for weight loss and could be dangerous without the proper therapeutic supervision.
- Massage does not break up fat and allow it to be burned off. Massage feels good and helps loosen tight muscles, but it does not cause weight loss.
- Saunas might feel great, but they have no effect on weight loss.
- Plastic or rubberized sweat and sauna suits make people sweat a lot, but they prevent the evaporation of heat from the body and hinder the ability of the body to cool itself. The weight loss that occurs when wearing these items is water loss, not fat loss. After you sweat off a few pounds of body fluids during a vigorous workout, you will regain the weight as soon as you drink fluids.
- Body wraps have been popular through the years. People selling these products claim that you can lose inches of fat rapidly by wearing them. Some body wraps are soaked in a solution that is supposed to have magical capabilities. There is absolutely no truth to the belief that people can lose weight or increase their physical fitness level by wearing body wraps. Body wraps will make you sweat a lot due to water loss, which will be quickly regained upon drinking additional fluids.
- Bust developers have been and still are a popular form of misleading advertising for more than a century. It is not surprising that such devices are still popular, since many adult females believe they need to have bigger breasts in order to

look more like the females seen in magazines and on television. Certain weight-training exercises for the chest may enhance breast appearance by firming up or toning the muscles underneath the breasts, but nothing outside of surgery can be done to increase the size of the breasts.

Fad Diets and Weight-Loss Drugs

Many Americans seem only too willing to pay any price for quick, simple, and comfortable methods of getting rid of excess body fat. At first glance, it might appear that a number of programs and products on the market could accomplish this, but the fact is that a simple, easy cure for being overweight or obese remains to be discovered. Some diets or remedies may bring about temporary weight reduction, but most are not only ineffective but also hazardous to your health. You should be very skeptical of crash diets recommended in popular diet books, as well as any miracle food that comes with money-back guarantees.

Metabolic Drugs

Appetite suppressants and thyroid hormones are two general categories of drugs commonly used in the treatment of overweight and obese people. These drugs supposedly increase the body's metabolic rate and, therefore, cause the body to burn more calories. Research has shown that only a small percentage of overweight and obese people have hormone problems. Most have simply developed extremely poor exercise and nutritional habits.

Diuretics

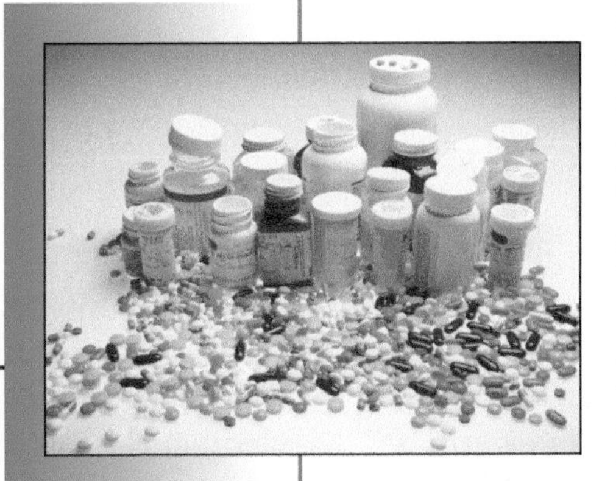

Many people think that the use of diuretics or diet pills can cause significant and permanent weight loss.

Photodisc

Diuretics are used to control different types of edema (accumulation of fluid in body tissues), congestive heart failure, and high blood pressure. They are occasionally prescribed for women with high blood pressure who experience weight gain due to water retention before their menstrual period.

Many people think that the use of diuretics or diet pills can cause significant and permanent weight loss. However, the reality is that, should any weight loss occur, it is only temporary, and can be accompanied by rapid weight gain, severe mood swings, and depression. The problem can be compounded with eating disorders such as bulimia and anorexia nervosa. The following are short-term effects of using diuretics/diet pills:

- Weight loss
- Fever
- Bed-wetting
- Frequent need to urinate
- Dehydration
- Headaches
- Thirst
- Menstrual irregularities
- Nausea
- Infections
- Change of appetite

Long-term damage is also possible:

- A dangerously low potassium level, which could cause heart problems
- Upset in the body's chemical balance
- Increased cardiovascular problems for people with high blood pressure
- Blood-clotting problems during menstruation
- Damage to the kidneys, if used continually

As you can see, diuretics are a very poor solution to a weight-gain problem. Remember that water loss is not true weight reduction because no calories are burned. Those who use diuretics are only fooling themselves! Be sure to share this information with anyone who is considering using diuretics for losing weight.

Anabolic Steroids

Athletes are vulnerable to claims that certain substances can enhance their performance. You have probably heard of the abuse of anabolic steroids by body builders, professional football players, and track athletes. Many other people experiment with these substances in an effort to improve their physical appearance or to become stronger. Research studies indicate that teenagers are also using steroids more frequently. It is extremely important that teenagers understand the very serious side effects of the use of anabolic steroids.

What Are Anabolic Steroids?

Anabolic steroids are a synthetic version of testosterone, the male sex hormone. Synthetic anabolic steroids are complex chemicals that the body does not handle easily or naturally. Synthetic anabolic steroids are similar to testosterone in chemical structure, but they affect the body differently.

Effects of Anabolic Steroids on the Body

The male testes produce testosterone naturally. At puberty, males may have as much as a twentyfold increase in testosterone naturally. Testosterone stimulates the growth of bone, muscle, and hair, and it also affects emotional development.

If anabolic steroids are administered orally or by injection, the body shuts down its own production of testosterone. The body reacts this way because it recognizes that it already has more than an adequate supply of testosterone. The testicles will shrink if anabolic steroids are taken for a long period of time, since the testosterone-producing cells in the body are no longer active.

Young people have more problems with anabolic steroids than older people. One reason has to do with the difference in bone growth. These drugs can cause premature closure of the growth plates on the ends of the long bones in your body. This can have a very serious effect on your growth. It can decrease the height to which you would normally grow.

The more a person uses steroids, the greater the risk of developing one of the many conditions identified as harmful side effects. You would be wise to adhere to the position taken by the American College of Sports Medicine. This group recommends that because of the many dangerous side effects, everyone should refrain from steroid use. Once again the answer to self-improvement is not found in a pill or a bottle. These drugs are extremely dangerous to anyone taking them. The following are some of the undesirable side effects associated with steroid use:

- Liver and kidney damage
- Decrease in ultimate height

- Increased risk of cancer
- Scalp hair loss
- Appearance of acne
- Decrease in size of the testicles and impotency
- Increased aggression and unpredictable mood changes
- Reduction of breast size in women

Evaluating Fitness Centers

At some point, you may wish to join a fitness club in order to start or maintain a PFP. There are many fitness clubs in most communities, but some are better than others, so you should investigate which one is the best one for you. A fitness club should be a place where you can pursue your fitness goals effectively and safely, and get sound professional advice. As you begin to look for a fitness club that meets your needs, there are three things you should focus on: facilities, programs, and personnel. Following is a list of questions you should ask under each of these areas.

Facilities

- Is the location of the club convenient?
- Do the operating hours of the facility fit into your schedule?
- Is the facility overcrowded at the time you would want to attend?
- Are the restrooms, showers, and equipment clean and well maintained?
- What are the prices, and does the club have package deals or season specials?
- How long has the club been in business? Check with the Better Business Bureau for complaints.
- Is the exercise area uncluttered and well monitored for safety?

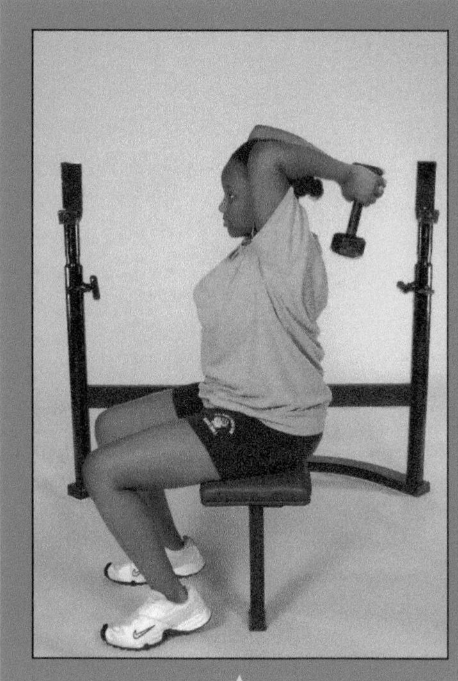

Ray Carson

Are individual exercise programs available?

Programs

- Are individual exercise programs available?
- Are educational programs available?
- Are aerobic classes offered? Are the class times convenient?
- Are racquetball, basketball or tennis courts available?

Personnel

- Are the instructors or personal trainers certified and well skilled in teaching weight training?
- Are the instructors certified in cardiopulmonary resuscitation (CPR) and first aid?
- Do the instructors seem to be sincerely interested in helping you set up a PFP?
- Do the instructors make a point of correcting any improper exercise techniques?
- Do the instructors move around the exercise room observing and offering help where needed?

Personal Trainers

Personal trainers are individuals who are very much into fitness and health and are committed to helping those who are anxious to improve their lifestyles through physical activities and the changing of health behaviors. Personal trainers will not only teach their clients how to exercise, they will also act as motivators, coaches, and friends. Personal trainers will not only help clients set goals, they will also monitor them and give advice about their progress.

Advantages of a Personal Trainer

Although personal trainers might be considered too costly, they can help you improve at a faster rate. The following are reasons why a personal trainer could help you reach your goals:

- *Safety:* A personal trainer will show you how to exercise safely and how to use exercise equipment in an appropriate manner.
- *Supervision:* Personal attention during exercise is a primary function of personal trainers. They should observe, assist, and correct if necessary.
- *Motivation:* Personal trainers should serve as a major source of motivation and encouragement. It is easy to lose one's motivation and to begin to slack off.
- *Consistency:* If you are having trouble keeping with your program, personal trainers can be of major assistance in helping to keep you on track.
- *Effective workouts:* Personal trainers can help you maximize your time by providing workouts designed to meet your goals quickly and efficiently.

- *Individualized instruction:* A personal trainer will develop the most effective program for you based on your fitness evaluation results and your personal goals.
- *Injury rehabilitation:* If you get injured, a personal trainer should be able to help you get back into action as quickly as possible.
- *Ego boost:* Personal trainers can provide positive feedback on your performance and bolster your confidence to take on new challenges.

Online Personal Trainers

It can be difficult to choose an online personal trainer.

Stockbyte

Hiring a personal trainer to design your personal fitness program has traditionally been the privilege of the rich and famous due to the cost factor. The average cost of hiring a personal trainer is probably between $35.00 and $100.00 per hour, which is a rather expensive fee for most people. Today, there are personal trainers available on the Internet, with some charging as little as $10.00 per month. Since online training is accessible to anyone with a computer and modem, and since new personal training sites are springing up all over the Internet, it can be difficult to pick the best one. There is also the added danger of unqualified trainers with questionable backgrounds giving out potentially dangerous fitness advice. With that in mind, consider the following tips for picking an online personal trainer as well as a local one.

- Check the qualifications of the staff who will be training you. Be sure to ask if the personal trainer is certified by a national organization. Web sites should provide this background information on all of their staff members.
- If nutritional advice is provided, make sure registered dietitians are on staff.
- Make sure the information provided is correct for your age. Some exercises, norms, and nutritional information is only correct for individuals over the age of 18.
- Determine how easy it is going to be to contact your trainer to ask questions either by e-mail or toll-free telephone number.
- Be absolutely honest when you respond to any questions asked by the personal trainer. Providing misinformation could reduce the effectiveness of your training program and lead to injury.

- The personal trainer should assist you in establishing behavioral objectives that will help you reach the goals you wish to achieve.
- It is important that your program is updated regularly. Whether you are using a local personal trainer or a Web site, they should provide you with an exercise planner to record your progress.
- Determine if the personal trainer or Web site provides you with feedback through e-mails about your progress.

Regardless of whether you use the services of a local personal trainer or an online one, they can help you pursue a healthier and more dynamic lifestyle. It is important to remember, though, that you will be competent to design your own personal fitness program and a wiser consumer, after you have completed this course.

Understanding Web Sites

As you are aware, there are thousands of Web sites on the Internet. Many of these are excellent sources of information for just about any topic. However, many Web sites are designed to promote products and services that can be purchased. These are not necessarily bad Web sites; they simply are set up to make money. These Web sites usually end with a .com, which stands for *commercial*. Web sites that end in .edu are sites dealing with any aspect of *education*. Web sites that end with .org represent *organizations*, while sites ending with .gov represent *government* materials. An important point to remember is that Web sites ending with .com are possibly biased because they are trying to sell products or services. Every network card has an identification number. Some .com Web sites will do a reverse search and find out your computer's IP address. Once the company finds out you are interested in similar products, they may send you e-mails or have ads pop up on your screen related to the Web sites you have visited. Remember, just because information is on the Internet does not make it true.

Selecting Fitness Equipment for Your Home

Having fitness equipment in your home has a huge advantage. The more convenient it is for one to exercise, the more likely they will engage in this healthy lifestyle behavior. Walk into any sporting goods store and ask to view the various exercise equipment for developing your physical fitness. Anyone would be confused about selecting the best piece of equipment after viewing all of the possibilities.

Although home-exercise equipment does not have to be fitness center grade, it should be sturdy and constructed of quality material. Here are a few considerations for the selection of home exercise equipment:

- Is it made out of steel, aluminum, or plastic?
- Are the joints welded or bolted? Welded joints are stronger than bolts.
- How convenient is it to use? Are you going to spend more time adjusting the equipment than in exercising?
- Is the equipment base large enough to provide ample stability when you are exercising? The general rule is, the larger the base of support, the greater the stability.
- Are handgrips provided to assist in getting into position or provide stability while exercising?
- Do you really need all of the electronics on a piece of equipment? Usually, the electronics are not needed and are added for motivational purposes.
- Do you have sufficient space to leave the equipment out all of the time, or must you break it down for storage after use?

You should also keep in mind that purchasing expensive aerobic and weight equipment may not be necessary. Depending on your weight-lifting goals, you can increase your muscular fitness significantly by doing exercises like push-ups, dips, pull-ups, and various abdominal exercises. Dumbbells are not only inexpensive, they are excellent in helping a person develop muscular fitness for all parts of the body. So, before you spend a lot of money for a fancy piece of equipment, explore the use of dumbbells and functional muscular exercises in which your body weight is used.

PFP Technology Activity

Using word-processing software, develop a check sheet to evaluate a local fitness center. Print out the check sheet to be included in your PFP for future use.

PFP Update

You are quickly closing in on the end of this class. How have you been doing with your goals? Stay determined to pursue your self-improvement desires. You should be feeling good about yourself by this time.

Advertisers dealing with health and fitness products are committed to convincing everyone, particularly women, that the simplest method of getting a lean, attractive body is to purchase a piece of equipment with the guarantee that positive results will occur quickly or to take a special supplement, with the same assurance of positive results. The unfortunate fact is that millions of consumers listen to these false ads and send their money to take advantage of such "miracle" products.

As you maintain your PFP in the future, don't purchase worthless products that promise everything. Remember, marketing people do not want consumers to be smart. They would rather have you uninformed, desperate and looking for a quick fix. Knowledge is the key, and you have it. All you need to do is use it.

Summary

Hundreds of unsound products are sold every year to consumers who want to be more physically attractive. People selling these products are experts in making you believe you can improve yourself easily and in a short period of time. They are successful in selling worthless products because many consumers do not have the necessary knowledge to recognize false statements. You can protect yourself, your family, and your friends from being ripped off by understanding some basic information related to how the body reacts to exercise and proper health practices. Become a strong and effective advocate for sound advertising and play an important role in getting rid of worthless products.

Goodshoot

Vocabulary Matching

Match the definitions to the correct term.

1. Consumer
2. Advertising
3. Diuretics
4. Edema
5. Fraudulent
6. Anabolic steroids

A. anything that has a powerful influence on your buying habits

B. substances used to control the accumulation of fluid in body tissue

C. a synthetic version of testosterone

D. accumulation of fluid in body tissue

E. a person who buys goods and services

F. misleading information designed to get consumers to buy products

Multiple Choice

Select the most correct answer.

7. Which is accurate when discussing spot reduction?
   A. An exercise myth is that sit-ups will reduce fat on the stomach.
   B. Research has shown that some products burn fat on specific body locations.
   C. Sit-ups are a very effective method of reducing fat on your stomach.
   D. Very few advertisements are seen on this subject.

8. The best way to combat false advertising is
   A. federal taxation.
   B. government laws.
   C. knowledge.
   D. to establish and follow a fitness program.

9. Which statement is most accurate?
   A. Most people have never been ripped off on health-related products.
   B. Teenagers are a very big target for advertisers.
   C. Teenagers spend little money on what might be called "glamour" products.
   D. Teenagers usually make smart buying decisions.

10. Advertisements
- **A.** can be relied on to be accurate.
- **B.** generally do not influence people's purchasing practices.
- **C.** are not as misleading as experts say they are.
- **D.** try to get consumers to buy goods so that they will be more attractive.

11. What influences buying decisions?
- **A.** advertisements
- **B.** your habits
- **C.** your friends
- **D.** all of the above

12. Which is most accurate when defining a consumer?
- **A.** Consumers are almost always satisfied with their purchases.
- **B.** Consumers are everyone who buys goods and services.
- **C.** Consumers usually have a very limited choice of what to buy.
- **D.** Teenagers do not spend much money as consumers.

13. Which side effects are associated with anabolic steroids?
- **A.** appearance of acne and scalp hair loss
- **B.** increased aggression and unpredictable mood changes
- **C.** liver and kidney damage
- **D.** all of the above

14. Anabolic steroids are
- **A.** a synthetic version of the male sex hormone (testosterone).
- **B.** no more dangerous for teenagers than for adults.
- **C.** not used by nonathletes.
- **D.** safe if you follow the advice of a body builder.

15. Diuretics will not
- **A.** cause damage to the kidneys.
- **B.** have any effect on the body at all.
- **C.** provide a good solution to a weight-loss concern.
- **D.** disrupt the chemical balance of the body.

16. False advertising claims about health and fitness products
- **A.** are prohibited from appearing on television by federal laws.
- **B.** rarely use testimonials from celebrities.
- **C.** use many misleading statements to increase sales.
- **D.** usually urge you to take your time deciding.

Authentic Assessment—Short Response

17. Identify something that you purchased recently. What influenced you to buy the item? What influenced you to buy from that specific store?

18. A friend is concerned about the fat on his stomach and tells you he is doing sit-ups to get rid of it. You immediately know he is on the wrong track. What should you tell him? Of what value are sit-ups?

19. Your mother is concerned about her legs because they are getting flabby. She asks you if flexibility exercises could do her any good. What is your answer? What type of exercise would be important for her to do? What other factor might be of extreme importance?

20. Your girlfriend wants to join a health club and she does not know which one to join. What advice could you give her?

21. Advertisers operate on the assumption that teenagers are not intelligent consumers. What can teens do to counter this belief?

Authentic Assessment—Extended Response

22. **Writing situation:** A friend of yours is trying very hard to develop his upper body. However, progress is slow. He has told you that he has decided to experiment with anabolic steroids and asks what you think.

Directions for writing: Make a list of the advantages and disadvantages of taking anabolic steroids to share with your friend. Rank your list in order of importance, giving a higher weighing to present and future health.

23. **Writing situation:** Several of your friends have complained about the types of advertisements that seem to be directed toward teenagers in regard to health and fitness items. One of your friends asks, "What can we do about it?" You have some ideas.

Directions for writing: Discuss the steps you could take if you wanted to become an advocate for teenage consumerism.

13

Evaluation of Activities

Photodisc

Objectives

As you read this chapter, look for answers to these key questions:

- Which activities are considered the best for improving physical fitness?
- What are some of the most popular exercise programs?
- Why is it important to develop skills in lifetime sports?
- Why should you consider health needs before selecting activities for your personal fitness program?
- Why are benefits from stress-diversion activities considered very personal?
- How do your personality and attitudes affect your selection of exercise programs and sports activities?
- How do the environment, the availability of facilities, and the cost enter into selecting activities for your personal fitness program?

"Quality is never an accident; it is always the result of effort."

V•A•L•U•E

The key to developing a successful personal fitness program is designing a program that is right for you. Before choosing exercise programs and sports activities for your personal fitness program, you should understand the benefits gained from each activity. The best activities are those that you enjoy and ones that also meet your individual needs. All of us enjoy doing those things that we can do successfully. Increase your skill in those activities that will help you reach your health-related fitness goals. This will increase the likelihood that you will take time to engage in physical activity.

Chapter Preview

- Which Activities Are Best?
- Categories of Activities
- Considerations Before Selecting Activities
- PFP Update
- Summary
- The Wrap-Up

Vocabulary

When you have completed this chapter, you should understand the meaning of these vocabulary terms:

planned programs
high-impact aerobics
low-impact aerobics
calisthenics
circuit training
interval training
sports skills activities
lifetime sports

Which Activities Are Best?

In order to be fit and healthy, as well as look good and feel good for a lifetime, you need to engage in some kind of regular exercise program. The key to developing a successful personal fitness program is to know what is right for you. The selection of activities depends, in part, on the answers to these questions.

- Which components of physical fitness do you need to improve most?
- What kind of exercises and activities do you enjoy?
- What kind of activities will help you manage your stress?
- What sports skills do you have?
- Will you be exercising alone or with others?
- Where will you be exercising?
- Will you need special equipment or facilities?

What kind of exercises and activities do you enjoy?

Photodisc

No single physical activity meets the needs of everyone. You have to select activities that best meet your own needs. Try to include a variety of activities in your personal fitness program to avoid boredom and to keep it fun and interesting. Do not be afraid to try a new or different activity; however, do not hesitate to stop doing an activity if you do not enjoy it. Do not become a physical fitness dropout just because you picked the wrong activity. Keep trying until you find activities you really enjoy. You are more likely to exercise regularly if you choose activities you enjoy.

Categories of Activities

In order to determine the activities that are best for you, you will need to become acquainted with and evaluate the many available exercise programs. Physical activities can be divided into two groups: (1) exercise programs and (2) sports activities.

Exercise Programs

Exercise programs can be designed by you or by someone else. It is important to remember that any exercise program should be based on the principles of training discussed in earlier chapters to assure both benefit and safety.

Gym balls can be used for a variety of exercises.

Ray Carson

GOAL SETTING

In order for your personal fitness programs to be successful, you must select exercise programs and/or sports activities that will address each of your health-related fitness goals. Some sports activities can be very beneficial in meeting your goals, if you possess the skill level required to obtain a sufficient workout.

Predetermined programs usually include specific exercises for persons of specific fitness levels or ages. These are sometimes referred to as **planned programs.** Aerobic dance classes, exercise programs seen on television and videotapes, circuit training, and fitness trails found in many recreation parks are examples of planned programs. Your overall personal fitness program should include several different exercise programs in order to meet all of your needs. You are encouraged to try different exercise programs. Some sample planned programs are provided to assist you in developing your own program. The following are some of the more popular exercise programs.

Aerobic Dance

Aerobic dance is a popular exercise program for people of all ages. Aerobic dance routines include a combination of dance steps and calisthenics done to upbeat popular music. Aerobic dance can be high-impact or low-impact. **High-impact aerobics** include jumping, bouncing, and running. **Low-impact aerobics** include vigorous arm movements while keeping one foot in contact with the ground at all times. You can develop your own aerobic dance routines, participate in programs at health clubs and recreation departments, or follow those seen on television and home videotapes.

Ray Carson

Aerobic dance is a popular exercise program for people of all ages.

Safety Awareness

Weather that is either very hot and humid or very cold could influence the type of activity you plan and time of day you plan to engage in the activity. In highly populated areas, air pollution and personal safety are also factors that must be considered when selecting activities.

Photodisc

Aqua Dynamics

Aqua dynamics is an exercise program done in the water. You do not have to be a swimmer to participate in this kind of program. Many exercises in aqua dynamics are similar to calisthenics. Because of the buoyancy provided by the water, aqua dynamics is a very popular exercise program among handicapped persons and those with injuries.

Bicycling

Bicycling is one of the most popular exercise programs for developing cardiovascular fitness and muscular endurance in the legs. Bicycling must be done continuously for at least 20 minutes in order to have an aerobic effect. When bicycling, try to maintain steady, continuous pedaling rather than coasting.

Table 13–1. Sample Bicycling Program

Week	Frequency/Wk	Distance	Time
1	3	2.0 miles	12:00
2	3	2.0 miles	10:00
3	3	2.5 miles	13:00
4	3	3.0 miles	20:00
5	4	3.0 miles	20:00

Calisthenics

Calisthenics are exercises in which body parts or body weight is used as the resistance. Such exercises are convenient to do because they require little or no equipment and can be done at home. Calisthenics are used for warm-up, flexibility, and development of muscular strength and muscular endurance. Running in place, side-leg raises, push-ups, sit-ups, and pull-ups are examples of calisthenics.

Circuit Training

Circuit training is an exercise program in which you move around a prescribed course, stopping at stations along the way to perform specified exercises. This exercise program stresses continuous activity. The intensity of a circuit can be made greater by increasing the repetitions of the exercise at each station, by decreasing the time required to complete the circuit, or by a combination of the two. (See the figures on page 291 for an example of circuit training.)

Bench Step
Upright Rowing
Sprinter
Front Curl
Pull-ups
Heel Raiser
Sit-ups
Bar Dips
Standing Press
Isometric-head
Push
Rope Jumping

Fitness Trails

Fitness trails can be found in many recreation parks and on school grounds. A fitness trail is an established route of considerable distance with exercise stations dispersed along the way. Signs that describe and illustrate each exercise and indicate the number of repetitions are posted at each station. You can walk or jog between stations, stop and perform the exercise at each station, and continue on to the end of the trail.

Interval Training

Interval training is an exercise program involving a series of exercises interspersed with rest periods. Interval training is usually associated with endurance training in running and swimming, but the general principles are applicable to any kind of exercise program. There are four variables in interval training: (1) speed or rate, (2) distance or length of time, (3) rest period, and (4) number of repetitions. One or all of the variables can be altered to change the intensity of the workout.

Table 13–2. Example of Interval Training Applied to Various Activities

Activity	Freq./Wk	Distance	Time	Rest	Repetitions
Jogging	3	220 yds.	0:45	2:00	5
Swimming	3	50 yds.	2:00	1:00	6
Bicycling	3	.5 miles	2:00	1:00	8

Internet Resources

Information on Actives Skills and Rules—VERB
http://www.verbnow.com

Fitness Awards Program—The President's Council on Physical Fitness and Sport
http://fitness.gov/sports/sports.html

Ad Council Videos on Exercise—President's Council on Physical Fitness and Sport
http://fitness.gov/video/video.html

Interactive Site to Select Activities—Centers for Disease Control and Prevention
http://www.bam.gov/fit4life/cards.htm

Photodisc

Jogging

Jogging is one of the most popular forms of aerobic exercise. Many people believe jogging is the best overall exercise for developing and maintaining cardiovascular fitness. You can jog almost anywhere at almost any time. You can jog alone, with someone, or with a group of people. The only special equipment required is a good pair of running shoes.

Table 13-3. Sample Jogging Program

Week	Frequency/Wk	Distance	Time
1	3	1.0 mile	12:00
2	3	1.5 miles	18:00
3	3	1.5 miles	16:00
4	3	2.0 miles	26:00
5	4	2.0 miles	24:00

Pilates

Pilates is an exercise program focused on improving flexibility and strength for the total body without bulking up. Many of the pilates exercises are performed in reaching or sitting positions and most are low impact and partially weight bearing. This popular exercise program is known for being used by Hollywood celebrities, top athletes, and professional dancers and models. Pilates instruction is available at many fitness facilities and on videos for home exercise.

Photodisc

Rope Jumping

Rope jumping is an excellent cardiovascular fitness activity that requires only a few simple skills and a rope. Many people jump rope when there is no opportunity to jog, swim, or bicycle, such as in a motel room when traveling. In jumping rope, you should use a continuous, progressive routine. Progress slowly in order to prevent injuries. The length of the rope should be such that it reaches your armpits when held to the ground beneath your feet.

Spinning

Spinning is an excellent cardiovascular fitness activity that utilizes a special stationary bike that you can change the pedaling resistance. Because you can establish the workload to suit your own ability and level of difficulty, people of all ability levels can participate together in spinning classes. The appeal of spinning classes is that it simulates a bike race. Many fitness facilities offer spinning classes.

Photodisc

Swimming

Swimming is an excellent exercise program for developing and maintaining physical fitness. Virtually every muscle is utilized as you propel yourself through the water. Swimming for physical fitness is done in laps at a mild or moderate pace. One advantage that swimming has over other exercise programs is that it is less likely to cause injury.

If you do not know how to swim, contact your local parks and recreation department, YMCA, college, or university. These organizations usually offer swimming classes for all ages. You may be surprised at how easy it is to learn to swim.

Stress Information

Stress-diversion activities include those activities that can help you manage your stress. Benefits from stress-diversion activities are very personal. If you are highly competitive and concerned with winning or losing, any competitive game or activity may be a stressor. If that is the case, you need to choose a noncompetitive activity as your stress diversion activity.

Table 13-4. Sample Swimming Program

Week	Frequency/Wk	Distance	Time
1	3	300 yds.	12:30
2	3	300 yds.	10:30
3	3	350 yds.	12:00
4	3	350 yds.	12:00
5	4	400 yds.	15:00

Tai Chi

Tai Chi is a very popular Chinese activity for improving flexibility and managing stress. This exercise program includes movements of your head, arms, hands, body, legs, and feet done in coordination with your mind and controlled breathing.

Photodisc

Walking

Walking is a very popular form of aerobic exercise. The biggest advantage to walking is that it can be done easily, without wear and tear on the body. You can walk almost anywhere at almost any time. A sturdy, comfortable pair of shoes is the only equipment necessary. When you are walking for physical fitness, do not stroll in a leisurely manner. Instead, walk at a steady pace brisk enough to make your heart beat faster and cause you to breathe more deeply and rapidly.

Table 13-5. Sample Walking Program

Week	Frequency/Wk	Distance	Time
1	3	1.0 mile	15:00
2	3	1.5 miles	22:30
3	3	2.0 miles	30:00
4	3	2.0 miles	26:40
5	4	2.0 miles	26:40

Nutrition Information

If you engage in a lot of physical activity, you may want to add one or two servings of bread, cereal, rice, or pasta, all of which are high in carbohydrates. If you are very active, you may also want to add one or two servings from the fruit and the vegetable food groups. Remember, when you are no longer as active, you should reduce your servings to meet the normal guidelines.

Learn to reduce fats and sugars added to foods in cooking or at the table. These foods include mayonnaise, butter, margarine, gravy, salad dressing, sour cream, and bacon bits. These foods pack on the extra calories.

Weight Training

Weight training is considered to be the quickest and most effective way to develop muscular strength and muscular endurance. It is a very popular exercise program among men and is gaining popularity among women, as the myths about femininity and muscle-boundness are discredited. Weight training can be done with either free weights or with machines.

Consumer Issues

Much of what you need for exercise is free. Many activities require little or no equipment. Many communities offer free or inexpensive recreation facilities and physical activity classes.

Analysis of Exercise Programs

Different exercise programs have different benefits. Select the programs that are best for you. The contributions of each exercise program to the health-related components of physical fitness and stress diversion are illustrated in Exercise Programs Analysis Table 13–6.

Table 13–6. Exercise Programs Analysis

Exercise Programs	Flexibility	Cardiovascular Fitness	Muscular Strength	Muscular Endurance	Body Composition	Stress Diversion
Aerobic Dance	H	H	L	M	H	H
Aqua Dynamics	M	M	M	M	M	H
Bicycling	L	H	M	H	H	H
Calisthenics	H	L	M	M	L	H
Circuit Training	M	M	M	H	M	H
Fitness Trails	M	M	M	H	M	H
Interval Training	L	H	M	M	H	H
Jogging	L	H	L	M	H	H
Pilates	H	M	H	H	M	H
Rope Jumping	L	H	L	H	H	H
Spinning	L	H	M	H	H	H
Tai Chi	H	L	L	L	L	H
Swimming	M	H	M	H	H	H
Walking	L	M	L	M	M	H
Weight Training	M	L	H	H	L	H

Rating Scale: H—High M—Medium L—Low

Photodisc

Sports activities may supplement more traditional physical fitness activities.

Sports Activities

Sports skills activities are those activities that help you develop sports skills and satisfy your need for competition. Some people prefer to get their exercise through participation in sports activities. Some individuals are more easily motivated by sports activities than by other forms of exercise. Keep in mind that even top athletes supplement their sports training with flexibility, cardiovascular, muscular strength, and muscular endurance programs. Whatever sports activities you choose, you will enjoy them more if you have an adequate level of physical fitness.

Your high-school years are generally oriented to team or group activities, but as you get older you may lose interest in these activities. You may also experience more difficulty finding opportunities to participate in team activities as you get older. That is why it is important to develop skills in individual sports. Individual sports are sometimes called **lifetime sports,** since they can be engaged in for a lifetime. Golf, racquetball, and tennis are examples of such activities. You should develop skills in as many lifetime sports as possible in high school because you can develop new skills more quickly now than later as an adult. Also, the more sports skills you possess, the less limited you will be in your physical activity choices, now and as an adult.

Photodisc

Photodisc

It is important to develop skills in lifetime sports.

Analysis of Sports Activities

Before choosing sports activities to be included in your personal fitness program, you should understand the benefits gained from each activity. Benefits from participation in sports activities vary according to the activity and the skill you possess. Some activities can be very beneficial in meeting your health-related fitness needs if you possess the skill level required to obtain a sufficient workout. The more skill you possess, the greater the benefit will be. Some activities, such as bowling and softball, contribute very little to the development of fitness. Others, such as soccer and basketball, are more conducive to the development of physical fitness.

The contributions of various sports activities on the health-related components of physical fitness and stress diversion are illustrated in Sports Activities Analysis Table 13–7. The contributions to health-related physical fitness are based upon an individual possessing a reasonable level of skill in the activities. The contributions to stress diversion are based on how a majority of people respond.

Considerations Before Selecting Activities

Certain factors should affect your decision about which activities will be most beneficial for your personal fitness program. These factors are listed as follows.

- Health needs
- Sports skills
- Stress diversion

Table 13-7. Sports Activities Analysis

Sports Activities	Flexibility	Cardiovascular Fitness	Muscular Strength	Muscular Endurance	Body Composition	Stress Diversion
Archery	L	L	M	M	L	H
Backpacking/Hiking	L	M	M	H	M	H
Badminton	M	H	L	M	M	M
Basketball	L	H	L	M	H	M
Billiards/Pool	L	L	L	L	L	H
Bowling	L	L	L	L	L	H
Canoeing/Kayaking	L	M	M	H	M	H
Dance (Social)	L	L	L	L	L	H
Diving	H	L	L	L	L	H
Fencing	M	M	L	M	M	L
Football (Flag/Touch)	L	L	L	L	L	M
Golf (Walking)	M	L	L	M	L	H
Gymnastics	H	L	H	H	L	M
Handball/Paddleball/Racquetball	M	H	L	H	H	H
Hockey (Field)	M	M	L	M	M	M
Hockey (Ice)	M	M	L	M	M	M
Horseback Riding	L	L	L	L	L	H
Judo/Karate	H	L	M	M	M	H
Lacrosse	M	M	L	M	M	M
Rock Climbing/Wall Climbing	M	L	H	H	L	H
Rugby	M	H	M	H	M	M
Sailing	L	L	L	L	L	H
Scuba Diving	L	L	L	M	L	H
Skate Boarding	L	M	L	M	L	H
Skating (Ice)	L	M	L	M	M	H
Skating (In-Line)	M	H	L	M	M	H
Skiing (Cross Country)	L	H	M	H	H	H
Skiing (Downhill)	L	M	M	M	L	H
Soccer	M	H	L	M	H	M
Softball	L	L	L	L	L	M
Surfing	L	L	L	M	L	H
Table Tennis	L	L	L	L	L	M
Tennis	M	M	L	M	M	M
Volleyball	M	L	L	L	L	M
Water Polo	M	H	L	H	M	M

Rating Scale: H—High M—Medium L—Low

- Personality and attitudes
- Financial considerations
- Availability of facilities
- Environmental considerations

Photodisc

Regardless of ability, all individuals must consider a number of factors in selecting activities.

Health Needs

How physically fit are you? Which health-related components of physical fitness do you need to improve the most? In order for your personal fitness program to be successful, you must determine your needs by assessing the health-related components of fitness. The component in which you are the weakest should be given the most attention. If, for example, you need to improve your cardiovascular fitness, you should participate in activities that will elevate your pulse rate and maintain it for at least 15 to 30 minutes. Activities such as jogging, bicycling, and swimming, or sports such as basketball and soccer, would be appropriate selections for improving cardiovascular fitness.

You should also consider any health problems or physical impairments you may have before selecting the activities. Swimming, jogging, and bike riding are all excellent ways of improving cardiovascular fitness, but each demands something different from you. An overweight individual might not want to begin jogging because of the strain it could place on the legs and feet. For this individual, walking, swimming, or bicycling may be better choices for improving cardiovascular fitness.

Following are other health needs that must be considered in the selection of activities.

- If you are trying to gain or lose weight, consider the caloric cost of activities.
- As you grow older, your interest in sports will change, the availability of other people for team sports will be less, and the amount of exercise time may decrease.
- If you have a physical disability, this may limit activities in which you are able to participate.
- A health problem may limit the degree to which you engage in vigorous activity. You should select specific activities that will help to improve your problem. For example, do exercises that will strengthen the lower back to prevent low-back pain.

Sports Skills

Your skill level will influence your success and continued participation in sports activities. Some activities require a great deal of skill. You should study the different sports activities to determine which ones are best for you, based on the level of skill you possess. Remember that an activity good for someone else may not be good for you. Try various sports activities, and evaluate them to determine if they are beneficial for you. Determine the skill requirements of the activity, such as agility, balance, power, reaction time, coordination, and speed. For example, if you are very agile and the sport selected requires a high degree of agility, you will be successful. If you experience success, you will be more likely to continue the activity and, therefore, improve your physical fitness.

Corel

Some activities can help you manage your stress.

Stress Diversion

Stress-diversion activities include those activities that can help you manage your stress. Activities that serve as stress diversion may also meet health or sports skills needs. Benefits from stress-diversion activities are very personal. What may be a good stress-diversion activity for you may not be good for your friends. Activities that are highly competitive are usually considered poor stress-diversion activities. However, if you can participate in a competitive activity such as tennis and not be caught up in winning and losing, it could be beneficial to you in controlling your stress.

In the Sports Activities Analysis table, the stress-diversion evaluations are based on how a majority of people respond. The table is meant only as a guide, since stress diversion is a personal matter. In evaluating activities for stress diversion, you must consider how you respond to stress.

Personality and Attitudes

Your personality and attitudes are important factors that should be considered in the selection of activities for your personal fitness program. Do you prefer to exercise alone or with others? Do you prefer to compete with others or only with yourself? Do you prefer activities that are self-directed or coached? Do you prefer to exercise indoors or outdoors?

Photodisc

Your personality and attitudes have a bearing on the activities you select.

Alone or with Others

Some people prefer to be alone with their thoughts during physical activity; some like to exercise with others. Some individuals are more successful in exercising regularly if they exercise with others. A partner, a group of friends, or family members can provide encouragement. Exercising with others may also help develop or reaffirm friendships. However, do not assume that you have to follow your friends' program. Remember that your exercise program must be individualized to meet your needs, or you will not be satisfied.

Competitive or Non-Competitive

Some individuals are highly competitive and prefer activities in which they compete against others. If this describes you, be careful not to let your exercise program become a contest. Exercise at your own level. Some people, on the other hand, do not like competing against others. They prefer to work on their personal fitness program alone by competing with themselves.

Self-Directed or Coached

Some people prefer self-directed activities. These are activities they themselves conduct, such as walking, jogging, or bicycling. Such individuals usually possess internal motivation and enjoy competing with themselves. However, some individuals prefer activities that are conducted or coached by someone else. Such individuals tend to get psyched up by their coaches or instructors.

Photodisc

Some individuals prefer activities in which they compete against others.

Indoors or Outdoors

Exercising outdoors offers variety in scenery and weather. The beauty of the outdoors motivates many people to participate in various activities such as hiking, skiing, sailing, and canoeing. Exercising indoors offers shelter from the weather and the convenience of exercising at home. Some activities, such as rope jumping, can be done indoors or outdoors. Because the activities you choose may be affected by weather, you may want to consider having an alternate time. You can then switch activities when necessary and still stay on your regular exercise schedule.

Financial Considerations

Much of what you need for exercise is free. Many activities require little or no equipment. For example, you can walk and jog at virtually no cost. Many communities offer free or inexpensive recreation facilities and physical activity classes. What you need to purchase will be determined by the kind of activities you include in your personal fitness program. The cost of an activity could be prohibitive, thus eliminating it from consideration.

Availability of Facilities

The availability of facilities should also be considered before selecting activities for your personal fitness program. Swimming is an excellent activity, but if a pool is not available, you need to consider something else. The same thing is true about the other components of your personal fitness program. Which facilities or equipment that can develop muscular strength and endurance do you have access to? You may need to rely on push-ups, sit-ups, and pull-ups, or on free weights if weight machines are not available.

Environmental Considerations

Often the environment is a major factor in determining the type of activity in which to participate. Weather that is either very hot and humid or very cold could influence the type of activity you plan and the time of day you do it. In highly populated areas, air pollution and personal safety are also factors that must be considered.

PFP Technology Activity

Choose a sports activity you think could meet one of your health-related fitness needs. Write a report to include the following: (a) How would you warm up before the activity? (b) How would you apply the principles of training? (c) How would you cool down? Also include what skill-related components of fitness are required in this activity to obtain a sufficient workout. When finished, save the information to your PFP file and/or print out the report and place it in your PFP notebook.

PFP Update

The information in this chapter has provided you with knowledge that will enable you to make sound decisions about the activities you select for your personal fitness program. Some activities can be used to fulfill more than one of your health-related fitness needs. For example, in addition to increasing cardiovascular fitness, jogging builds muscular endurance in the legs, and swimming develops the arm, shoulder and chest muscles. If you select the proper activities, it is possible to fit parts of your muscular endurance workout into your cardiovascular fitness workout and save time.

Choose activities that you think you will enjoy. Most people will stick to their exercise program if they are having fun, even though they are working hard. Vary your exercise program. Change activities or invite friends or family members to join you to make your workout more enjoyable. Remember, there is no "best exercise"—just the one that works best for you.

From the information and confidence you have gained from establishing and following a PFP for an extended period of time, you should have the knowledge and competence to follow a PFP for a lifetime of health. You are equipped with the necessary knowledge not only to help yourself plan a program, but also to help your friends and family members do the same.

Summary

The numbers of exercise programs and sports activities to choose from are virtually endless. An exercise program should be based on the principles of training to assure both benefit and safety. The best activities are those that you enjoy and that also meet your individual needs.

Before choosing exercise programs and sports activities for your personal fitness program, you should understand the benefits gained from each activity. Benefits vary according to the activity and the skill you possess.

In order for your personal fitness program to be successful, you must determine your physical fitness needs. Once you identify your fitness needs, specific activities can be selected for the various health-related components in need of improvement. Health problems, sports skills, stress diversion, personality and attitudes, cost, availability of facilities, and environment are also factors that affect your selection of activities. The key to developing a successful personal fitness program is designing a program that is right for you.

Photodisc

The Wrap-Up

Vocabulary Matching

Match the definitions to the correct term.

1. Planned program

2. High-impact aerobics

3. Low-impact aerobics

4. Calisthenics

5. Circuit training

6. Interval training

7. Sports skills activities

8. Lifetime sports

A. exercises in which body parts or body weight is the resistance

B. exercise program involving a series of exercises interspersed with rest periods

C. activities that help you develop sports skills and satisfy your need for competition

D. predetermined programs that usually include specific exercises for persons of specific fitness levels or ages

E. exercise that includes vigorous arm movements, while keeping one foot in contact with the ground at all times

F. individual sports that can be engaged in for a lifetime

G. exercise program in which you move around a prescribed course, stopping at stations along the way to perform specified exercises

H. exercise that includes jumping, bouncing, and running

Multiple Choice

Select the most correct answer:

9. When selecting activities for your personal fitness program, choose those
- **A.** selected by friends so you have someone with whom to exercise.
- **B.** that best meet your needs.
- **C.** that you like the most.
- **D.** that include all of the above.

10. Which item is an example of a planned exercise program?
- **A.** aerobic workout videotape
- **B.** bicycling
- **C.** fitness trails
- **D.** A and C

11. Which exercise program is considered to be the quickest and most effective way to develop muscular strength and muscular endurance?
A. calisthenics
B. circuit training
C. swimming
D. weight training

12. Which exercise program is least effective for developing cardiovascular fitness?
A. aerobic dance
B. bicycling
C. rope jumping
D. weight training

13. Which activity would provide the greatest benefit for flexibility?
A. backpacking/hiking
B. basketball
C. cross country skiing
D. gymnastics

14. Which activity would provide the greatest benefit for cardiovascular fitness?
A. football
B. judo
C. soccer
D. volleyball

15. Which item should be considered when selecting activities for your personal fitness program?
A. health needs
B. sports skills
C. stress diversion
D. all of the above

16. Which item would provide the greatest benefit for stress diversion?
A. backpacking/hiking
B. racquetball
C. softball
D. tennis

17. When you exercise with a friend, you should
A. choose the same activities.
B. each exercise at your own level.
C. exercise at the same level.
D. race to see who is the fastest.

18. The key to developing a successful personal fitness program is
  A. designing a program like that of your friends.
  B. designing a program that is right for you.
  C. participating in planned programs.
  D. participating in sports activities.

Authentic Assessment—Short Response

19. What are the advantages of planned exercise programs?

20. Why is walking a popular form of aerobic exercise?

21. Why should you be physically fit before participating in a sport?

22. What are the factors you should consider when selecting activities for your personal fitness program?

23. What is the value of exercising with a friend?

Authentic Assessment—Extended Response

24. **Writing situation:** Before choosing activities to be included in your personal fitness program, you should understand the benefits gained from each activity.

    Directions for writing: Rate each of the following activities either good, average or poor regarding their contribution to cardiovascular fitness. Illustrate your ratings in a bar graph and explain why you rated the activities as you did.

aerobic dance	basketball	bowling
golf	jogging	cross country skiing
swimming	weight training	karate
backpacking	bicycling	canoeing
football	handball	volleyball

25. **Writing situation:** Anna recognizes that she needs to improve her cardiovascular fitness and muscular strength. She has fairly good sports skills. Anna enjoys the outdoors. She likes to participate in activities with friends and with other people.

    Directions for writing: Identify activities you think would best meet Anna's needs. Explain why you selected these activities.

Photodisc

14 Designing Your Own Program

Objectives

As you read this chapter, look for answers to these key questions:

- What are the physical fitness components that you should address when designing your personal fitness program?
- What should you consider when beginning a fitness program?
- What are the steps in designing a personal fitness program?
- What motivational strategies may help you keep your program going?

"You cannot hope for success, you've got to plan for it."

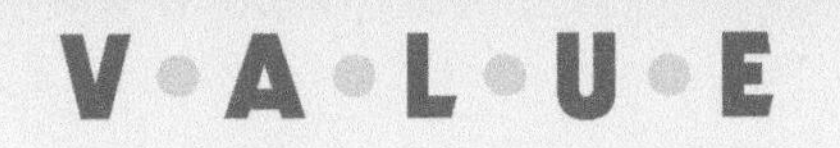

V•A•L•U•E

The information in this chapter will assist you in designing a personal fitness program that will help you achieve all the benefits of a personal fitness program. You will not be dependent on going to a fitness center and paying someone to help you. This chapter will provide you guidelines that will allow you to develop a balanced fitness program that includes the health-related components of fitness, nutrition, sleep, and stress management; program that will assist you in looking good and feeling good.

Chapter Preview

- Developing a Total Personal Fitness Program
- Starting Your Program
- Designing Your Personal Fitness Program
- Steps in Designing Vanessa's Personal Fitness Program
- Keep It Going
- PFP Update
- Summary
- The Wrap-Up

Vocabulary

When you have completed this chapter, you should understand the meaning of these vocabulary terms:

lifestyle choices

periodic assessment

Wellness Connection

Develop a Total Personal Fitness Program

When you hear people talk about a physical fitness program, the image that probably forms in your mind is of someone either running, swimming, or lifting weights. Although each of these activities is a good fitness activity, that image or picture is not a complete one. A single vigorous exercise is only one element of a total Personal Fitness Program (PFP). This approach usually results in an exercise program that does not develop all of the health-related components of physical fitness and may not be safe. Your personal program should be one that results in you looking good and feeling good. A well-rounded personal fitness program is made up of several components that require personal lifestyle choices to help you become a winner.

At this point in the course, you have all the information you need to make the necessary decisions about your Personal Fitness Program. Each chapter has given you information that you can use to make choices. You have been given information about assessment, and in most cases, alternative methods that you can choose. You have been provided the information about assessment of the health-related components of fitness, body composition, nutrition, and stress. If you have completed all of the chapters, you may already have all of the components of your Personal Fitness Program planned.

Photodisc

This chapter is to serve as a guide to help you plan, modify or assess your PFP. In addition, it will assist for you in putting together all of the components of your program that you have worked on, into one product. This chapter takes you through the steps with a typical teenager as she develops her program. Follow along with your own planning, keeping what you have already developed, modifying when you want, and if you missed one component, developing that component for yourself along with Vanessa.

Starting Your Program

Basic guidelines to follow when beginning a personal fitness program include (a) determining the need for a medical examination, (b) conducting a physical fitness evaluation, (c) setting realistic goals, and (d) selecting activities that help you reach those goals. Keep in mind that you have personal choices to make based on your lifestyle. Your choices should be your own, not the choices of your friends or family.

Above all, you should make sure your personal fitness program includes all of the health-related components of physical fitness. You must decide if you want to improve each component of physical fitness, or if you only want to improve one or two components while maintaining the others. You might want to lose a few pounds or you might want to become stronger. Any personal fitness program decision you make should be based on your physical fitness assessment.

Designing Your Personal Fitness Program

Now is the time to begin putting your own personal fitness program into action, using what you have already developed, modifying where needed, or developing an entirely new plan. Your current level of physical fitness should be the basis for designing your future program. Use your physical fitness test scores to establish goals. Evaluation of your current level of physical fitness is essential for a number of reasons. It is important to know what your level of fitness is in each of the health-related components of physical fitness. Once you have this information, you will be able to make good decisions, set realistic goals, design an exercise program that will bring about improvement, and use baseline data to periodically evaluate the level of improvement.

Based on your physical fitness test scores and your goals, begin designing each element of a total personal fitness program. Set realistic goals. If your physical fitness level is very low, it will take time to condition your muscles, ligaments, and other parts of your body without causing injury.

A beneficial exercise program must follow the principles of training. You should apply the principles of overload, progression, and specificity that you learned about earlier in this book. Your exercise program should be designed to overload the body systems that you want to improve. It must progressively demand more of those body systems and will only improve the specific part of the body that it was designed to benefit.

Goal Setting

What do you hope your physical self-image will be like in five years? In most cases, hoping for a particular body composition will not do the job. You will need to be a continual goal setter, if you are to realize your desired goals related to your physical self in five years. There is little doubt that you will get what you want if you establish an on-going physically active and dynamic lifestyle.

SAFETY AWARNESS

The most dangerous bicycle accidents are those that involve collisions with motor vehicles. Such accidents occur at intersections and are primarily the result of the bicyclist not obeying traffic laws.

In order to design a sound personal fitness program, you should follow these specific steps:

1. Evaluation
2. Goal setting
3. Selection of activities
4. Application of training principles in program design
5. Periodic assessment

To help guide you in the process of designing your own program, look at the following example of a typical high-school student. Study her physical fitness scores, lifestyle, realistic goals, and common-sense approach in meeting those goals. Go through this process with Vanessa to develop your own program. Using what you have already developed in each chapter, revise what you choose and develop along with Vanessa those components that you did not have an opportunity to do when you covered a specific topic.

Steps in Designing Vanessa's Personal Fitness Program

Vanessa was a 15-year-old ninth-grader who had never been very active. She spent a lot of time watching television, wishing she had the energy to learn how to play tennis and participate in some of the other activities her classmates enjoyed. Even though Vanessa enjoyed swimming, she was a little overweight and felt self-conscious in a bathing suit.

Emmanouel G. Harageones

Evaluation

All students in physical education classes were given a physical fitness test during the first two weeks of school. Vanessa recorded her physical fitness test scores on the form provided: (1) cardiovascular fitness-mile run, 14:00 minutes; (2) flexibility, 18 centimeter; (3) sit-ups, 17; (4) pull-ups, 0; (5) body composition, 44 millimeter.

Goal Setting

After the class had taken the first physical fitness test, Vanessa's teacher sat down with the students and talked about setting personal goals. The teacher emphasized that the students should compare their results only to themselves. This sparked an interest in Vanessa because she thought she could be successful if all she had to do was compete with herself.

Health-Related Fitness Profile

NAME Vanessa **AGE** 15 **CLASS** 2nd Period

Body Weight: ____ pounds ____ kilograms Height: ____ feet/inches ____ meters

Fitness Components	Test Item	Test #1 Date	Health Fitness Standard	Goal	Test #2 Date
Flexibility	Sit and Reach	18 cm	25 cm	24 cm	
Cardiovascular	One-Mile Run	1400	1030	1030	
Abdominal Strength/Endurance	Sit-ups	17	34	37	
Upper Body Strength/Endurance	Pull-ups	0	1	1	
Body Composition	Skinfolds				
	1. Tricep	29			
	2. Calf	15			
	Sum of 1 & 2	44 cm	15–35	34	

With help from the teacher, Vanessa developed both short-term and long-term goals to provide direction for her personal fitness program. For the final step in goal setting, she wrote down what she thought would be the benefits of accomplishing these goals:

Emmanouel G. Harageones

Walking and jogging are excellent cardiovascular exercises.

1. Improved appearance
2. Improved self-concept
3. Better posture
4. Improved cardiovascular endurance
5. Improved muscular endurance
6. Improved upper body strength

To keep herself motivated, Vanessa made a poster for her room listing the benefits she would obtain from her Personal Fitness Program.

Selection of Activities

The next step for Vanessa was to decide on the activities in which she would like to participate. Using the Exercise Programs and

Sports Activities Analysis charts in Chapter 13, Vanessa compared the health-related benefits of each activity to her physical fitness goals. For example, she wanted to improve her cardiovascular fitness, so she reviewed those activities that were rated high in this component of physical fitness. Vanessa then considered her personality, attitudes, cost of activities, availability of facilities, and environmental conditions under which she would exercise. Based on all of these factors, Vanessa selected activities that would help her reach her personal fitness goals.

Evaluation of Activities

NAME Vanessa AGE 15 CLASS Second Period

Activities	HR/SR	CV	Flex	Mus Str	Mus End	Body Com
	Components					
Riding Bicycle	HR	X			some	some
Walk/Jog	HR	X			X	X
Stretching Exercise	HR		X			
Negative Pullups	HR			X	X	
Sit-ups	HR			X	X	

Internet Resources

Just Move!—American Heart Association
http://www.justmove.org

On Line Activity Log—The Center for Health and Health Care in Schools
http://www.healthinschools.org/2003/july18_alert.asp

National Association of Governor's Councils on Physical Fitness and Sports
http://www.fitnesslink.com/Govcouncil/

Nutrition Information

Include a nutrition plan and appropriate amount of water consumption as part of your Personal Fitness Program.

Application of Training Principles in Designing a Program

Vanessa's next step was to apply the training principles to the activities she had selected. Using the information she had learned in class, Vanessa was able to personalize her program by applying the principles of overload, progression, and specificity.

Cardiovascular Goal Setting

Table 14–1. Test Score: Mile Run = 14:00 Minutes

Goal: To run the mile in 10 minutes and 30 seconds on the post-test

Cardiovascular Goal Setting			
	Distance from Health Fitness Standard		
	Less	Close	Exceeds
Difference between Test Score and Health Fitness Standard	2 minutes+	0–2 minutes	0 or better
Recommended Range for Goals	30 seconds to 5 minutes	15 seconds to 90 seconds	0 to 45 seconds

First, Vanessa designed an exercise program that would help her improve cardiovascular fitness. She decided to ride her bicycle to school each day, rather than ride in the car with her father. She did not expect to ride her bicycle at a pace that would allow her heart rate to reach the lower level of her target heart rate zone of 137 beats per minute. Nor would the one-mile distance provide her sufficient time for aerobic training. However, biking the one mile to and from school each day would improve muscular endurance in her legs and help her reach her cardiovascular fitness goal. See Table 14–1.

STRESS INFORMATION

Learn to identify the source of your anger. Whenever you become angry, take a minute to focus on why you are angry. This will make it easier for you to identify the source of frustration and what the appropriate reaction should be.

She had learned that she needed to exercise at least 3 days a week (frequency), at 60 to 90 percent of her maximum heart rate (intensity), for at least 20 minutes (time) to obtain all of the aerobic benefits. Vanessa decided she would walk/jog 3 days a week as soon as she got home from school. Her plan was to begin slowly, since she knew she was not in very good condition, based on her physical fitness test score. Therefore, in designing her program, she chose to start with low intensity for a short period of time.

Her goal for the first 2 weeks would be to walk one mile as fast as she could (intensity). After the first 2 weeks, she would begin to walk and jog 1 mile, and then continue walking until she had been exercising for 30 minutes (time). She decided to jog slowly for one block, walk fast for one block, and continue alternating jogging and walking for 1 mile. She would do this for at least 4 weeks.

After 4 weeks of alternating jogging and walking, Vanessa thought she would be in good enough shape to try to jog for a full mile, walk for a short distance, and then jog some more. After completing this routine, she would again continue walking fast until she had exercised for 30 minutes. By the end of 3 months, she hoped to be able to jog 2 miles at a steady pace. After she had reached that level of fitness, her goal for the rest of the semester would be to continue exercising for 30 minutes, 3 days a week, progressively increasing her pace and the distance covered. See Table 14–2.

Table 14-2. Cardiovascular Training Program

	Bicycling	Walk/jog
(F) **Number of sessions per week**	10*	3
(I) **Target heart rate for 10 seconds**	23–31	24–28
(T) **Length of session**	1 mile/10 mins.	30 mins.

*Includes riding to and from school five days a week.

Flexibility Goal Setting

Table 14-3. Test Score: Sit-and-Reach Test = 18 cm

Goal: To obtain a score of 24 cm on the post-test	Flexibility		
	Distance from Health Fitness Standard		
	Less	Close	Exceeds
Difference between Test Score and Health Fitness Standard	More than 10 cm	1–10 cm	At or above standard
Recommended Range for Goals	5–15 cm	1–4 cm	0–2 cm

Next, Vanessa looked at flexibility. She would have to do stretching exercises, since she was not skilled at any other type of activity that could improve her flexibility. Her initial goal was to improve her fitness test score in the sit-and-reach test. Her teacher had said that they should warm up by stretching before they exercise, and repeat those same stretches in their cool-down. Vanessa decided she might as well do a warm-up,

Stretching exercises should be included in your exercise program not only to improve flexibility, but as part of your warm-up and cool-down to reduce the chance of injury or soreness.

Emmanouel G. Haragoenes

work on her flexibility, and cool down in each workout session. See Table 14–3.

She decided to add a 5-minute stretching session (time) to her warm-up and cool-down for all 5 days (frequency) of planned exercise. She selected 10 stretching exercises and planned on holding each one for 15 seconds. Each exercise would be performed as one repetition for three sets. Her goal would be to work toward holding the stretches longer and, hopefully, to be able to do 30-second stretches by the end of the semester. See Table 14–4.

Table 14–4. Flexibility Training Program

	Routine of 10 static stretches
(F) **Number of sessions per week**	10*
(I) **Length of stretch**	point of slight discomfort
(T) **Time of stretch**	15 sec./3 sets/per exercise

*Includes warm-up and cool-down 5 days a week

Muscular Strength Goal Setting

Table 14–5. Test Score: Pull-Ups = 0

Goal: To be able to perform 1 pull-up by the post-test

Goal Setting for Upper Body Strength	Distance from Health Fitness Standard		
	Less	Close	Exceeds
Difference between Test Score and Health Fitness Standard	More than 1	1–2	at or better
Recommended Range for Goals	1–3	2–5	1–3

Consumer Issues

Before joining a fitness center, call several to compare cost, as well as services offered. Visit two or three centers to be sure that the staff is well trained and the equipment is in good repair.

Vanessa's teacher had told her that she should place more emphasis on muscular endurance than on muscular strength if she wanted to improve muscle tone and decrease her percentage of body fat. However, since Vanessa was unable to perform even one pull-up on the physical fitness test, she realized she had a long way to go before she could lift her body weight. Vanessa's teacher had described different exercises that could be used to improve her muscular strength, including weight training. She was going to have to exercise at school, since she did not have any way to do pull-ups at home. Vanessa chose to use negative pull-ups to help her reach her goal of one pull-up. See Table 14–5.

Vanessa decided to work on this component of physical fitness each day at the beginning of class (frequency). She would begin by doing three negative pull-ups, trying to make each last for 5 seconds (intensity) and trying to work up to five (time). See Table 14–6.

Table 14–6. Muscular Strength Program

	Negative Pull-ups
(F) Number of sessions per week	5
(I) Resistance	body weight/5-second count
(T) Length of session	3–5 repetitions

Muscular Endurance Goal Setting

Table 14–7. Test Score: Sit-Ups = 17

Goal: To be able to do 37 by the post-test

Goal Setting for Abdominal Strength and Endurance	Distance from Health Fitness Standard		
	Less	Close	Exceeds
Difference between Test Score and Health Fitness Standard	More than 15	1–15	0 or better
Recommended Range for Goals	5–15	2–10	1–4

Designing a program to help her reach her muscular endurance goal was Vanessa's next task. See Table 14–7. She knew that none of the activities she had picked would help her abdominal muscles. The best thing to do was sit-ups, even though she did not enjoy doing them. Vanessa wanted to do as few as possible

Sit-ups, like push-ups, may be modified in different ways to increase or decrease their difficulty.

Emmanouel G. Harageones

to reach her goal. She decided to do one set (time) of maximum sit-ups (intensity) three nights a week (frequency) before going to bed. By the middle of the semester, she would have to reach 27 sit-ups or make an adjustment in her activity level. Her physical education teacher agreed with her assessment. See Table 14–8.

Table 14–8. Muscular Endurance Program

	Sit-ups
(F) **Number of sessions per week**	3
(I) **Resistance**	Body weight using regular sit-ups
(T) **Length of session**	1 set of maximum sit-ups

Body Composition Goal Setting

Table 14–9. Test Score: Skin-fold measurement = 44 mm

Goal: To have a body composition measurement of 34 mm by the time of the post-test

	Body Composition		
	Distance from Health Fitness Standard		
	Less	Close	Exceeds
Difference between Test Score and Health Fitness Standard	More than 10 mm	1–10 mm	0 or better
Recommended Range for Goals	1–15 mm	1–10 mm	1–3 mm

How could Vanessa cut calories without eliminating the food she liked to eat?

Emmanouel G. Harageones

Body composition was the last component of physical fitness Vanessa had to address. Vanessa liked to eat, but she knew she had to cut down a little on her intake. She was consuming an average of 2,400 calories per day, or 16,800 per week. However, Vanessa's daily activity level required only 2,143 calories, or 15,000 per week. The extra 1,800 calories per week were being stored in her body as fat. See Table 14–9.

Vanessa tried to eat additional servings of vegetables when available.

Emmanouel G. Harageones

Since she had been sitting around and watching a lot of television, the exercise program that she designed would help her body composition. How could she cut calories without eliminating any of the foods she liked to eat? After reading some examples that her teacher had handed out, Vanessa got an idea. Why not cut out the butter and mayonnaise that she used every day? One little pat of butter had 70 calories, and one tablespoon of mayonnaise had 100 calories. Vanessa determined that she could reduce her caloric intake by 200 calories per day without giving up any food. She liked that idea.

The personal fitness program that Vanessa designed would greatly improve her body composition. Although she occasionally engaged in physical activity, she did not burn as many calories as she took in. Using the calorie expenditure formula and the chart on Caloric Costs of Activities in Chapter 10, Vanessa calculated that she could burn an additional 272 calories per day, or approximately 1,900 calories per week. This would result in her expending 1,500 calories more than she took in. See Table 14–10.

Table 14–10. Body Composition

Calories Taken In		Calories Burned	
Present # of calories consumed each week	16,800	Present # of calories burned each week	−15,000
Planned calorie reduction each week	−1,400	Additional calories burned in exercise	− 1,900
	15,400		−16,900
	Total excess calories burned each week = 1,500 caloric reduction		

The additional calories burned each week and the planned calorie reduction would allow Vanessa to lose one-half pound of body weight per week, or approximately 2 pounds per month. During the next 16 weeks, Vanessa would lose 8 pounds, or approximately 26 pounds in a year. One year seemed a long way off. However, Vanessa had learned in class that if she wanted to permanently lose body weight, she had to change her lifestyle and not depend on fad diets.

Nutrition

Vanessa knew that a good personal fitness program should include a good nutritional plan. When the class covered nutrition in Chapter 9, the teacher had them keep a personal diet diary, and analyze their diet using MyPyramid. Based on that analysis, they developed a nutritional plan. She knew that she ate too much fat, red meat, and starches. She did not eat the total number of servings from vegetables and fruits that she could have based on what her family had available. She decided to implement the nutritional plan that she developed for Chapter 9.

Her plan called for her to eat an additional serving of vegetables at each meal when they were available. She would also take at least one piece of fruit with her to school each day for a snack. The third goal in her nutritional plan was to decrease the amount of fat and red meat that she consumed. She had already planned to cut out some butter and mayonnaise in her personal fitness plan. In addition to this, she would cut down on fast foods that she now ate.

Water

Water is an essential element that the body needs. Vanessa drank very little water, with most of her fluid intake being made up of soft drinks, fruit juices, and milk. Since she was beginning an exercise program, adequate water consumption was even more important. She would continue to drink the same amount of milk, reduce the amount of fruit juice, and substitute a glass of water for a soft drink twice a day. Additionally, she would drink a glass of water immediately before she did her cardiovascular walk/run, and another glass when she had completed her workout.

Emmanouel G. Harageones

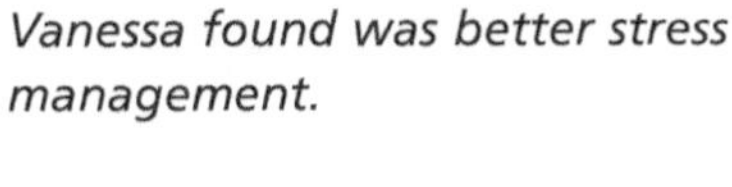

One benefit of improved fitness Vanessa found was better stress management.

Stress Management

Vanessa's grades were above average, and her home life was stable. She got along with her brother and sisters fairly well, and she found it easy to talk with her parents. What stress Vanessa did have was the result of her interaction with her peers. Since many of the activities she had selected were stress-diversion activities, she planned to use those activities for **stress management**. She would also use the benefits of improved fitness to manage her stress. In addition, she identified some of her weaknesses and developed goals and a plan of action for self-improvement.

Sleep

Vanessa liked to watch television, and often stayed up late at night watching her favorite shows. She had learned in class that insufficient sleep could cause a student problems. Her teacher had said that all teenagers should get at least 8 to 9 hours of sleep. She was not getting that much every night. She decided to videotape some of her favorite television shows that came on late, and watch them at a different time. She set as a goal to be in bed by 10 P.M. That would allow her to get nine hours of sleep and still be able to get up early enough in the morning to get her chores done and get ready for school. Since she was beginning to be more physically active, she figured she would be tired and not have a problem going to sleep at the time she had set.

Periodic Assessment

Vanessa built short-term goals into her program that could be used as targets to help her periodically assess her progress toward her long-term goals. She would time herself in the mile run halfway through the semester, with her goal being 12:15. This would put her halfway to her long-term goal of being able to complete the mile run in 10:30.

Vanessa had her own program and goals; she was competing only against herself.

Emmanouel G. Harageones

In order to test her flexibility, Vanessa asked her physical education teacher if she could occasionally use the sit-and-reach box to test her progress. She decided to check her flexibility once a month. She knew her goal was slightly more than touching her toes. This information allowed her to monitor her rate of improvement without having to use the sit-and-reach box daily.

Vanessa had a long way to go before reaching her ultimate goal of being able to do one pull-up on the physical fitness test. She decided that she would try to do a regular pull-up once a week, prior to doing her sets of negative pull-ups.

Since she was going to do the maximum number she could perform, the sit-up workouts would be self-testing. She would be able to determine her progress each day.

She decided to use a combination of ways to monitor her body composition. She would weigh herself once a week, use the mirror test, ask her teacher to take her skin-fold once a month, and let the fit of her clothes serve as the final judge.

Vanessa understood the importance of managing stress. She set aside thirty minutes each week to evaluate her stress level.

Reflecting on the week's activities would allow her to make modifications in her stress management program.

Periodic assessment was going to be a lot of record keeping, but Vanessa thought that it could be fun and that she would be successful. Vanessa and her physical education teacher thought that the goals she had set were realistic and challenging. Her teacher also agreed that the planned personal fitness program would allow her to reach those goals. Vanessa was not sure she could reach her goals, but she was sure of one thing: she was tired of being embarrassed because she was in such poor condition. This was her program, her goals, and she was competing only against herself.

Keep It Going

Starting an exercise program is not a difficult task. People do it every day. In fact, it is so easy that some individuals start a program 6 to 10 times a year. The difficulty is continuing the program and making it a part of your lifestyle. This problem is almost always mental, seldom physical.

Photodisc

Plan for a variety of activities.

Fight Boredom with Variety

Boredom is possibly the biggest threat to an exercise program. You must build those elements into your program that will continue to interest you and motivate you to exercise regularly. Variety is a must. Plan for a variety of activities, a variety of people with whom you exercise, and a variety of places in which you exercise. If you only jog, you may want to jog different distances over different courses at different times of the day.

Exercise with a Friend

Most people are sociable individuals and like the social interaction provided by certain types of exercise. Ride your bike with people you enjoy being around. Play tennis with people whose company you enjoy. Make your self-improvement program a social activity whenever possible.

Keep Records

Record keeping and periodic evaluation can also be motivating. You should not depend on remembering the amount of the weight lifted, the number of repetitions completed, the distance covered, or the elapsed time. Writing down your performance provides you with objective measurements to help you monitor your progress. Your records will help you in setting new goals, modifying your program, and avoiding injuries. The type of information that you might want to record includes date, number of repetitions and sets, resistance, resting heart rate, exercise heart rate, distance covered, time required, weekly distance, and cumulative distance since the start of the program.

You might want to test your skills periodically against people who are better than you. Enter a road race, a tennis tournament, or a racquetball tournament. Compare the results with your previous efforts to determine how you are doing.

Make a commitment to looking good and feeling good. Make a commitment to exercising on a regular basis. Make lifestyle choices that will make you a winner.

PFP Technology Activity

Update your database with your latest health-related test scores. Develop charts showing improvement made in your post scores, as compared to your pre-test scores. Using a word processing software, write a summary of your progress, reflecting on your self-concept at the beginning of the course. State how you feel about yourself today, as compared to when you began your Personal Fitness Program. In addition, identify new goals and strategies for continuing the positive habits of a healthy lifestyle. Share your completed PFP with family members so they too can live a longer and happier life.

PFP Update

If you have followed the PFP updates at the end of each chapter, you should have your program almost complete and have established healthy lifestyle habits. At this point, you should not feel dependent on having to go to a fitness center and pay someone to help you develop a PFP. As a result of this course, you have the knowledge to do it on your own. Keeping your program up to date and putting it into practice will have an impact on how much you enjoy life, as well as how long you live. On your fortieth birthday, write your teacher to let him/her know this truly was the most important course you took in high school.

Summary

A total fitness program should include: (1) physical activities that increase health-related fitness components, (2) nutrition, (3) sleep, and (4) stress management. When making decisions about your personal program, you must take into account a number of factors, including assessment of your current level of physical fitness. You might want to design a program for improving specific health-related components of physical fitness based on your test results, while only maintaining other components.

You should follow five basic steps before beginning your physical fitness program: (1) evaluate your current level of physical fitness; (2) set goals; (3) select activities needed to improve your level of physical fitness; (4) design your fitness program based on the training principles; and (5) plan periodic assessment of your progress.

Start a physical fitness program and continue to make it a part of your daily routine. Fight boredom with variety. To be a winner, make a commitment to lifestyle choices that will aid you in looking good and feeling good.

Corel

The Wrap-Up

Vocabulary Matching

Place the letter of the correct answer in the place provided.

1. Lifestyle choices

2. Periodic assessment

A. decisions you make regarding the way you lead and conduct your life

B. scheduled evaluation of short-term goals

Multiple Choice

Choose the most correct answer.

3. In designing your total fitness program, you should be concerned with
- A. good nutrition, the programs of your friends, and health-related and sports skills activities.
- B. health-related, sleep, and stress-management, and good nutrition.
- C. sports skills and stress-diversion activities, good nutrition, and the programs of your friends.
- D. stress-diversion and health-related activities, good nutrition, and the programs of your friends.

4. Beginning a program by simply starting to jog with a friend usually results in a program that
- A. is safe and balanced.
- B. meets your personal needs.
- C. may cause soreness or injury.
- D. will motivate you to continue.

5. The most important thing you should consider when making decisions about your fitness program should be
- A. financial concerns.
- B. the environment.
- C. what friends are doing.
- D. your personal needs.

6. Which basic principle of training should you follow in order to improve your level of fitness?
- A. overload
- B. progression
- C. specificity
- D. all of the above

7. What is the first step in designing your personal fitness program?
   A. determine basic guidelines
   B. evaluate fitness level
   C. goal setting
   D. selection of activities

8. The reason you should monitor your heart rate during exercise is to properly apply the overload variable of
   A. frequency.
   B. intensity.
   C. specificity.
   D. time.

9. The reason why Vanessa did not include sports skills activities in her program was that she
   A. believed her fitness level was too high.
   B. did not enjoy sports.
   C. did not have enough skill.
   D. thought they were too easy.

10. Vanessa decided to work on her cardiovascular fitness 3 days a week. In making that decision, she was applying the overload variable of
   A. intensity.
   B. frequency.
   C. specificity.
   D. time.

11. Once Vanessa could jog 2 miles at a steady pace, she planned to slowly increase her pace and distance. By doing this, she would be applying which principle of training?
   A. frequency
   B. overload
   C. progression
   D. specification

12. Vanessa planned to reach her goal for body composition by
   A. dieting only.
   B. exercising only.
   C. exercising and dieting.
   D. none of the above.

Authentic Assessment—Short Response

13. What are the key decisions you should make before beginning a personal fitness program?

14. How should health-related activities, sports skill activities, and stress-diversion activities be used in developing your total personal fitness program?

15. What basic guidelines should be used in developing your personal fitness program?

16. Identify and explain the key steps that you should go through in designing your personal fitness program.

17. What should you do to motivate yourself to continue your personal fitness program?

Authentic Assessment—Extended Response

18. **Writing situation:** Kathy is considering starting a personal fitness program.

Directions for writing: Briefly explain what steps Kathy should take prior to beginning her fitness program, and why these steps should be taken?

19. **Writing situation:** Clay is a 15-year-old ninth-grader. He has never been very active, and spends a lot of time watching television, watching sports, and wishing he could be a great athlete. His physical education class took a physical fitness test during the first week of school. Clay's score on the fitness test items were (a) cardiovascular: 14:05 for the mile run;
(b) flexibility: 13 centimeter for the sit-and reach;
(c) muscular strength and endurance: 5 sit-ups, 0 pull-ups;
(d) body composition: skinfold of 44 mm.

Directions for writing: What advice would you give Clay about his cardiovascular fitness program?

Appendices

Appendix A
Assessment Standards

Health Fitness Standards Chart

Males												
Age	13		14		15		16		17		17+	
HFZ	Lower	Upper	Lower	Upper	Lower	Upper	Lower	Upper	Lower	Upper	Lower	Upper
FLEXIBILITY												
Trunk Lift (inches)	9	12	9	12	9	12	9	12	9	12	9	12
Back Saver Sit-and-Reach** (inches)	8		8		8		8		8		8	
Shoulder Stretch	Passing = touching fingertips together behind the back											
V-Sit Reach (inches)	1		1		1		1		1			
Sit-and-Reach (centimeters)	21		21		21		21		21			
CARDIOVASCULAR												
PACER (# laps)	41	72	41	83	51	94	61	94	61	94	61	94
One-Mile Run (min:sec)	10:00	7:30	9:30	7:00	9:00	7:00	8:30	7:00	8:30	7:00	8:30	7:00
One-Mile Run (min:sec)	8:00		8:00		7:30		7:30		7:30			
MUSCULAR STRENGTH AND ENDURANCE												
Curl-Up (# complete)	21	40	24	45	24	47	24	47	24	47	24	47
Partial Curl-Up (# complete)	25		25		30		30		30			
Pull-Up (# complete)	1	4	2	5	3	7	5	8	5	8	5	8
Pull-Up (# complete)	2		3		4		5		6			
Flexed Arm Hang (seconds)	12	17	15	20	15	20	15	20	15	20	15	20
Push-Up (# complete)	12	25	14	30	16	35	18	35	18	35	18	35
Push-Up (# complete)	10		12		14		16		18			
BODY COMPOSITION												
Skinfold Measurement (% fat)	25	10	25	10	25	10	25	10	25	10	25	10
Body Mass Index	23	16.6	24.5	17.5	25	18.1	26.5	18.5	27	18.8	27.8	19
Body Mass Index	24.7	15.4	25.4	16.1	26.4	16.6	26.8	17.2	27.5	17.7		

* Number on left is lower end of HFZ; number on right is upper end of HFZ.
** Test scored Pass/Fail; must reach this distance to pass.
*** Non-shaded rows—source: With permission from The Cooper Institute for Aerobics Research, *Fitnessgram Test Administration Manual* (Dallas, TX: 1999), 38.
****Shaded rows—source: With permission from The President's Council on Physical Fitness and Sports, *The President's Challenge* (Bloomington, IN, 2002–2003), 23.

Health Fitness Standards Chart

Females

Age	13		14		15		16		17		17+	
HFZ	Lower	Upper	Lower	Upper	Lower	Upper	Lower	Upper	Lower	Upper	Lower	Upper
FLEXIBILITY												
Trunk Lift (inches)	9	12	9	12	9	12	9	12	9	12	9	12
Back Saver Sit-and-Reach** (inches)	10		10		12		12		12		12	
Shoulder Stretch	Passing = touching fingertips together behind the back											
V-Sit Reach (inches)	3		3		3		3		3			
Sit-and-Reach (centimeters)	25		25		25		25		25			
CARDIOVASCULAR												
PACER (# laps)	23	51	23	51	23	51	32	61	41	61	41	61
One-Mile Run (min:sec)	11:30	9:00	11:00	8:30	10:30	8:00	10:00	8:00	10:00	8:00	10:00	8:00
One-Mile Run (min:sec)	10:30		10:30		10:00		10:00		10:00			
MUSCULAR STRENGTH AND ENDURANCE												
Curl-Up (# complete)	18	32	18	32	18	35	18	35	18	35	18	35
Partial Curl-Up (# complete)	25		25		30		30		30			
Pull-Up (# complete)	1	2	1	2	1	2	1	2	1	2	1	2
Pull-Up (# complete)	1		1		1		1		1			
Flexed Arm Hang (seconds)	8	12	8	12	8	12	8	12	8	12	8	12
Push-Up (# complete)	7	15	7	15	7	15	7	15	7	15	7	15
Push-Up (# complete)	7		7		7		7		7			
BODY COMPOSITION												
Skinfold Measurement (% fat)	32	17	32	17	32	17	32	17	32	17	32	17
Body Mass Index	24.5	17.5	25	17.5	25	17.5	25	17.5	26	17.5	27.3	18
Body Mass Index	25.3	15.5	25.3	16.2	26.5	16.6	26.5	16.8	26.9	17.1		

* Number on left is lower end of HFZ; number on right is upper end of HFZ.
** Test scored Pass/Fail; must reach this distance to pass.
*** Non-shaded rows—source: With permission from The Cooper Institute for Aerobics Research, *Fitnessgram Test Administration Manual* (Dallas, TX: 1999), 39.
****Shaded rows—source: With permission from The President's Council on Physical Fitness and Sports, *The President's Challenge* (Bloomington, IN, 2002–2003), 23.

Appendix B
Goal Setting

Setting Goals to Improve Flexibility

	Distance from Health Fitness Standard		
	Less	Close	Exceeds
Difference between Test Score and Health Fitness Standard	More than 10 cm	1 to 10 cm	At or above standard
Recommended Range for Goals	5 to 15 cm	1 to 4 cm	0 to 2 cm

Setting Goals for Cardiovascular Improvement

	Distance from Health Fitness Standard		
	Less	Close	Exceeds
Difference between Test Score and Health Fitness Standard	2 minutes+	0 to 2 minutes	0 or better
Recommended Range for Goals	30 seconds to 5 minutes	15 seconds to 90 seconds	0 to 45 seconds

Goal Setting for Abdominal Strength and Endurance

	Distance from Health Fitness Standard		
	Less	Close	Exceeds
Difference between Test Score and Health Fitness Standard	More than 15	1 to 15	0 or better
Recommended Range for Goals	5 to 15	2 to 10	1 to 4

Goal Setting for Upper Body Strength			
	Distance from Health Fitness Standard		
	Less	Close	Exceeds
Difference between Test Score and Health Fitness Standard	More than 1	1 to 2	at or better
Recommended Range for Goals	1 to 3	2 to 5	1 to 3

Goal Setting for Body Composition			
	Distance from Health Fitness Standard		
	Less	Close	Exceeds
Difference between Test Score and Health Fitness Standard	More than 10 mm	1 to 10 mm	0 or better
Recommended Range for Goals	1 to 15 mm	1 to 10 mm	1 to 3 mm

Appendix C
Minimum Principles of Training Guidelines

Summary of Flexibility Training Guidelines	
Frequency	At least 3 times per week
Intensity	Controlled stretch until mild tension is felt
Time	Static: Hold each stretch 15–30 seconds. Dynamic: 10 to 20 repetitions and 1 to 3 sets

Summary of Cardiovascular Endurance Training Guidelines	
Frequency	At least 3 times per week
Intensity	60–90% maximum heart rate 50–85% maximum heart rate reserve
Time	Minimum of 20 minutes of continuous large muscle group activity

Summary of Muscular Fitness Training Guidelines	
Muscular Endurance	
Frenquency	Every other day for each muscle group
Intensity	Low resistance (30–50%, 1 RM)
Time	High repetitions (12 to 20 reps, 1 to 3 sets)
Muscular Strength	
Frenquency	Every other day for each muscle group
Intensity	Heavy weights (60–90%, 1 RM)
Time	Low repetitions (4 to 8 reps, 1 to 3 sets)

Appendix D
Percentage of Maximum Heart Rate

(220 – age) × 60 percent = lower level of target heart rate zone

Percentage of Maximum Heart Rate Calculation

	Lower Limit	Upper Limit
1. Lunetta subtracted 14 (age) from 220 to obtain her maximum heart rate of 206. 220 – age = maximum heart rate	220 –14 206 MHR	220 –14 206 MHR
2. She decided that 60% should be the lower limit of her target heart rate zone and that 90% would be a safe upper limit for optimum training effect.	× 60%	× 90%
3. Lunetta multipled step 2 by the value of step 1. It was determined that 123.6 was the lower limit of her target heart-rate zone and 185.4 was the safe upper limit.	123.6	185.4

[(220 – age) – resting heart rate] × 50 percent + resting heart rate = lower level of target heart rate zone

Percentage of Heart Rate Reserve

	Lower Limit	Upper Limit
1. Chris subtracted 14 (age) from 220 to obtain his maximum heart rate of 206. 220 – age = maximum heart rate	220 –14 206 MHR	220 –14 206 MHR
2. Using the method described in this chapter, he determined his resting heart rate to be 70, which was subtracted from 206.	–70 RHR 136	–70 RHR 136
3. Chris decided that 50% should be the lower limit of his target heart rate zone and that 85% would be a safe upper limit for training.	× 50%	× 85%
4. He multiplied step 3 by the value of step 2.	68	122.4
5. Chris then added his resting heart rate.	+70 RHR	+ 70 RHR
6. It was determined that 138 was the lower limit of his target heart-rate zone and 186 was the safe upper limit.	138	185.6

Appendix E
Aerobic Training Program

Aerobic Training Program for 14- to 17-Year-Olds

The following can be used to help you in developing your cardiovascular personal fitness program. Depending upon your current level of cardiovascular fitness as determined by your fitness assessment such as the one mile run and by your previous involvement in physical activity, you may wish to start at week five rather than week one for example. This program can be used with any aerobic actvity such as walking, jogging, cycling, swimming, aerobic dance, racquet sports, and cross country skiing.

Week	Frequency (sessions/wk.)	Intensity (heart rate/min.)	Pulse (10 sec.)	Time (Min.)
1	3	40	13–14	15
2	3	40	13–14	15
3	3	45	14–15	15
4	3	45	14–15	20
5	3	50	16–17	20
6	3	50	16–17	25
7	3	55	18–19	25
8	4	55	18–19	30
9	4	60	20–21	30
10	4	60–70	20–24	30
11	4	60–75	20–26	35
12	4–5	60–80	20–28	40
13	4–5	60–85	20–29	50
14	4–5	60–90	20–31	55
15	4–5	60–90	20–31	60

Appendix F
Muscular Fitness Program

Muscular Fitness Program

The following exercises are only a few that can be used to improve muscular endurance and muscular strength. These exercises were selected because they require no or little equipment and as a group, offer a complete body workout. Regardless of age, start your program and progress as outlined in Chapter 8 by implementing the principles of training.

Activity	Body Area	Muscle Group
Curl ups	Abdominal	Abdominal
Push ups	Arms, chest, shoulders	Pectoralis major Deltoid Serratus anterior Tricep
Bicep curl	Arms	Bicep brachii Brachialis
Wrist curl	Arms	Wrist extensors
Reserve wrist curl	Arms	Wrist flexors
Overhead press	Arms, back, shoulders	Trapezius Deltoid Tricep
Single arm row	Back, shoulder	Trapezius Rhomboids Latissimus dorsi Deltoid
Shoulder shrug	Shoulder	Trapezius Rhomboids
Heel raises	Legs	Gastrocnemius Soleus
Leg extension	Legs	Quadriceps
Squat	Legs, back	Erector spinae Gluteus maximus Quadriceps Hamstrings

Appendix G
Flexibility Program

Flexibility Program

Remember to always stretch any muscle that was contracted. The exercises below stretch the muscles that were contracted in the suggested muscular fitness program.

Activity	Body Area	Muscle Group
Overhead stretch	Abdominal, back, shoulder, chest	Pectoral major Rhomboids Latissimus dorsi Abdominal
Triceps stretch	Arms, back	Latissimus dorsi Tricep
Cat stretch	Back	Trapezius Rhomboids Latissimus dorsi Erector spinae
Modified hurdler	Legs, back	Erector spinae Gluteus maximus Hamstrings
Neck stretch	Chest, back	Sternocleidomostoid Trapezius
Shoulder stretch	Back, shoulder	Rhomboids Latissimus dorsi Deltoid
Groin stretch	Legs	Adductors (thigh)
Hamstring stretch	Legs	Gluteus maximus Hamstrings
Quadriceps stretch	Legs	Quadriceps Tibialis anterior

Appendix H
Caloric Values of Common Foods

Number of Servings Daily to Meet Individual Needs			
	Women & some older adults	Children, teenage girls, active women, most men	Teenage boys & active men
Calorie level*	about 1,600	about 2,200	about 2,800
Bread group	6	9	11
Vegetable group	3	4	5
Fruit group	2	3	4
Milk group	**2–3	**2–3	**2–3
Meat group	2, for a total of 5 ounces	2, for a total of 6 ounces	3, for a total of 7 ounces

*These are the calorie levels if you choose low fat, lean foods from the five major food groups and use foods from the fats, oils, and sweets group sparingly.
**Women who are pregnant or breast feeding, teenagers, and young adults to age 24 need 3 servings.
Source: USDA

Serving Size and Caloric Values of Common Foods

Bread, Cereals, Rice, and Pasta Group	Serving Size	Calories
Bagel	1 (3")	165
Biscuit	1 (2")	100
Bread:		
White	1 slice	70
Whole Wheat	1 slice	65
Italian	1 slice	85
Corn	1 2½" square	160
Cereal, dry (varies with type, check label)	1 cup	90
Cooked Grain Products		
Oatmeal	½ cup	65
Grits	½ cup	65
Spaghetti	½ cup	80
Macaroni	½ cup	80
Egg Noodles	½ cup	100
Rice	½ cup	110
Crackers:		
Saltine	4	50
Graham	2 squares	55
Hush Puppies	3	150
Muffin:		
Blueberry	1 medium	110
Bran	1 medium	105
Corn	1 medium	125
Pancake	1 (4")	60
Popcorn, popped with oil	1 cup	40
Roll:		
Hamburger/Hot Dog (1)	1	120
Submarine	1 large	390
Brown 'n Serve	1	85
Waffle	1 (7")	210

Vegetable Group	Serving Size	Calories
Beans:		
Lima	½ cup	85
Pinto	½ cup	105
Green	½ cup	15
Broccoli	½ cup	20
Cabbage	½ cup	10

Continued on next page

Vegetable Group	Serving Size	Calories
Carrots:		
Raw	1 large	40
Canned	½ cup	25
Cauliflower	½ cup	15
Cole Slaw	½ cup	85
Corn	4" ear	100
	½ cup	70
Greens:		
Collard	½ cup	30
Spinach, mustard, turnip	½ cup	20
Lettuce	1 cup	5
Mixed vegetables	½ cup	60
Peas:		
Green	½ cup	75
Blackeyed	½ cup	100
Potatoes:		
Baked, no skin	1 large	140
Boiled, no skin	1 medium	70
French fries	10	110
Hash Browns	½ cup	230
Sweet:		
Baked	1 medium	160
Candied	½ medium	145
Squash:		
Summer	½ cup	15
Winter	½ cup	50
Tomato, raw	1 medium	25
Turnip	½ cup	15

Fruit Group	Serving Size	Calories
(Unless otherwise noted, values are for raw fruits and cooked vegetables)		
Apple	1 medium	85
Banana	1 medium	125
Grapefruit	½ medium	40
Grapes	10	35
Juices:		
Apple	8 oz.	120
Grape	8 oz.	165
Grapefruit	8 oz.	100
Lemon	1 Tbsp.	4
Orange	8 oz.	110
Orange	1 medium	65
Peach:		
Fresh	1 medium	40
Canned, heavy syrup	2 halves	80
Pear:		
Fresh	1 medium	100
Canned, heavy syrup	2 halves	75
Plum	1 small	30
Strawberries	½ cup	42
Watermelon	4" × 8" piece	110

Milk, Yogurt, and Cheese Group	Serving Size	Calories
Cheese:		
Cheddar	2 oz.	230
Swiss	2 oz.	210
Mozzarella, part skim	2 oz.	160
Cream	2 oz.	200
Cottage, 4% fat	1 cup	200
Cheese Pizza:		
Thin crust	¼ 13" pie	340
Thick crust	¼ 13" pie	390
Ice Cream, vanilla		
Hard	1 cup	270
Soft	1 cup	375
Milk:		
Whole	8 oz.	150
2% lowfat	8 oz.	120
2% chocolate	8 oz.	180
Skim	8 oz.	90
Buttermilk	8 oz.	90
Thick Shake:		
Vanilla	10 oz.	350
Chocolate	10 oz.	355
Yogurt:		
Plain	8 oz.	150
Vanilla, lemon	8 oz.	200
Fruit	8 oz.	260

Meat, Poultry, Fish, Dry Beans, Eggs, and Nuts Group	Serving Size	Calories
(These figures are for meat without bone)		
Bologna	2 slices	170
Chicken:		
Breast		
Fried	½ breast	230
Broiled, no skin	3½ oz.	165
Drumstick, fried	2 small	125
Chili con carne, with beans	1 cup	340
Chuck Roast:		
With fat	3 oz.	365
Visible fat removed	3 oz.	210
Eggs:		
Boiled	1 large	80
Scrambled	1 large	110
Fish Sticks	3 oz.	150
Ham:		
With fat	3 oz.	315
Visible fat removed	3 oz.	185
Hamburger:		
21% fat	3 oz.	245
10% fat	3 oz.	185
Hot Dog	1 (2 oz.)	150
Macaroni and cheese:		
Home recipe	1 cup	430
Canned	1 cup	230

Serving Size and Caloric Values of Common Foods—*continued*

Meat, Poultry, Fish, Dry Beans, Eggs, and Nuts Group	Serving Size	Calories
Peanut Butter	2 Tbsp.	380
Pork Chop:		
With fat	3 oz.	310
Visible fat removed	3 oz.	215
Round Steak:		
With fat	3 oz.	375
Visible fat removed	3 oz.	205
Sausage	2 small	140
Spaghetti and meat sauce	1 cup	295
Tuna Salad	1/2 cup	175
Turkey, light meat	3 oz.	150

Fats, Oils, and Sweets Group	Serving Size	Calories
Bacon	2 slices	85
Beer:		
Regular	12 oz.	150
Light	12 oz.	100
Butter or margarine	1 Tbsp.	100
Cake:		
Angel Food, 10"	1/12 cake	160
Chocolate with icing	1/16 cake	275
Yellow with icing	1/16 cake	275
Candy:		
Chocolate	1 oz.	145
Caramel	1 oz.	115
Hershey Bar	1 ½ oz.	220
Snickers	2 oz.	270
Peanut M&M's	1.7 oz.	240
Peanut Butter Cups	2 large	260
Chocolate Syrup	1 Tbsp.	45
Coca Cola	12 oz.	145
Cookies:		
Chocolate Chip	1 (2¼")	50
Oatmeal Raisin	1 (2½")	60
Oreo	1 (1¾")	60
Fig Newton	1	50
Brownie	1 (1¾")	95
Granola Bar	1	120
Doughnut:		
Cake	1	100
Glazed	1	205
Ginger Ale	12 oz.	135
Gin, Rum, Vodka, Whiskey	1½ oz.	125
Hawaiian Punch	8 oz.	120
Honey	1 Tbsp.	60
Ice Cream Sandwich or bar	1	165
Jam	1 Tbsp.	55
Kool Aid	8 oz.	100
Lemonade	8 oz.	110
Mayonnaise	1 Tbsp.	100
Nuts:		
Peanuts, roasted	¼ cup	340
Cashews	¼ cup	280
Pecans	¼ cup	205
Oil	1 Tbsp.	125
Pie:		
Apple	⅛ pie	300
Cherry	⅛ pie	310
Lemon Meringue	⅛ pie	270
Pecan	⅛ pie	430
Pumpkin	⅛ pie	240
Potato Chips	10	115
Pretzels, twisted	10	235
Pudding:	1 cup	
Chocolate	1 cup	385
Vanilla	1 Tbsp.	285
Salad Dressing:	1 Tbsp.	
Blue Cheese	1 Tbsp.	60
Italian	1 Tbsp.	70
Thousand Island	1 Tbsp.	80
Sour Cream	1 Tbsp.	25
Sprite	12 oz.	145
Sugar	1 Tbsp.	45
Tang	8 oz.	135
Tartar Sauce	1 Tbsp.	75
Tom Collins	10 oz.	180
Wine:		
Sweet	3½ oz.	135
Dry	3½ oz.	85

From Take Control: Manage Your Weight to Look Good and Feel Great. Published by Nutrition Education and Training Program. N.C. State Dept. of Public Instruction, Healthful Living Section, Raleigh, N.C.

Caloric Values of Fast Foods*

Arby's	Calories
Beef and Cheese Sandwich	450
Club Sandwich	560
Ham 'n Cheese Sandwich	380
Junior Roast Beef Sandwich	220
Roast Beef Sandwich	350
Super Roast Beef Sandwich	620
Turkey Deluxe Sandwich	510
Turkey Sandwich	410

Burger Chef	Calories
Big Chef	542
Cheeseburger	304
Double Cheeseburger	434
Hamburger	258
Mariner Platter	680
Rancher Platter	640
Shake, Vanilla	326
Skipper's Treat	604

Burger King	Calories
Cheeseburger	305
French Fries	214
Hamburger	252
Hot Dog	291
Shake, Vanilla	332
Whaler	486
Whopper	606

Dairy Queen	Calories
Banana Split	540
Big Brazier, deluxe	470
Big Brazier, regular	457
Big Brazier with Cheese	318
Brazier Chili Dog	330
Brazier Cheese Dog	330
Brazier Dog	273
French Fries, large	320
French Fries, regular	200
Onion Rings	300
Brazier, regular	260
Oyster Bar	390
Chocolate Dipped Cone, medium	300
Chocolate Malt, medium	600
Chocolate Sundae, medium	300
Float	330
Freeze	520
Parfait	460
Ice Cream Sandwich	140
Dilly Bar	240
Fiesta Sundae	570

Dairy Queen	Calories
Fish Sandwich	400
Fish Sandwich with Cheese	440
Hot Fudge Brownie Delight	570
Mr. Misty Float	440
Mr. Misty Freeze	500
Super Brazier Chili Dog	555
Super Brazier Dog	518
Super Brazier Dog with Cheese	593

Hardee's	Calories
Apple Turnover	282
Big Twin	447
Cheeseburger	335
Deluxe	675
Double Cheeseburger	495
Fish Sandwich	468
French Fries, large	381
French Fries, regular	239
Hamburger	305
Hot Dog	346
Milkshake	391
Roast Beef Sandwich	390

Kentucky Fried Chicken	Calories
Drumstick	136
Breast	283
Rib	241
Thigh	276
Wing	151
9 Pieces Chicken	1892
Chicken Dinner, original	830
Chicken Dinner, extra crispy	950

McDonald's	Calories
Apple Pie	300
Big Mac	541
Cheeseburger	306
Cherry Pie	298
Chocolate Shake	324
Egg McMuffin	352
English Muffin, buttered	186
Fillet O'Fish	211
Hamburger	257
Hot Cakes, with butter & syrup	472
Cookies	294
Quarter Pounder with Cheese	518
Sausage	184
Scrambled Eggs	162
Strawberry Shake	345
Vanilla Shake	323

Caloric Values of Fast Foods*—*continued*

Mexican Foods	Calories
Enchilada:	
Beef, one	260
Beef, topped with cheese, one	340
Cheese, one	280
Guacamole, ½ cup	140
Refried Beans, ½ cup	150
Taco Salad, 1 serving	234
Tamales, one	115
Tortillas, one	40

Wendy's	Calories
Cheeseburger:	
Single with Cheese	580
Double with Cheese	800
Triple with Cheese	1040
Chili	230
French Fries	330
Frosty	390
Hamburger:	
Single	470
Double	670
Triple	850

Pizza Hut	Calories Thin	Calories Thick
Standard Cheese	180	208
Standard Pepperoni	202	224
Standard Pork/Mushroom	196	227
Super Supreme	266	300
Superstyle Cheese	213	235
Superstyle Pepperoni	233	244
Superstyle Pork/Mushroom	230	244
Supreme	216	244

Steak House	Entree	Dinner
Baked Potato	145	
Chopped Beef	324	727
Double Deluxe	362	791
Extra-Cut Prime Rib	409	812
Extra-Cut Ribeye	358	761
Fillet of Sole Dinner	251	654
Fillet of Sole Sandwich	122	551
French Fries	230	
Junior Patty	98	446
Prime Rib	286	689
Rib Eye/Shrimp	398	801
Shrimp	220	623
Steakhouse Deluxe	181	611
Strip Sirloin	277	680
Super Sirloin	383	786
T-Bone	374	777
Tartar Sauce, 1 Tbs.	95	

*Values are for a standard single serving size.

Bibliography

Alter, Michael J. (1998). *Sport Stretch*. Champaign, IL: Leisure Press.

American College of Sports Medicine. *ACSM's Guidelines for Exercise Testing and Prescription*. Philadelphia, PA: Lippincott Williams and Wilkins Publisher.

American Heart Association (ed.). *American Heart Association Fitting in Fitness: Hundreds of Simple Ways to Put More Physical Activity into Your Life*. American Heart Association.

The American Heart Association (1995). *The Healthy Heart Walking Book: The American Heart Association Walking Program*. Dallas, TX: Hungry Minds, Inc.

Bailey, C. (2001). *The New Fit or Fat*. Boston: Houghton Mifflin.

Branner, T. T. (2000). *The Safe Exercise Handbook*. Dubuque: Kendall/Hunt Publishing.

Coleman, E. L. (2003). *Eating for Endurance*. Palo Alto, CA: Bull Publishing.

De Vries, H. A., and T. Houch (1994). *Physiology of Exercise*. Dubuque, IA: Brown and Benchmark.

Elkin, A. (1999). *Stress Management for Dummies®*. New York: For Dummies.

Fenton, M. (2002). *The Complete Guide to Walking for Health, Weight Loss, and Fitness*. Readers Digest; Revised edition.

Fleck, S. J., and W. J. Kraemer (1997). *Designing Resistance Training Programs*. Champaign, IL: Human Kinetics.

Fox, E. L., R. W. Bowers, and M. L. Foss (1998). *The Physiological Basis for Exercise and Sport*. Philadelphia: Saunders College Publishing.

Gaede, K., A. Lachica, D. Werner (2001). *Fitness Training for Girls: A Teen Girl's Guide to Resistance Training*, Chula Vista, CA: Cardiovascular Conditioning and Nutrition, Tracks Publisher.

Goliszek, A. (1992). *60-Second Stress Management: The Quickest Way to Relax and Ease Anxiety*. Far Hills, NJ: New Horizon Press.

Graves, J. and B. Franklin (eds.) (2001). *Resistance Training for Health and Rehabilitation*. Champaign: IL: Human Kinetics.

Greenberg, J. S., G. B. Dintiman, and B. M. Oakes (1995). *Physical Fitness and Wellness*. Englewood Cliffs, NJ: Prentice-Hall.

Hauri, P. and S. Linde (1996). *No More Sleepless Nights*, 2nd ed. New York: Wiley.

McArdele, W. D., F. I. Katch, and V. L. Katch (2001). *Exercise Physiology: Energy, Nutrition, and Human Performance*. Philadelphia: Lea and Febiger.

Oswald, C., and S. Bacso (July 2003). *Stretching for Fitness, Health & Performance: The Complete Handbook for All Ages & Fitness Levels*. London: Sterling Publications.

Pollock, M., and J. Wilmore (2004). *Exercise in Health and Disease*. Philadelphia: W. B. Saunders.

The Cooper Institute for Aerobics Research (1999). *FITNESSGRAM: Test Administration Manual*. Champaign, IL: Human Kinetics.

The President's Council on Physical Fitness and Sports (2002–2003). *The President's Challenge Physical Activity and Fitness Awards Program*. Washington, D.C.: PCPFS.

Williams, M. (1996). *Lifetime Fitness and Wellness*. Dubuque, IA: William C. Brown.

U.S. Department of Health and Human Services. *Healthy People 2000 Objectives and The National Education Goals*. Public Health Reports 107 no. 1 (1992):9–14.

U.S. Department of Health and Human Services (1998). *The Surgeon General's Report on Nutrition and Health*. DHHS (PHS) Publication No. 88-50211. Washington, D.C.: U.S. Government Printing Office.

Glossary

A

abdominals—group of muscles forming the supporting wall of the abdominal region

acclimatization—the process of the body slowly adapting to a new temperature

Achilles' tendon—tendon connecting the calf muscle to the heel of the foot

adipose tissue—fat tissue

adrenaline—chemical secreted by the adrenal glands which moves the body into the fight or flight response

advertising—describing or presenting a product in order to induce people to buy, support, or approve it

aerobic—with oxygen; term refers to energy-producing biochemical pathways in cells that use oxygen to produce energy

agility—the ability to change the position and control the movement of the whole body

alarm stage—first stage of stress where the stressor is identified and adrenaline is released

alveoli—small air sacs in the lungs where exchange of air into the blood takes place

amino acids—chemical substances that make up protein

anabolic steroids—a synthetic version of the male sex hormone testosterone

anaerobic—without oxygen; term refers to energy-producing biochemical pathways in cells that do not require oxygen to produce energy

anorexia nervosa—an eating disorder in which a person refuses to eat normally, resulting in extreme thinness and even starvation

antioxidants—a special group of vitamins that help protect the body from cell damage

aorta—large artery that carries blood away from the heart to be carried throughout the body

arteriosclerosis—hardening of the arteries that occurs in advanced stages of cardiovascular disease

artery—a vessel that carries blood away from the heart

atherosclerosis—a condition in which fatty deposits build up on inner walls of arteries, causing narrowing of the arterial passageway

atrium—the top two chambers of the heart that receive blood from the veins and force it into the lower two chambers of the heart

atrophy—the wasting away or decrease in size of a body part, particularly muscle

avoidance—refusing to act on a situation

B

balance—ability to keep an upright posture while either standing still or moving

ballistic stretching—stretching that involves bobbing, bouncing, or jerky movements that make use of the body's momentum

basal metabolism—the amount of energy required to maintain the body at rest

behavior modification—the technique used to promote desirable changes in behavior

blood pressure—the measure of blood force against the walls of the arteries

body composition—the ratio of fat to muscle, bone, and other body tissues

body image—the way one sees oneself physically

body mass index (BMI)—provides an indication of the appropriateness of your weight relative to your height

bulimia—an eating disorder characterized by overeating followed by self-induced vomiting, use of laxatives, or very strenuous exercise to avoid weight gain

burnout—the point at which you cannot deal with the accumulated effect of all stressors

C

calisthenics—exercises in which body weight is used as the resistance

calorie—the amount of energy needed to raise the temperature of 1 kilogram of water 1 degree centigrade; a unit that measures the energy in foods

concentric contraction—the shortening of a muscle due to contraction; also called positive work

capillary—a network of small vessels located between the arteries and veins in which exchanges of vital substances occur between tissue and blood

carbohydrates—the essential nutrients that are the body's primary source of energy

cardiovascular fitness—the ability of the heart, blood vessels, and respiratory system to supply oxygen and nutrients to the muscles during exercise

carotid artery—a major artery (or pair of arteries) located on each side of the neck allowing blood to flow from the aorta to the head

cholesterol—a waxy, fat-like substance found in animal tissue

circuit training—an exercise program in which one moves around a prescribed course, stopping at each station to perform a specified exercise

circulatory system—the system consisting primarily of the blood, heart, and blood vessels

compensation—overreacting to make up for a feeling of inadequacy

consumer—a person who buys goods and services

cool-down—a 10- to 15-minute period of mild exercise following vigorous exercise that allows the body and heart rate to return to normal

coordination—the integration of eye, hand, and foot movements

creeping obesity—the gaining of fat slowly over a period of time

criterion-referenced tests—physical fitness tests in which specific standards are used to judge fitness levels

cross-train—to engage in a variety of activities and exercises from day to day

D

dehydration—the loss of water from body tissues

diabetes—the body's inability to regulate sugar metabolism

diaphragm—a large muscle in the upper abdomen

diastolic blood pressure—the blood pressure exerted during the relaxation phase of the heart cycle

distress—negative stress resulting from difficulties

diuretics—the drugs used to control accumulation of fluids in body tissues, congestive heart failure, and high blood pressure

dynamic stretching—stretching done in a continuous, slow, and controlled manner

E

eccentric contraction—isotonic contractions in which the muscle exerts force while the muscle lengthens; also called negative work

ectomorph—a body type with a slender, slight build

edema—an accumulation of fluid in body tissues

electrical impedance—method of determining body fat by measuring electrical resistance encountered in the body

endormorph—a body type with a large, soft, bulging body and pear-shaped appearance

eustress—positive stress resulting from something good

evaluation—determining your current level of fitness

exercise prescription—a personalized amount of exercise that promotes physical fitness

F

fad diets—diets that promote weight loss without sound nutritional practices

fallacy—an idea that is the result of deception or incorrect information

fast-twitch fibers—white muscle fibers that contract quickly, allowing explosive muscular contractions

fat—an efficient storage of energy; excess fat is stored in fat cells called adipose tissue located under the skin and around internal organs

fat-soluble vitamins—vitamins that can be stored in fat deposits in the body; for example, vitamins a, d, e, and k

fight or flight response—an involuntary physical response to a stressor that gives an individual the capacity for sudden and quick action

F.I.T.—the three ways to achieve overload in a physical fitness program: frequency, intensity, and time

flexibility—the range of possible movement at various joints

fraudulent—characterized by deceit or trickery used to gain an unfair or dishonest advantage

frequency—the number of times one should exercise to improve a component of physical fitness

G

general adaptation syndrome—body's response to a specific stressor

general stressors—those types of stimuli that trigger the stress response but are not easily identifiable by the body

glucose—the only sugar molecule that can be used by the body in its natural form and that serves as a valuable source of energy

glycemic index—classifies carbohydrates by how strongly and quickly they cause a person's blood glucose level to rise after they are digested

goal setting—a process designed to motivate people to make lifestyle changes toward self-improvement

H

HDL—high-density lipoprotein that helps remove excess cholesterol

health-related fitness—components of physical fitness that contribute to the operation of the systems of the body

health-related fitness standards—satisfactory or healthy levels of flexibility, cardiovascular fitness, muscular strength and endurance, and body composition

health risk factors—those factors associated with disease, disability, and premature death

healthy eating pyramid—an alternative food pyramid that differentiates between the more and less healthy nutritional food sources

heart attack—the damage of heart tissue as a result of the heart not receiving a sufficient blood supply

heart rate—the number of heart beats per minute

heat cramps—a heat-related problem in which certain muscles contract involuntarily and cause pain

heat exhaustion—a condition characterized by profuse sweating, dizziness, and extreme weakness

heat stroke—a medical emergency characterized by hot, dry skin and a rising body temperature

hemoglobin—an iron-rich compound in the blood that helps carry oxygen to the muscles, tissues, and organs

high-density lipoprotein (HDL)—a type of cholesterol that is associated with lowering fatty plaque accumulation in the coronary arteries that lead to heart disease. HDL-cholesterol is often called *good cholesterol*.

high-impact aerobics—aerobic dance that includes jumping, bouncing, and running

homeostasis—the internal balance of the body

humidity—the amount of water vapor in the air

hydrostatic weighing—a method of determining body composition that involves weighing a person both outside and inside a tank of water

hypertension—an unstable or persistent elevation of blood pressure above normal range, commonly called high blood pressure

hyperthermia—an increase in body temperature with a reduction of body fluids

hypothermia—an excessive decline in body temperature

I

ideal body weight—the amount a person weighs if he or she has an appropriate percentage of body fat

inactivity—the lack of physical activity and exercise

intensity of exercise—the degree to which one should exercise to improve fitness

intermediate-twitch fibers—muscle fibers that possess a combination of the fast- and slow-twitch fiber characteristics

interval training—an exercise program that involves a series of exercises interspersed with rest periods

isokinetic exercises—exercises done with special machines that allow for maximum resistance over the complete range of motion

isometric exercises—exercises in which one contracts muscles but does not move body parts

isostatic stretching—a form of stretching in which the body is pushed beyond its initial limit

isotonic exercises—exercises in which a muscle lengthens and shortens through its full range of movement while lowering and raising a resistance

J

joint—point at which two bones come together

L

lactic acid—a waste product built up in the body as a result of severe muscular exercise

LDL—low-density lipoprotein that leads to a buildup of cholesterol on artery walls

lean body mass—body mass made up of muscle tissue and other nonfat tissue such as bones, ligaments, and tendons

lifetime sports—individual sports that can be engaged in for a lifetime

ligament—strong, fibrous tissue that attaches one bone to another

lifestyle—daily choices you make in regards to what you eat, consume, and activities in which you engage

long-term goals—those goals that take a long time, perhaps years, to reach

low-impact aerobics—aerobic dance that includes vigorous arm movements while keeping one foot in contact with the ground at all times

M

maximum heart rate—the heart rate that should not be exceeded during exercise; calculated by subtracting one's age from 220

media—newspapers, magazines, television, and radio

meditation—focusing one's thoughts for the purpose of relaxation

mesomorph—a body type with a solid, muscular, and large-boned physique

metabolic rate—total calories burned or expended as heat

minerals—the essential nutrients needed by the body in small amounts to prevent deficiencies and diseases

muscle—meaty tissue that surrounds the bone

muscle-bound—characterized by an imbalanced development of strength between the antagonist and agonist muscle in which a loss of flexibility occurs

muscular endurance—the ability to use muscles for a long period of time

muscular strength—the ability of muscles to exert a force one time

MyPyramid—a visual guideline established by U.S. Department of Agriculture to ensure that all of the essential nutrients are included in the daily diet.

N

negative coping techniques—those responses that ease or disguise the symptoms of stress and that are harmful to an individual and those around him or her

negative stress (distress)—reacting in a negative manner to something bad

norm-referenced tests—physical fitness tests in which norms are used to indicate fitness levels

nutrient—a substance contained in food that is necessary for good health

O

obese—having an excessive amount of body fat

obesity—a condition characterized by excessive deposits of fat on the body

omega-3 fatty acids—polyunsaturated fats found primarily in oily fish from cold waters

one-repetition maximum (1 rm) test—a measurement of the maximum amount of weight that can be lifted one time

osteoporosis—the loss of bone mass and strength, which increases risk of bone fractures

overload principle—a basic principle of fitness training in which the body is stressed and adapts to that stress

overuse injury—an injury caused by not following the correct progression, doing an exercise too much, too soon, or too often

overweight—a condition that exceeds the desirable body weight by 10 percent, according to height and weight charts

P

percentage of heart rate reserve—a method of calculating cardiovascular exercise intensity based on 50 to 85 percent of your maximum heart rate reserve

percentage of maximum heart rate—a method of calculating cardiovascular exercise intensity based on 60 to 90 percent of your maximum heart rate

personal fitness program (PFP)—a plan designed to help you select activities to improve your lifestyle

personal trainer—certified fitness professional who designs personal fitness programs

physical fitness—the capacity of the whole body to function at optimum efficiency; determined by the condition of the heart and circulatory, respiratory, and muscular systems, the degree of flexibility, and the percentage of body fat

planned program—a program that includes specific exercises for persons of specific fitness levels or ages

positive coping strategies—strategies designed to deal with unavoidable stress

positive stress (eustress)—reacting in a positive manner to something good

power—ability to do strength performances at a rapid pace

principle of overload—exposing the muscles, joints, and cardiovascular and respiratory systems to more work and stress than is normally experienced

principle of progression—a progressive increase in the level of exercise in order to sustain improvement in physical fitness

principle of specificity—the performance of specific exercises in order to improve specific components of physical fitness in specific body parts

prioceptive neuromuscular facilitation (PNF) stretching—stretching based on a contract-and-relax technique requiring the help of another person

progression, principle of—principle of training that dictates that overload should be increased gradually

progressive muscle relaxation—relaxation program where muscles are relaxed group by group

projecting—blaming someone else for your own fault

proteins—the essential nutrients needed for growth and repair of body tissues

pulse—a regular throbbing caused by pressure of blood on an artery wall that corresponds to heartbeat

Q

quack—one who promotes useless and sometimes harmful practices as beneficial

quackery—the promotion of useless and sometimes harmful practices as beneficial

R

rationalizing—making up reasons why the situation turned out the way it did

reaction time—the amount of time needed to move once the senses signal the need to move

recommended daily allowance (RDA)—the amount of nutrients recommended daily by the U.S. Department of Agriculture

recovery heart rate—the existing heart rate just after exercise

red blood cell—the cell that carries oxygen to the tissues

rehydration—the replacement of fluids that have been lost from the body

relaxation techniques—those activities that reduce muscle tension and stress in the body through concentration of the mind

repetition—the completion of a single, full-range movement of the body part being exercised

respiratory system—the system composed of lungs and air passages that help supply oxygen to the body

resting heart rate—the existing heart rate just after waking and before getting out of bed

resting metabolic rate (RMR)—calories expended while at rest

resistance—the amount of weight you lift

R.I.C.E.—the letters stand for the first letters of words used in first aid for certain injuries: R = rest; I = ice; C = compression; E = elevation

risk factor—a trait that increases the likelihood one will develop chronic diseases

S

saturated fats—those fats contained in animal products

set—a group of repetitions performed one after the other

set point theory—the theory that body weight is controlled at a set point by a weight-regulating control center within the brain

shin splint—an inflammation of the membrane on the front of the bones in the lower leg

short-term goals—those goals that can be reached in a short period of time

skill-related fitness—the components of physical fitness that contribute to the ability to successfully participate in sports

skinfold caliper—a device used to measure a fold of skin and its underlying layer of body fat

slow-twitch fibers—red muscle fibers that are slow to contract but have the ability to continue contracting for long periods of time

somatotype—body type

specificity, principle of—principle of training that states the exercise training effect is specific to those muscles involved in the activity

speed—the ability to cover a distance in a short time

sports skills activities—those activities that help develop sports skills and satisfy the need for competition

spot reduction—the mistaken belief that exercising muscles in a particular area of the body will remove fat from that area

static stretching—the slow movement of a muscle to the stretching point at which it is held for 15 seconds

stimulus—an incident that initiates the alarm stage of general adaptation syndrome

stitch in the side—sharp pain in the side just under the ribs

strain—damage to a ligament that occurs if excessive force is applied to a joint

stress—the nonspecific response of the body to demands made upon it

stress management—activities and strategies that reduce stress

stress-diversion activities—those activities, both active and passive, that reduce or divert stress

stress fracture—tiny cracks or breaks in bone, usually caused by overuse

stressor—a stimulus (event, situation, or activity) that causes stress

stroke—brain damage that occurs when blood supply to the brain is reduced

stroke volume—the amount of blood the heart pumps out of the left ventricle on each contraction

systolic blood pressure—the blood pressure during the contraction phase of the heart

T

target heart rate—60 to 90 percent of the maximum heart rate; results in greatest cardiovascular benefits from exercise

tendon—connective tissue that anchors muscles to bones

testosterone—male hormone that helps build muscle

time—how long one exercises to improve fitness

time line—a tool used to organize and plot the course toward a major goal

time management—learning to manage your time

trans fats—unsaturated vegetable oils that have had hydrogen added to them, producing a fat that worsens blood cholesterol because it increases blood LDL and lowers blood HDL

U

unsaturated fats—those fats found in plant sources

V

vegetarian—one who does not eat animal products

vein—a vessel that carries blood to the heart

ventricles—the bottom two chambers of the heart

vitamin—a nutrient that helps control growth and maintain body functions

W

warm-up—a 10- to 15-minute light exercise period during which the body is prepared for vigorous exercise

water—makes up about 65 percent of your body weight

water-soluble vitamins—those vitamins that dissolve in water and cannot be stored in body tissues

wellness—term used to describe someone's commitment to live a healthy and active lifestyle; encompasses mental, physical, environmental, spiritual, emotional, and social health

Index